UNITY THROUGH DIVERSITY

CURRENT TOPICS OF CONTEMPORARY THOUGHT

A series devoted to the publication of original and thought-evoking works on general topics of vital interest to philosophy, science and the humanities.

Edited by **Rubin Gotesky** and **Ervin Laszlo**

Dr. LUDWIG von BERTALANFFY

Unity Through Diversity

A Festschrift for Ludwig von Bertalanffy

Edited by

WILLIAM GRAY and NICHOLAS D. RIZZO

PART II

GORDON AND BREACH SCIENCE PUBLISHERS

New York   London   Paris

TABLE OF CONTENTS

VOLUME I

Section I

LUDWIG VON BERTALANFFY: PERSON AND WORK

Section II

GENERAL AND OPEN SYSTEMS

Introduction

VOLUME II

Section III

Section IV

*Deceased

581

---

*Deceased

SECTION III
GROWTH AND MALIGNANT GROWTH

INTRODUCTION

GROWTH AND MALIGNANT GROWTH

During the interval between 1930 and 1950 von Bertalanffy's biological research was primarily concentrated in the fields of comparative physiology, cellular physiology, and animal growth. A large number of his experimental investigations dealt with total metabolism, tissue respiration under varying conditions, the allometric growth of organs, and related topics.

The Bertalanffy growth equations which resulted from these studies enjoyed wide attention and frequent application. Biological growth has been the object of many mathematical studies, formulas, and models. Bertalanffy's theory of animal growth is based chiefly on plausible physiological assumptions. It is derived from those families of equations which apply to the growth curves of many species as well as to the qualitative descriptions of many growth phenomena. The growth theory was logically developed and, in its present form, represents a far reaching series of formulations of basic phenomena. It follows his own maxim that theoretical biology should emerge from the close cooperation and mutual control of both experimental design and theoretical ideas. By contrast, neither the reliance on merely empirical formulas describing biological events, nor the exclusive reliance on mathematical constructs without sufficient experimental backing, has yielded theories of more than passing value. Bertalanffy's growth theory is, furthermore, one specific application of the view that a living organism is an open or general system. This application contributes mightily to his expectation that the basic fields included in physiology — i.e., metabolism, excitation, morphogenesis — would eventually be united under the guidance of the theory of open systems [1].

585

His expectation has been repeatedly confirmed by many investigations, examples of which are contained in Section II
of the present work.

Bertalanffy's theory is admittedly based on a highly
simplified model of the growth process; actually it is one
of the simplest models derived from the theory of open
systems. He does not consider it as ultimate, but rather
expects that it will undergo further modifications with
continuing research. Nevertheless, it turned out that this
simplified model works to a rather amazing extent. The
Bertalanffy growth equations are the only ones now available which (1) present a simple rationale of the process of
animal growth, (2) are readily applicable to a wide range
of empirical facts, and (3) have allowed predictions which
were widely, and often surprisingly, confirmed by experimental data. A recent survey [2] has enumerated no less
than 14 different categories of verifications, many of which
were supported by large arrays of empirical facts.

One field especially concerned with laws of growth is
fisheries research. Because of this and the fact that the
growth of fish often follows the Bertalanffy equations with
an exactitude approaching that of physical law, those equations are routinely applied in international fisheries
research [3].

The first part of this Section is devoted to discussion
and elaboration of the theory of growth. Professor A.E.
Needham, Oxford, presents an excellent survey from the
vantage point of a zoologist. Dr. K. Radway Allen, of the
Fisheries Research Board of Canada, examines the Bertalanffy
equations and develops generalized formulations [4,5]. In a
comparable theoretical framework Professor F. Krüger of the
University of Kiel examines the energetics of animal growth.
Professor F. Scharf, Chairman of the Anatomy Department of
Halle University and a former student of von Bertalanffy,
has done extensive work in the calculation of growth by computer and in the analysis of the oscillations in the difficult case of the human growth curve. This Section, it is
hoped, will be valuable to zoologists, fisheries authorities
and administrators, biologists, physiologists, and students
of human growth. It presents fields of research by leading
European workers who are not widely known in the United
States [6,7,8,9].

It was natural that von Bertalanffy would proceed from
the study of normal growth to abnormal growth and to problems of early cancer detection. His work started in the
1940s, shortly after Casperson and Brachet first directed
attention to the fundamental importance of desoxyribonucleic
acid (DNA) and ribonucleic acid (RNA). Using a then novel
instrument, the fluorescence microscope, Bertalanffy developed the acridine-orange fluorescence technique for cyto-
topochemical detection of RNA and its application for the
detection of malignant cells in cancer screening. High
RNA content is characteristic of growing cells, especially
so of malignant cells. The high RNA content of cancer
cells produces a flaming red fluorescence that makes them
easy to identify. Naturally it is urgently necessary to
study, also, morphologic features in cancer screening.
This approach has found wide-spread interest. More than
300 papers and clinical research programs have been published in many countries. Bertalanffy's fluorescence
method has proved its value as a research tool, for differential diagnosis, in biochemical studies of nucleic acids,
in virology, and in embryology. It is characterized by
the fact that the technique is not merely empirical, but
based on estimation of a substance (RNA) which is intimately
connected with the mechanism of cell growth and malignancy.
This is, therefore, an example of a theoretically planned
approach which has paid valuable dividends and presumably
will continue to do so.

The contribution by Professor M.N. Meissel of the
U.S.S.R. Academy of Sciences is remarkable in various
respects. He applied the technique of acridine-orange
fluorescence to the study of animal tissues independently
of, and even prior to, von Bertalanffy although he used a
somewhat different technique. Meissel employed fresh instead fixed preparations. This independent discovery and
priority was emphasized by von Bertalanffy, but Professor
Meissel and his co-workers have graciously and repeatedly
acknowledged von Bertalanffy's important and pioneering
work. Of added importance is the fact that Meissel and
Zelenin's carefully balanced account surveys research work
in the U.S.S.R. which is not otherwise available.

Professor Felix D. Bertalanffy of the University of
Manitoba is the son of Ludwig and Maria von Bertalanffy.
For many years father and son have been co-workers and

collaborators in cancer research. Felix Bertalanffy's chapter demonstrates the inter-relatedness of tissue renewal, anatomy, and certain cancerous processes. Exfoliative cytology has been the important technique for elaborating these associations. The biological basis presented in the report is not too well understood by many clinicians who study exfoliated cells.

The contributions by Dr. J.M. Ayre, Director of the National Cancer Cytology Center; by C.M. Lucena and co-workers, of the Gynecological Service, Buenos Aires, who won an award of the International Federation of Gynecology and Obstetrics for their work in early diagnosis of cervical cancer by fluorescence cytology; and by T.C. Arminsky, Detroit surgeon, present further clinical aspects of the Bertalanffy method. International interest is well illustrated by these contributions.

Section III pays homage to von Bertalanffy for his research in experimental and laboratory physiology. It confirms the belief that von Bertalanffy is indeed more than philosopher or theoretician. His theoretical contributions can be appreciated along with his experimental findings and observations. Although von Bertalanffy is known by scholars the world over for his contributions to general and global theories, his practical and experimental work is an affirmation of the principle that general theories must have general application.

Nicholas D. Rizzo

REFERENCES

1. von BERTALANFFY, L., *Theoretische Biologie*, Berlin: Borntraeger, 53, 1932.

2. von BERTALANFFY, L., "Principles and Theory of Growth," In: NOWINSKI, W.W., (ed.), *Fundamental Aspects of Normal and Malignant Growth*, Amsterdam: Elsevier, 1960.

3. ABRAMSON, N.J.,"von Bertalanffy's Growth Curve II", IBM 7094, UNIVAC 1107, Fortram IV. *Transaction Am. Fisheries Soc.*, *94*, 195-196, 1965.

4.   ALLEN, K.R., "A Method of Fitting Growth Curves of the
     von Bertalanffy Type to Observed Data", *J. Fish. Res.*
     Bd. Canada, 23, 163-179, 1966.

5.   ALLEN, K.R., "Fitting of von Bertalanffy Growth-Curves,
     IBM 709, Fortran IV", *Transactions of the American*
     Fisheries Society, 95, No. 2, 231-232, April 1966.

6.   FABENS, A.J., "Properties and Fitting of the von
     Bertalanffy Growth Curve", *Growth, 29,* 265-289, 1965.

7.   SHOMURA, R.S., "Age and Growth Studies of Four Species
     of Tunas in the Pacific Ocean", *Proceedings of the*
     Governor's Conference on Central Pacific Fishery
     Resources, Honolulu-Hilo, February-March, 1966.

8.   SOUTHWARD, M.G. and CHAPMAN, D.G., "Utilization of
     Pacific Halibut Stocks: Study of von Bertalanffy's
     Growth Equation", *Rept. International Pacific Halibut*
     Commission, No. 39, 33, 1965.

9.   TOMLINSON, P.K. and ABRAMSON, N.J., "Fitting a von
     Bertalanffy Growth Equation by Least Squares",
     Calif. Dept. Fish and Game, Fish Bull., No. 116, 1961.

THE MATHEMATICAL DEFINITION OF GROWTH

A.E. NEEDHAM

Department of Zoology, South Parks Road, Oxford, England

Embryonic development was the subject of Ludwig von Bertalanffy's first monograph (1928) and it is probably true to say that ontogenesis, particularly its growth component, has remained his main biological interest and research-field. His work on metabolism is directly related to growth and his concern with the thermodynamics of open systems is closely associated with both of these subjects. It was primarily embryology which prompted his organismic theory of biological function and led to his work on *systems theory*. From this already broad range of fundamental subjects, his dynamic interest spread rather naturally to the general problems and theories of life. As he says (1960, p. 139), "Growth is not an isolable phenomenon but rather a certain aspect of the process of life." His cytological work has been largely concerned with cancer and other aspects of growth. The centre of his interest in growth, however, has been essentially the application of quantitative techniques, and he has pressed forward with this approach through times when it could not boast a very festive bandwagon. His most important contributions have been on absolute growth.

ABSOLUTE GROWTH (SIZE/TIME)

Viewing growth as essentially a quantitative phenomenon, von Bertalanffy has avoided the difficulties

and complications which arise if it is not clearly distinguished from the differentiation component of morphogenesis. Growth can be defined simply (von Bertalanffy,
1960, p. 137) as "the quantitative increase of a living
system, which results from the prevalence of anabolism of
building materials over catabolism." In outline, the
whole story of growth is latent in the simple graph of
size/time and the definition of this has been his primary
objective. It has also been the objective of many
previous workers for, unlike most biological subjects,
growth was, from the outset, eminently amenable to
mathematical study. Partly as a result of this, publications accumulated in excess of the digestive enzymes which
other approaches could have provided, and there resulted a
satiated inability to choose decisively between the 150 or
more algebraical relations (Richards and Kavanagh, 1945)
which had been fitted to available size/time data
(Needham, 1964).

The first aim of the mathematical approach is to
describe size/time more succinctly, even if purely
empirically. The relation so obtained can then serve as a
short-hand definition for that species, can be made the
basis for a ready-reckoner, valid for growth in that
species, and so on. The next aim is to generalize the
relation fitted to this particular species so that it
defines growth in all organisms with only the parameters
of the relation varying between species. If such a
universal relation can be found, then the general
principles of growth underlying it should be inducible
from it. Students of a more theoretical bent reverse the
whole procedure and deduce a general relation or 'model'
from biological rationale and then test the fitting of
this to actual data. In either case, the generalized
relation can, in principle, be used for further analysis
and prediction, for estimating the effect of relevant
agents on growth, for comparisons between species, etc.

For empirical, ready-reckoner purposes, a number of
different relations have appeared to fit particular bodies
of data tolerably well, though none so closely and
uniquely as to inspire general confidence in it as well as
in the particular biological rationale underlying it.
Gray (1929) pointed out that considering the errors of

measurement and of individual variation, two or more very different relations could be fitted equally well to the same body of data; it was therefore pointless, or worse, to look for the biological rationale latent in any one relation. One answer to this impasse was to use purely empirically the simple polynomial, in size or in time, or in their logarithms (Backmann, 1941). Taken to sufficient terms, this type of relation will fit any body of data. In practice, the number of useful improvement-terms is often quite limited (Needham, 1957), and one may be tempted to look for biological rationale in the relation.

Backmann used transformation and scaling factors to develop a universal form of his relation, essentially by expressing size as a function of the final, limiting size and time in units determined by the growth-rate of the species. This species dimension, or *species scale,* technique has been applied also to other relations (Waddington, 1933; Brody, 1945). It has relevance to *similarity analysis* (p.611) in that the species dimensions are in effect ratios or dimensionless numbers. Ideally, all species reach a particular ontogenetic stage at the same value of species size and time. Backmann attempted to show that the significant stages in fact constituted a simple arithmetic progression in the specific units.

However empirical the relation, it is impossible to use it for long without feeling a compulsion to induce biological rationale into it, or else to make the same manipulations on one which has this added advantage. Moreover since, as just indicated, a number of relations are amenable to the same manipulations, there is only one reasonable basis for choosing finally, and this is optimal biological rationale. As a preliminary it is possible, on this basis, to reduce the 150-odd candidates to a comfortable short list. To convince auxologists in general of the virtue of the final choice, it must also be the relation which fits actual growth data most consistently. On both counts, the *metabolic relation* of von Bertalanffy (1960, 1964) ranks very highly. It has been emphasized repeatedly (Gray, 1929; Richards and Kavanagh, 1945; Sholl, 1950) that excellence of fit to one body of data is no absolute verdict in favour of a particular relation, and we should place more reliance on one which

fits a large amount of data, provided it does so reasonably well. This is in fact true of the metabolic
relation.

The typical curve of size/time is sigmoid, a phase of
growth-acceleration being followed by one of increasing
retardation, so that the curve inflects and eventually
tends to a limiting size, typical of the species. In
special, usually experimental, cases there is no
inflection and a simple climbing exponential relation fits
the data:

$$w = ae^{bt} \tag{1}$$

where w = weight (size), t = time and a,b are parametric
constants. This has universal appeal since it implies a
constant intrinsic or 'specific' growth-rate:
$(1/w)(dw/dt) = b$ which would be maintained under ideal,
non-limiting conditions. All of the more plausible
relations which have been fitted to the normal, sigmoid
curve likewise have been based on exponential, but more
complex, expressions. Brody fitted two separate, simple
exponential relations to the two halves of the sigmoid
curve, the first having a positive and the second a
negative exponent. The main objection to this is the
implication that two sharply separated phases are
involved. In fact, the curve itself and its various
derivatives, such as that of growth-rate, dw/dt, and that
of specific growth-rate, $(1/w)(dw/dt)$, are all smoothly
continuous.

In some cases the curve of specific growth-rate
itself very closely approximates to a declining
exponential function (Medawar, 1940; Laird *et al.*, 1965)
and size/time therefore has been fitted by the exponent
of an exponent in t, namely:

$$w = ae^{-be^{-kt}} \tag{2}$$

This was first fitted to growth-data by Sewall Wright
(1926) but was originally used by Gompertz for actuarial
purposes. The rationale (Medawar, 1940) is that the

specific growth potential of the cells is subject to an
inhibitor which itself increases exponentially with time,
a self-propagating factor perhaps. This relation gives an
inflection at $w = 0.37$ of its final limiting value
(w max), and this is consistent with some of the available
data. However, it implies that surface and linear
measurements also are sigmoid in time, and this is not
always the case. The simplest way of representing the
accelerating and retarding components of growth, acting
without any discontinuity, is to put

$$dw/dt = aw^m - cw^n \qquad (3)$$

where, provided that $n > m$ and $a > c$, the first term will
determine an initial acceleration which will later be
overtaken by the effect of the second, retardation-term.
This is the general form of the von Bertalanffy metabolic
relation. Robertson (1908) in his *logistic* relation put
$m = 1$ and $n = 2$, which permits a simple factorization of
the expression: $dw/dt = w(a - cw)$, with the biological
rationale that growth-rate is proportional to the interaction of a factor which increases as w (the intrinsic
exponential tendency) and a second factor which decreases
linearly in w. The main objection to this logistic
relation is that it implies an inflection at

$w = \frac{1}{2} w_{\max}$. which is later than in most actual records.

Pearl and Reed (1925) attempted to modify the logistic to
correct this feature, but the relation then became very
cumbersome and also less plausible biologically. The

derived logistic, $w = e^{-t}/(1 + e^{-t})^2$, which Robertson
later used (Baas Becking, 1945), retains reasonable
simplicity and gives an asymmetrical curve, but again is
biologically inferior and does not fit the data-very well.
In this setting, von Bertalanffy's metabolic relation
seems the best, if not the only reasonable, solution.

THE METABOLIC RELATION OF GROWTH

    To give the observed early inflection in the size/
time curves, $n - m$ must be less than unity and it is
difficult to find rationale for this if either m must be

unity or n must $= 2$. The problem is removed if $n = 1$, when m may take values between 2/3 and unity. This implies an acceleratory factor proportional to body-surface, or partly to surface and partly to mass, and a deceleratory component proportional simply to mass. This is the basis of von Bertalanffy's metabolic model of growth (1957, 1960, 1964).

It is reasonable to suppose that growth represents the excess of anabolism over catabolism and that these are respectively represented by the terms aw^m and cw^n in equation (3). It also seems that catabolism is indeed proportional to the active mass of the body. There is evidence for this from nitrogen-excretion (von Bertalanffy, 1960, p. 203) and from weight-loss during starvation (1960, p. 179). Accepting this value for n, the expression (3) becomes:

$$dw/dt = aw^m - cw \qquad\qquad (4)$$

which integrates relatively easily to:

$$w = \left[a/c - (a/c - w_0{}^{1-m})\, e^{-(1-m)\,ct}\right]\, 1/(1-m) \qquad (5)$$

where w_0 is the value of w at t_0, the time of onset of the phase of growth covered by the relation, and a/c is the cube-root of the limiting value of w. It will be noted that this value is a species constant and is independent of the time variable. This is in keeping with actual evidence and, in fact, is recognized in all of the more plausible relations proposed: growth is said to be *equifinal*. A printer's error in one version of this relation, in the 1960 paper, has been pointed out (von Bertalanffy, 1966).

As long as m is not greater than 2/3 there is the interesting situation that weight and volume will give a sigmoid curve in time whereas length and other linear measurements will follow a so-called *decaying exponential* relation, without an inflection. Now logically the value of m cannot be less than 2/3 since this would imply a rate of anabolism inversely proportional to size (v.B., 1960,

p. 202). Nevertheless, this discriminating difference
between the length and the weight curves does appear to
hold in many species (v.B., 1960; Beverton and Holt, 1957)
so that here the evidence in favour of a precisely
surface-dependent anabolism-term is as strong as it could
possibly be. However, it is necessary to emphasize that
in fact there are also records of sigmoid length/time
curves, implying a higher value of m, and that they
indicate considerable variation in this value (see below).
Since an inflection must appear in the length curve
immediately when m exceeds 2/3, it is remarkable that
uninflected curves should be observed at all frequently.
It might be anticipated that any slight fluctuation in
conditions would introduce a slight early inflection in
the length/time curve of organisms even when, in effect,
they do obey an m = 2/3 relation. Such early inflections
have been recorded, but not frequently, so the relation is
not very easily disturbed by fortuitous factors and the
2/3 rule is adhered to very closely.

Indeed the decaying exponential relation effectively
fits linear measurements often enough to have been used
rather extensively (Pütter, 1920; von Bertalanffy, 1934).
At one time, this type of curve was thought to correspond
to that of a monomolecular reaction $(dw/dt = a - cw)$, but
this is now felt to be too naive. A zero value of m would
be inadmissible by the theory of von Bertalanffy.

There is positive evidence also that anabolism really
is often related to surface-area, the 2/3 power of weight.
In micro-organisms the intake of materials appears to be
surface-dependent (v.B., 1960, p. 180) and the plankton-
intake of the sardine is proportional to gut-size, which
in turn is related to body-area (Yoneda and Yoshida, 1955;
Yoshida, 1956). In the rat the weight of the gut
increases very nearly as the square of the body-length
(Spencer and Coulombe, 1965); the gut is a hollow tube so
that its area is proportional to its weight, and
assimilation-surface is again proportional to body-area.
This has been shown also for a planarian (von Bertalanffy,
1940).

The measurement of assimilation-areas is not always
easy, and the active area is often an uncertain fraction

of the total. Further, the rate of assimilation may not remain simply proportional to area of assimilation. For these and other reasons, von Bertalanffy has made more use of oxygen-consumption as the measure of anabolic rate. According to Rubner's classical surface rule, oxygen consumption is typically related to surface-area and this seems well established for many invertebrates and poikilo-thermic vertebrates. In general, it is these same animals which have a value of m, in the growth-equation, approximating to 2/3, a sigmoid curve of weight-growth, and a decaying exponential for length. In a number of cases respiratory rate and growth have been measured on the same species. Often this was performed by independent workers.

When $m = 2/3$, equation (5) simplifies to:

$$w_o = \left[\sqrt[3]{w_{max}} - (\sqrt[3]{w_{max}} - \sqrt[3]{w_o})\, e^{-ct/3} \right]^3 \qquad (6)$$

This may also be written:

$$(pl)^3 = p^3 \left[l_{max} - (l_{max} - l_o)\, e^{-ct/3} \right]^3$$

where p is the proportionality constant between l and $\sqrt[3]{w}$ ($p = \sqrt[3]{w}/l$).

Hence: $$l = l_{max} - (l_{max} - l_o)\, e^{-ct/3} \qquad (7)$$

or: $$1/1_{max} = 1 - ke^{-ct/3} \qquad (8)$$

where $k = (1 - l_o)/l_{max}$.

Consequently $w/w_{max} = \left[1 - ke^{-ct/3} \right]^3$.

In mammals (Kleiber, 1947), pulmonates (von Bertalanffy and Müller, 1943) and other animals (Zeuthen, 1947), metabolic rate and oxygen-consumption are proportional to a power of w nearer to 3/4 than to 2/3; and the growth-curves in these groups are consistent with this, being sigmoid for both length and weight. Like the

value of m, the size-dependence of respiratory rate varies
quite considerably between species, for instance, even
within the sub-class Prosobranchia and the sub-class
Pulmonata (Berg and Ockelmann, 1959). If the m value of
the growth-curve could be shown statistically to be highly
correlated with the size-dependence index of respiration,
throughout a large sample of species, then the whole
theory would be well established, including the
respiration-dependence of anabolism (p.602).

If m is as high as unity, of course, dw/dt is simply
related to w and growth should be exponential (p.594). It
does indeed appear to approximate to this pattern in
insects, in some pulmonates (von Bertalanffy, 1960,
p. 197) and in some rod-shaped bacteria (1960, p. 180).
Moreover it is in these organisms that either respiration
or assimilation has been found simply weight-dependent.
The respiration-index seems to be highest in the most
fully terrestrial animals (Will, 1952). The fish,
Savelinus, therefore, seems to be exceptional in having a
respiration-index approaching unity and an exponential
size/time curve (von Bertalanffy, 1960, p. 205).

Ludwig von Bertalanffy (1960, 1964) recognizes three
growth-types according to these values of the anabolism-
index, m, namely 2/3, 1, or some intermediate value.
Because of the sharp changes in the size/time curves at the
two extremes, this is perhaps reasonable though it might
be equally fair to emphasize that there is a continuous
spectrum of values, and to concentrate on demonstrating a
close correlation between the respiration- and anabolism-
indices, whatever their actual values. There are in fact
a few awkward values recorded for the respiration-index.
Berg and Ockelmann (1959) recorded values as low as 0.45
in some pulmonates and Whitney (1942) and Mann (1956)
found values probably significantly greater than 1 in some
planarians and leeches. It will be important to obtain
the parameters of the growth-curves in authentic cases of
such extreme respiration-pattern.

The size-dependence of respiration in a particular
species is not absolutely constant. For instance, it
varies with season in some gastropods (Berg and Ockelmann,
1959). However, von Bertalanffy and Müller (1943) found

that the growth of the snail, *Eulota fructicum*, has a
similar seasonal variation. Exercise affects the
respiration-relation and is also well known to compete
with growth. These variations may prove support for von
Bertalanffy's relation since they provide additional means
for testing it. This is equally true for variations in
the coefficients a and c. Thus in the guppy, *Lebistes
reticulatus*, the ratio of the values of a obtained from
the growth curves of the male and female is 1.5, and the
respiratory rates of the two sexes bear precisely the same
ratio (von Bertalanffy, 1960, p. 198). Values of c,
calculated from the growth-curves of various organisms,
agree with values obtained from studies of protein-
turnover in the same organism. Protein does not account
for the whole of catabolism but it is probably a fairly
constant fraction of this.

Much of the strength of the metabolic relation lies
in its general flexibility, its recognition that the
parameters vary between species and with varying
conditions in the same species. For instance, it can
probably explain also the observation of Hugget and Widdas
(1951) that in the mammalian foetus, body-length increases
linearly in time. This may be because the catabolic term
is negligible, not only because w is small but also
because the mother performs the catabolic function for the
foetus. Consequently, $dw/dt = aw^{2/3}$, so that $3w^{1/3} = at + b$
where b is the constant of integration. It is important
to be sure that such tests really do demonstrate
flexibility and strength rather than laxity and backlash,
and that the gain in generality outweighs the loss in
specificity. Some cells grow linearly in time (Needham,
1964): again w is small, and catabolism may be negligible
in rapidly proliferating cells.

This flexibility is very relevant to Medawar's
important verdict (Medawar, 1945, p. 159) that there is
no such thing as a universal growth-equation. The
conclusion was partly based on the variety of equations
which had been fitted to available data; a single flexible
relation might very well remove this difficulty. At the
same time, it also disposes of the logical demand for a
rigid, universal law of growth, which dominated work in
the field for so long. Medawar's judgment depended also

on the fact that no biologically significant growth-relation considered up to that time could be mathematically valid for both the whole organism and for its constituent parts. This disability applies equally to the metabolic relation. The sum of a set of equations of this type is not itself an isomorphous relation except in special, and therefore biologically trivial, cases. In general, therefore, the conclusion has been that such relations could be useful only for empirical ready-reckoning and not for biological interpretation. The metabolic relation must also face this judgment.

Quite apart from the particular merits of this, or any other relation, the time has perhaps come to re-examine the finality of the demand for a universal relation in these two senses, i.e. for all taxa and for all parts of the body. In both, the views of logician, mathematician, physical scientist, and biological mechanist all tend to concur and are not to be challenged without good reason. However, in their application to biology the views of all must be screened by biological reality. Their authority depends entirely on the supposition that biological activity is simply mechanistic. In *Modern Theories of Development*, von Bertalanffy (1933) advocated an organismic theory of life in preference to mechanism and to other theories, and his case has strengthened in certain respects in the intervening years. There are certainly no grounds for supposing that living systems contravene any law of the physical sciences, but there is growing evidence that the emergent complexity and variety of biological systems has been under-estimated. Natural selection has produced end-results which often answer simple purposes, and so on the surface they may betray little clue to the complexity of the processes of intermediation.

In the present context, the possibility is that the overall growth of an organism may be controlled by a few dominant factors so that a relatively simple mathematical relation usefully and significantly defines them. On the other hand, the details of growth in the individual organs may be controlled by a wide variety of regional and regionally varying factors. There is often a good deal of differential growth within the body and the size/time

curve for some measurements must differ very considerably
from that of the body as a whole. In passing it may be
suggested that this is equally relevant to the objection
of Haldane (see Huxley, 1932, p. 81) to the allometric
relation of differential growth (Huxley, 1932; Reeve and
Huxley, 1945) on the grounds that this relation (p.609)
can not apply both to a particular measurement and to its
component parts.

Some degree of variation between the growth-relations
for different taxonomic groups, as countenanced by the
metabolic equation, also seems reasonable, both on the
grounds already considered and on genetic grounds. The
broad genetic features tend to be universal and the
details subject to essential variation and selection. For
this reason a vast amount of parallelism and convergence
is possible, and it need not prove fatal to the metabolic
theory of growth that within any one group of animals the
parameters can take virtually the full permissible range
of values.

In this emancipated situation it is worth reconsider-
ing all reasonable size/time relations, but it does seem
that the metabolic relation at present has the strongest
appeal at this initial level of analysis. Criticisms have
been levelled at it but none seem to threaten its
foundations seriously. One further criticism which might
at first seem pertinent is that catabolism makes much
greater demands than anabolism on respiratory energy and,
therefore, it should prove to be the component most
closely related to respiration. In mammals, for instance,
surface-dependent heat-loss has been considered the main
determinant of the respiration index. By contrast, the
fabric formed in growth is not more fully oxidized than
the materials from which it is formed and, indeed, in
plants it is much more fully reduced while the energy
expended in the process, the *work of growth*, is a
relatively small percentage of the total energy-exchange
of the growing body (Needham, 1964). However, it must be
appreciated that the anabolism term in the metabolic
relation in fact represents the *whole* of metabolism, since
growth is there symbolised as the amount by which it
exceeds catabolism. Within the catabolism term must be
envisaged not only the work of growth, maintenance and all

other activities but also the repair of damaged fabric.
Like the work function this repair item increases
proportionately to body weight and so contributes to the
ultimate arrest of growth, as expressed in the relation.
Ultimately catabolism comes to equal total metabolism, or
'gross anabolism.'

These considerations should also help to resolve an
objection (Medawar, 1945, p. 159) to this type of relation
on the grounds that there is no biochemical entity to
which the term 'growth-metabolism' may be applied. The
postulated entity is in fact gross anabolism and the net
growth is obtained, mathematically, as the excess of this
term over the catabolism-term. With the increasing use of
labelled raw materials, of course, it is becoming possible
to measure more directly metabolic turnover and the
relative proportions of neoformation (growth) and replacement. Consequently, methods of measuring growth-
metabolism and, at the same time, additional means of
testing the von Bertalanffy relation are now available.
He himself has made considerable use of the results of
turnover-studies. As expected, the rate of outflow from
turnover agrees well with the catabolism coefficient, c,
obtained from growth data. It is not certain that von
Bertalanffy himself always visualizes the anabolism-term
as precisely gross anabolism or total assimilation (e.g.,
1960, p. 195), but this would seem essential. Assimilated
material either contributes to growth or is oxidized to
spare energy reserves or replaces reserves which have been
oxidized. Unless the anabolism term has this gross significance, it can scarcely be closely related to
respiration. There is, of course, a certain amount of
assimilated material which is excreted incompletely
oxidized and this product should be excluded from the
gross anabolism-term. If the latter is equated with total
metabolism, in effect it is excluded, but there is
probably no great error in equating the term with gross
assimilation.

The metabolic relation has been used by a number of
workers in recent years (von Bertalanffy, 1960, p. 204),
particularly for fitting the growth of fish (Yoneda and
Yoshida, 1955; Beverton and Holt, 1957; Tomlinson and
Abramson, 1961; Wohlschlag, 1962; Abramson, 1965;

Southward and Chapman, 1965; Allen, 1966; Phillips and
Campbell, 1968). Beverton and his colleagues have
formulated in great detail the dynamics of fish size and
numbers for commercial purposes so that accuracy of
fitting is more important perhaps than biological
rationale, but they have also considered from this aspect
the relative merits of the relation compared with its most
serious rivals. Their decision was entirely in its favour
and they introduced a simplifying modification to facilitate its incorporation into models defining aspects of the
behaviour of the population. Wohlschlag (1962) was able
to explain sex differences in growth and metabolism in the
fish, *Trematomus*, in terms of the von Bertalanffy
relation. Among recent studies is that of Fabens (1965)
using computer methods of fitting to data by Barwick on
the lizard, *Hoplodactylus*. Approximate values of the
parameters of the equation were first obtained from the
raw data by least squares methods and the computer was
then used to improve the values by reiteration of the
Newton-Raphson formula. It is probably significant that
usually only about six reiterations were necessary,
compared with the hundreds required by McCredie *et al*
(1965) when fitting the Gompertz relation (p.605) to other
data. Computer methods were used by Tomlinson and
Abramson (1961), Abramson (1965), Southward and Chapman
(1965), and Allen (1966) as well.

OTHER RELATIONS OF SIZE/TIME

At present, the Gompertz relation in fact seems to be
the most serious rival to the metabolic relation at this
level while the logistic (p.596) appears to be losing
favour increasingly. In addition to the reasons already
given for this, Beverton and Holt (1957) object to the
implication that growth rate is dependent on a term in w^2.
Feller (1940) concluded that the logistic had no
advantages over other relations and Spiegelman (1946)
objected that one, if not two, of its parameters are
biologically meaningless. Kavanagh and Richards (1934)
pointed out that the logistic is approximated by a
probability distribution whereas Beverton and Holt (1957)
emphatically rule out fortuity as the basis of growth-
control in fishes. Harris (1959) and others however have

been prepared to regard growth at the cellular level as
the sum of many stochastic events, and it is perhaps significant that Leslie (1957) found the logistic to fit very
well some of Gause's data on populations of *Paramecium*.
Nelder (1961) has used a generalization of the logistic,
which includes the exponential, monomolecular (p.597), and
Gompertz relations as special cases, and this might be
claimed to re-establish the logistic as the focus of a
comprehensive group comparable in scope to the metabolic
spectrum of relations. The greater heterogeneity of the
group, however, and the objections to the logistic itself
react strongly in favour of von Bertalanffy's set of
relations. The generalized logistic certainly seems to
lose more in specificity than it gains in generality.

Notwithstanding its esoteric, transcendental form,
the Gompertz relation fits some data very well, and has
recently been used by Laird *et al.*(1965) and McCredie *et
al.*(1965). The former found a straight line relationship
between the logarithm of the specific growth rate and
time, as required by the Gompertz relation, and they
showed that the logistic implies a very different curve.
They rejected the von Bertalanffy relation because they
were dealing with tissues *in vitro* and considered that
metabolism plays only a subsidiary role here. It would be
useful to know if in fact, and in consequence, this
relation fits their data less well than the Gompertz one.

McCredie *et al.*used a computer to fit the Gompertz to
their own data on the growth of tumours *in vivo*, as well
as to existing data by Streeter on human foetal growth.
The fitting to some of their own results was very good and
that to Streeter's data rather poorer, so that it seems
possible that the Gompertz is particularly appropriate to
metazoan cell-populations *in vitro*, or in the semi-
isolation of a tumour. Medawar (1940) also was working
with cells *in vitro* but a systemic metazoan type of
inhibitor figured in his rationale for selecting this
relation. Weymouth *et al.*(1931) in fact fitted the
relation to growth in a lamellibranch and to Donaldson's
data on the intact rat, so that its application needs
further examination.

FURTHER LEVELS OF ANALYSIS

The most important of recent new approaches in the field of absolute growth, because it increases the depth of analysis, is that of Weiss and Kavanau (1957), extended by Kavanau (1960). They fitted to data on the growth of the chick a relation of the same general type as that of von Bertalanffy, i.e., in which growth-rate is determined by the algebraical sum of promotor and depressor terms, but in these terms they specified a promotor/depressor pair of control-factors in addition to anabolism and catabolism. Their formulation also included the effect of differentiation in cells, regarded as terminating their growth-activity. The preliminary formulation and fitting, as well as the computer-work, were formidable tasks and for the present preclude the general use of the method by practicing auxologists. It was necessary to use, in all, 30 mathematical symbols, a large proportion of them parameters which had to be evaluated from the data. Moreover, with this number and the computer facility, the excellence of fit was naturally outstanding and this might be taken to weaken rather than strengthen any claims for a unique relevance of the factors postulated.

At the most, of course, the relation confirms the operation of unspecified promotor and depressor factors and the authors' use of the terms 'templates' and 'anti-templates' was perhaps unfortunate. The former is now somewhat outmoded and both are rather hypothetical in the context. The identification of the latter with organ-specific inhibitors is even more uncertain and in any case the data used were for the whole animal. To settle for unspecified promotor and depressor agents would greatly improve the general acceptance of the formulation and the recognition ofı its merit in extending the level of growth-analysis. As von Bertalanffy says (1960, p. 211) "... it may lead to a more detailed analysis of the overall process of growth."

The authors point out that for a population of micro-organisms the formulation should be simpler, since there is no complication of differentiation or of systemic controls. There are, however, systematic changes in the

cells in the course of a population cycle, and there are
also communal influences (Needham, 1964) so that the
mathematics may not differ very greatly from those of
growth in a metazoan.

The formulation has the great additional merit of
accommodating any disturbance of growth, and this was
tested on liver-regeneration (Kavanau, 1960). It should
also lead to realistic estimates of the relative
proportions of proliferating and non-proliferating cells,
for comparison with independent estimates of the ratio of
non-differentiated to differentiated cells; unfortunately,
however, good independent estimates of the latter are
still very scanty. Since the postulated depressor factor
is autogenous it forms part of a negative feedback-
mechanism and the relation gives an oscillatory approach
to the limiting size. The authors suggest that this is
usual, in practice (cf. Richards and Kavanagh, 1945,
p. 194), but has been overlooked or ignored by most
observers. Goodwin (1964) in fact suggests that such
oscillatory ('talandic') behaviour may be more general and
may underlie circadian and other observed periodic
activities. In population-dynamics such oscillations are,
of course, commonplace (Andrewartha and Birch, 1954), and
they may play a more important part in individual growth
than so far admitted. The more detailed formulation may
be necessary to fit these complications, though in
population-growth, in fact, the simple logistic predicts
them under certain conditions (Cook, 1965).

Diurnal and other short-term oscillations are of
course invisible on the typical, rather coarse-grained
records of growth, but seasonal and other long-term cycles
are often evident. Other, more obscure, periods also are
sometimes found. There are three main cycles in the
growth curve of man (Thompson, 1942, p. 160) and four in
that of the mouse. Because it is easier to collect the
data, so-called growth-curves are often in fact size-
distribution curves against age for a population of the
species (Cook, 1966). This may smooth out small
oscillations in individual growth and it may convert sharp
changes into smooth sigmoid phases (Medawar, 1945). For
this level of analysis adequate reliable data on the
growth of individuals under steady, natural conditions

is a first essential. This is a very stringent condition
for any but a few laboratory animals.

Fig. 1. Ventral view of female (above) and male
pea-crab, *Pinnotheres pisum*, to show the markedly
differential growth of the abdomen relative to
the cephalothorax, in the female, and the change
in shape within the abdomen. That of the
juvenile female is similar to that of the male
(which is not much bigger than a juvenile
female).   [Photo: J.S. Haywood]

DIFFERENTIAL GROWTH

Once size/time has been adequately defined, it is
logical to turn to shape/time (Medawar, 1945), i.e., to
the distribution of growth within the body. Actually, it
is evident from the literature that these interests have
run parallel and not in series, and this is not without
justification in view of the difficulties in mathematically defining absolute growth. Clues for the whole may come
from a study of its parts. It was of course intuitively
evident that regional growth is often strongly differential, as for instance the abdomen of the female of
the pea crab (Fig. 1) relative to thorax (Needham, 1950).
D'Arcy Thompson (1942), in his Cartesian transformation
method, developed a particularly striking and directly
pictorial method of demonstrating this as a continuous
function of two dimensions. The geographical contour
method (Needham, 1937; 1964) is less directly pictorial
but potentially more quantitative. Both have the limitation of presenting only two points in time. Ideally, a
complete definition of shape/time should give each point
in the three-dimensional body as a continuous function of
its position and of time, i.e., $p = f(x, y, z, t)$. Some
success has been achieved in this direction (p.610) but as
in the case of absolute growth less ambitious methods have
much practical value. Recently, Sneath (1967) has
extended the Cartesian transformation method by applying
the geological technique of trend-surface analysis, an
extension with considerable potentialities, though
laborious and technically demanding.

As a counterpart of the Cartesian transformation
method, defining space continuously for two selected
times, the algebraical, simple allometry relation (Huxley,
1932; Reeve and Huxley, 1945) relates two selected measurements as a continuous function of time. If the two
measurements are y and x, it is found that they are often
related quite simply by the power-relation, $y = bx^k$, where
b and k are constants. The rationale for this is that the
specific growth rates of y and x maintain a constant
ratio, as may be seen if the relation is written in its
logarithmic form. This simple allometry relation has
proved very useful in many ways, not least in stimulating

interest in differential growth.   There are, however,
serious objections to regarding it as a general law even
if we do not consider Haldane's criticism as insuperable
(p.605).   At least this criticism proves that the
relation can not hold between every two measurements in
the body.

von Bertalanffy (1957; 1960) has remained strongly in
favour of the simple allometry relation also because, in
some cases, there are sound functional reasons why it
should hold.   For instance, the gut may increase in weight
proportionately to the surface of the body (p.597), a
terrestrial animal's legs must increase in sectional area
proportionately to the weight of the body, and the bird's
wing-muscles in weight proportionately to the 7/6 power of
body-weight (Thompson, 1942, p. 41).   Modifications of the
simple allometry equation have been suggested, but it
remains the most satisfactory relation between two
selected measurements taking all considerations into
account.   Many physiological functions (Adolph, 1949) and
biochemical components (J. Needham, 1934) are thus related
to body-size - as, for instance, respiration (p.599).   If
one of these materials or activities in turn determines
the size of a particular organ or part, then this also
might have a simple allometric relation to body-size.
This is to imply that the relation may have specific
rather than universal validity.   As in the case of
absolute growth (p.603) a flexible outlook seems
justified.

For empirical use, and as a taxonomic label, the
value of the simple allometry relation has been repeatedly
stressed (Huxley, 1932; Reeve, 1941; Hersh, 1941; von
Bertalanffy and Pirozynski, 1952; Rensch, 1956; von
Bertalanffy, 1960; Gould, 1966).   After Huxley, Teissier
(1937; 1948; 1960) has probably done most to develop and
exploit the relation and its corollaries.   It is an
invaluable aid in *similarity analysis* (see below).

The first serious attempt to define shape, or form
(shape × size), in detail as a continuous function of
space and time, i.e., integrally, was that of Medawar
(1944, 1945).   Data were available only for a single
spatial dimension.   Needham (1950) adapted the method to

a somewhat different situation. Hewlett (1944) used a
different method, again for a single spatial dimension.
Richards and Kavanagh (1945) developed general relations
giving the specific rate of growth in volume, area and
linear measurements at any point and any moment, the
linear growth being further defined in all directions at
that point. They applied their relations to an actual
case in two dimensions. Unfortunately, the relations are
too complex for ready integration so as to define form/
time. As in the more ambitious methods of analysis of
absolute growth (p.606), the mathematical labour becomes
formidable. Computer methods should materially improve
this situation.

On the assumption that the shape of an organism is
essentially a functional property, it should be possible
to define its change during growth by the technique of
similarity analysis as used by engineers to scale up or
down their working models. Lambert and Teissier (1927)
and, more recently, Günther and Guerra (1955) have applied
this technique to biological growth and the latter
attempted to apply Newton's reduction coefficient for
mechanical similarities, to simplify the procedure. This
reduces to one the effective scaling factors, called
similarity criteria (Stahl, 1963 a. and b.). Stahl dis-
cusses the method in the broader context of physiological
functions in general, and (1963 b.) uses the von
Bertalanffy relation in applying it to growth. The first
aim of this approach is to obtain a *scaling law* for each
anatomical and physiological variable as a power function
of some one standard dimension, length or mass. The rule
of dimensional homogeneity should be observed in all
equations and the standard dimensions, mass, length, time,
etc., must be regarded as an Abelian system, amenable to
multiplication and division but not to addition or sub-
traction. In practice different variables may have
different scaling factors, and in constructing model
systems it is rarely possible to hold more than two or
three similarity criteria constant. Biological systems
are complex, and Günther and Guerra were probably not
justified in seeking the simplicity of a single similarity
criterion. This method of defining form therefore is not
necessarily simpler than the more direct methods already

considered. However, among its advantages is the ability
to pool anatomical and physiological data.

This view that shape is determined by its prospective
function is not necessarily incompatible with the
suggestion (p.609) that simple allometry is due to
regional variations in growth-potential. The latter could
be the more proximate cause for the former. More
intriguing would be evidence that differential growth is
sometimes dictated by the exigencies of the growth process
itself (Needham, 1964). Possible examples of this include
those of Turing (1952) and Green (1965). Turing showed
how distinctive structural patterns might be the automatic
result of certain intrinsic features of growth, and a
simpler example of this, perhaps relevant to growth, is
the Liesegang periodicity (Hedges, 1932). It is, of
course, questionable if any functional malformations
resulting from exigencies of the growth-process could
survive for long the test of natural selection, but this
question is worth specific investigation.

Another group of indirect techniques for investigating growth-patterns is that of multi-factorial analysis
(Yates, 1950; Olson and Miller, 1958; Kraus and Choi,
1958; Blackith, 1965). This aims at expressing a group of
variables in terms of their significant controlling
factors. Each variable is defined as a linear regression
on its relevant factors and the whole is then treated as a
typical matrix, here called the *factor pattern* (Harman,
1960). Unless the factors are all uncorrelated it is
necessary to derive a further matrix, the *factor
structure*, giving the correlations between all factors and
all variables. This set of equations can then be solved
for the individual coefficients of the various factors
affecting each variable.

As applied to growth in an individual organism, the
so-called P-technique (Olson and Miller, 1958), the
variables are a set of size-measurements over a relevant
time-interval and the operative factors are any which
influence the growth of the measurements. The factors are
mathematically extracted from the matrix of growth-data by
a reiterative procedure, until the residual 'variance' in
size-change becomes insignificant. There are a number of

alternative methods of obtaining the factors, each with its particular merits and demerits. The factors obtained are initially mathematical abstractions, to which biological meaning or identity must be attributed by the investigator (Yates, 1950; Harman, 1960). The method gives simply (1) the number of *general factors*, common to all the variables, (2) the number common to a group of variables (*group factors*), (3) any factors peculiar to particular variables (*unique factors*), and (4) the total variance due to each. It settles the problem of how many and what type of factors there are, which must eventually be given biological meaning. Its further great contribution is in concentrating on the control or interpretation of form rather than on its mere definition - bypassing the means for the end, in fact. Nevertheless we do also require the definition, as a record of the precise mode of operation of the factors.

In the growth of the legs of the crab, *Maia*, Teissier (1948), using Sewall Wright's *path coefficients* method, found that one general factor accounted for as much as 92-94% of the growth variance, a group factor for a further 3-6%, and a local factor, acting most strongly on the most anterior legs, for a further 3%, leaving a residual variance of less than 1%. Kraus and Choi (1958) analyzed the growth of the limb skeletons of the human foetus and obtained very similar results. The first principal factor is a general one and takes out 94.1% of the total variance. The second, a group factor affecting mainly the distal phalanges, takes out 3.3%, the third affects mainly the middle phalanges and accounts for only 1.0%, while the fourth affects mainly the proximal phalanges, with a variance-contribution of 0.6%. The residual variance is less than 1% and no more significant factors need be visualized. This result is in keeping with existing knowledge of a number of genetically distinct types of brachydactyly, each affecting particular phalanges or metacarpals. It seems possible that a single distal growth-centre, moving its position with time, might account for factors 2-4.

The multi-factorial method is applicable also to a single measurement through a number of individuals (Baker, 1954) or through a set of type-members of a number of

species, i.e., to genetic factors again (Cock, 1966).   In
principle it could also be applied to one measurement at a
series of time-intervals, the latter being the variables;
the aim here would be to see if different factors operate
on the one measurement in different phases of the growth
period.   The method has been applied to taxonomic studies
by Sokal (1962) and by Sokal and Sneath (1963).   Its
application to these and to finer-grained genetic
variation is very critically discussed by Cock (1966) in
the wider setting of current quantitative approaches to
the analysis of growth and form.

Of course, in all these methods the choice of mea-
surement-variables is somewhat arbitrary, and necessarily
a restricted abstraction from the integral growth pattern.
Moreover, in principle, the direct, integral methods also
can be used for a kind of factor analysis.   For instance,
in the Medawar method (p.610) each point (p) was first
defined as a function of its position along one body-axis
(x), and the parameters of this relation were then defined
as a function of time (t).   In principle the residual
parameters could, in turn, be similarly defined as
functions of the remaining spatial dimensions (y, z) and
then of such relevant factors as temperature (T),
nutritional level (n), hormonal level (h), etc., giving:

$$p = f(x, \ y, \ z, \ t, \ T, \ n, \ h, \ \ldots)$$

The result could be a definition rivalling in precision
those of the more exact sciences and certainly surpassing
them in complexity.   In practice, however, the project
would grind to a halt after two or three steps, except in
the most trivial of cases, and it is doubtful if computer
methods could yet make the method practicable.   In
addition, the successive approximations in the fitting
procedure place a heavy onus on the accuracy of the
initial measurements.

Both problems might be significantly, if not
dramatically, eased by skillful exploratory methods to
find the best order of treating the relevant variables;
for instance, the three spatial dimensions should
probably be taken in direct sequence, if not

simultaneously as in Richards and Kavanagh's method (p. 21).
It is reasonable to anticipate that various other simplifi-
cations could be effected and that this might improve the
veracity as well as the utlity of the relations obtained.
It might indeed make its own contribution to the analysis
of growth by helping to decide between alternative theories
about how factors act and interact so as to produce the
observed growth-patterns. This is not the technical counterpart of the circular argument but applies the principle of
expediency, which is considered a legitimate part of the
scientific method (Harman, 1960, p. 21). The similarity
method (p. 21) can be developed in a rather comparable way
to embrace all relevant factors (Stahl, 1963, a., p. 315)
and might perhaps claim to be the simplest method of doing
so.

    In the exact sciences, remarkable success has been
achieved with very simple relations, and, indeed, the most
important have usually been the simplest. It would be
pertinent, therefore, to question the value of relatively
complex biological relations and still more of any attempts
to define growth-patterns in great detail and so to complicate them still further. The main answer to this is
that the biologist is interested in the individual and not
in the statistical mean, even down to the macromolecular
level. This outlook, and the complexity, therefore, are
unavoidable. The simple universal relation may be suspect
(p. 10) for this reason also. Ludwig von Bertalanffy has
achieved, in his relation, the greatest simplicity consistent
with biological rationale, and, at the same time, he has
fully recognized biological variability.

CONCLUSION

    In all, there appears to be strong vindication of
von Bertalanffy's faith that mathematical methods, of reasonable simplicity, can contribute materially to the study of
both absolute and differential growth. As an empirical
and labelling device, for taxonomic and other comparative
purposes, any reasonably well-fitting relation may be adequate. Even so, where two or more have equal claims to
best fitting then preference should be given to the one

with greatest biological rationale. Moreover, for comparative studies, which probably make most call on available data, reasonably comprehensive relations are very desirable, so that in fact the further quest for a biologically meaningful mathematics is inevitable. This has also been von Bertalanffy's conviction.

The initial choice of a comprehensive and biologically ideal relation is necessarily somewhat arbitrary, but the arbitrary choice of a working hypothesis, provided it is responsibly exercised, is considered legitimate even in the exact sciences. We may join Harman (1960, p. 21) in quoting from Moulton, on such a crucial subject as the relation for obtaining the velocity of light: "... every set of phenomena can be interpreted consistently in a great variety of ways, in fact in infinitely many ways. It is our privilege to choose among the possible interpretations the ones which appear to us most satisfactory, whatever the reason for our choice." In fact the biologist has very good reason when he invokes biological rationale, and on this score von Bertalanffy's relation is as acceptable as any. Having made the choice, there is no call to recant unless it subsequently proves inadequate. In this instance there has been more favourable than contrary evidence, and more support than for alternative relations. However, a thesis can not remain indefinitely in the no-man's-land between non-rejection and full acceptance, and the stronger the evidence in its favour the greater the desire to finalize the position. To this end, it would be useful to have more examples, from a variety of groups of animals, in which there were adequate parallel data on both aspects - growth and metabolism. The present apparent difficulties and uncertainties could then be resolved. The intuitive feeling is that the thesis may need minor modifications but will not be rejected.

There is already some movement towards a more detailed representation of growth, particularly of regional growth, but this still presents formidable technical problems. In the future, therefore, there will probably be increasing emphasis on more indirect methods - methods with some of the qualities of impressionism in art. They share with this technique the virtues of

simplicity and speed without serious loss of effectiveness, thereby avoiding the clutter of unnecessary detail.
It is relevant here to quote with Stahl (1963a.) from
K.S. Cole on the subject of a model of the axonal
membrane: "... the further progress of physiology may
depend to a large extent on phenomenonological generalizations such as this ... in which sordid details of
mechanism can be ignored without loss of operational
utility." In the present context, there is the possibility of adding further details later, as required, with
a precision impossible without the cartographic framework.

The study of growth illustrates very well the advantages of combining a number of independent approaches to a
subject. This applies not only within the mathematical
field but also between this and the genetic, morpho-
genetic, physiological and biochemical approaches. Ludwig
von Bertalanffy has contributed to all of these fields but
particularly to the combination of the mathematical and
the physiological and biochemical approaches. Moreover,
his contributions have been made mainly during a period
when, with few exceptions (Krebs, 1950), biochemists
interested in growth were carried along too rapidly by the
tide of their own new techniques to be able to collaborate
with other disciplines (Needham, 1964). His name stands
with those of Rubner (1908), Robertson (1923), Huxley
(1932), Thompson (1942), and Brody (1945). On this
important occasion for stock-taking, students of growth
everywhere will wish to add their tribute to this and
other aspects of his achievement.

REFERENCES

ABRAMSON, N.J., *Trans. American Fisheries Soc.*, *94*, 195,
1965,

ADOLPH, E.F., *Science*, *109*, 579, 1949.

ALLEN, K.R., *Journal of the Fisheries Research Board of
Canada*, *23*, 163, 1966.

ANDREWARTHA, H.G., and L.C. BIRCH, *The Distribution and
Abundance of Animals*. Chicago: Chicago University Press,
1954.

BAAS BECKING, L.G.M., *Acta biotheoretica, 8, 42, 1945.*

BACKMANN, G., *Arch. Entw. mech. Org., 141, 455, 1941.*

BAKER, G.A., *Growth, 18, 137, 1954.*

BERG, K., and OCKELMANN, K.W., *Journal of Experimental Biology, 36, 690, 1959.*

VON BERTALANFFY, L., *Kritische Theorie der Formbildung.* Berlin: Borntraeger, 1928.

————————————, *Modern Theories of Development.* Translated and arranged by J.H. Woodger, London: Oxford University Press, 1933.

————————————, *Arch. Entw. mech. Org., 131, 613,* 1934.

————————————, *Arch. Entw. mech. Org., 140, 81,* 1940.

————————————. Wachstum. In Kukenthal's *Handbuch der Zoologie, 8,4(6).* Berlin: De Gruyter, 1957, *Quart. Quart. Rev. Biol., 32, 217, 1957.*

————————————, *Fundamental Aspects of Normal and Malignant Growth.* NOWINSKI, W.W., (ed.), Amsterdam: Elsevier, 137-259, 1960.

————————————, *Helgol. Wiss. Meeresunters, 9,* Nos. 1-4, 5-38, 1964.

————————————, *Growth, 30, 123, 1966.*

VON BERTALANFFY, L., and MÜLLER, I., *Riv. Biol. (Perugia), 35, 48, 1943.*

VON BERTALANFFY, L., and PIROZYNSKI, W.J., *Evolution, 6, 387, 1952.*

BEVERTON, R.J.H., and HOLT, S.J. *Fishery Investigations,* Series II, Vol. XIX. London: Her Majesty's Stationery Office, 1957.

BLACKITH, R.E., *Theoretical and Mathematical Biology.* WATERMAN, T.H., and MOROWITZ, H.J., (eds.). New York: Blaisdell, 225-249, 1965.

BRODY, S., *Bioenergetics and Growth.* NewYork: Reinhold, 1945.

COCK, A.G., *Quart. Review Biol.*, *41*, 131, 1966.

COOK, L.M., *Nature*, *207*, 316, London, 1965.

FABENS, A.J., *Growth*, *29*, 265, 1965.

FELLER, W., *Acta biotheoretica*, *5 (A)*, 51, 1940.

GOODWIN, B.C., *Sympos. Soc. exp. Biol.*, *18*, 301, 1964.

GOULD, S.J., *Biol. Rev.*, *41*, 587, 1966.

GRAY, J., *J. exp. Biol.*, *6*, 248, 1929.

GREEN, P.B., *J. Cell. Biol.*, *27*, 343, 1965.

GÜNTHER, B., and E. GUERRA, *Acta Physiol. Latinoamer.*, *5*, 169, 1955.

HARMAN, H.H., *Modern Factor Analysis*. Chicago: University Press, 1960.

HARRIS, T.E., *Kinetics of Cellular Proliferation*. STOHLMAN, F.(ed.), New York: Grune & Stratton, 1 1959.

HEDGES, E.S., *Liesegang's Rings and Other Periodic Structures*. London: Chapman and Hall, 1932.

HERSH, A.H., *Growth*, *5*, Suppl. 113, 1941.

HEWLETT, P.S., *Nature*, *154*, 611, London, 1944.

HUGGETT, A.G., and W.F. WIDDAS, *Journal Physiol.*, *114*, 306, 1951.

HUXLEY, J.S., *Problems of Relative Growth*. London: Methuen, 1932.

KAVANAGH, A.J., and O.W. RICHARDS, *Amer. Nat.*, *68*, 54, 1934.

KAVANAU, J.L., *Proc. Nat. Acad. Science*, *U.S.*, *46*, 1658, 1960.

KLEIBER, M., *Physiol. Rev.*, *27*, 511, 1947.

KRAUS, B.S., and CHOI, S.C., *Growth*, *22*, 231, 1958.

KREBS, H.A., *Biochem. Biophys. Acta*, *4*, 249, 1950.

LAIRD, A.K., TYLER, S.A., and BARTON, A.D., *Growth*, *29*, 219, 233, 1965.

LAMBERT, R., and G. TEISSIER, *Ann. Physiol.*, *3*, 212, 1927.

LESLIE, P.H., *Biometrika*, *44*, 314, 1957.

LUMER, H., *Growth*, *1*, 140, 1937.

MANN, K.H., *J. exp. Biol.*, *33*, 615, 1956.

McCREDIE, J.A., W.R. INCH, J. KRUUV, and T.A. WATSON, *Growth*, *29*, 331, 1965.

MEDAWAR, P.B., *Proc. Royal Society Lond. B.*, *129*, 332, 1940

—————————, *Proc. Royal Society Lond. B.*, *132*, 133, 1944.

—————————, *Essays on Growth and Form.* LeGROS CLARK, W.E., and MEDAWAR, P.B., (eds.), Oxford: Clarendon Press, 157-187, .945.

NEEDHAM, A.E., *Proc. Zool. Soc. Lond. A.*, *107*, 289, 1937.

—————————, *Proc. Royal Soc. Lond. B.*, *137*, 115, 1950.

—————————, *Nature*, *180*, 1293, London, 1957.

—————————, *The Growth Process in Animals.* London: Pitman, 1964.

NEEDHAM, J., *Biol. Rev. Cambridge Philos. Soc.*, *9*, 79, 1934.

NELDER, J.A., *Biometrics*, *17*, 89, 1961.

OLSON, E.C., and MILLER, R.I., *Morphological Integration.* Chicago: University Press, 1958.

PEARL, R., and J. REED, *Proc. Nat. Acad. Sci. U.S.*, *14*, 573, 1925.

PHILLIPS, B.F., and N.A. CAMPBELL, *Growth*, *32*, 317, 1968.

PÜTTER, A., *Pfluger's Arch. ges. Physiol.*, *180*, 298, 1920.

REEVE, E.C.R., *Proc. Zool. Soc. Lond. A.*, *111*, 279, 1941.

REEVE, E.C.R., and J.S. HUXLEY, *Essays on Growth and Form.* LeGROS CLARK, W.E., and MEDAWAR, P.B., (eds.), Oxford: Clarendon Press, 121-156, 1945.

RENSCH, B., *Amer. Nat.*, *90*, 81, 1956.

RICHARDS, O.W., and A.J. KAVANAGH, *Essays on Growth and Form.* LeCROS GLARK, W.E., and MEDAWAR, P.B., (eds.), Oxford: Clarendon Press, 188-230, 1945.

ROBERTSON, T.B., *Arch. Entw. mech. Org.*, *25*, 4, 1908.

——————————, *The Chemical Basis of Growth and Development.* Philadelphia: Lippincott, 1923.

——————————, *Journal gen. Physiol.*, *8*, 463, 1926.

RUBNER, M., *Das Problem der Lebensdauer und seine Beziehungen zu Wachstum und Ernahrung.* Munich and Berlin: Oldenburg, 1908.

SHOLL, D.A., *Proc. Roy. Soc. Lond. B.*, *137*, 470, 1950.

SNEATH, P.H.A., *J. Zool. Lond.*, *151*, 65, 1967.

SOKAL, R.R., *J. Theoret. Biol.*, *3*, 230, 1962.

SOKAL, R.R., and SNEATH, P.H.A., *Principles of Numerical Taxonomy.* San Francisco and London: Freeman & Co., 1963.

SOUTHWARD, M.G., and CHAPMAN, D.G., *Rep. Internat. Pacific Halibut Commission,* No. 39, 1965.

SPENCER, R.P., and COULOMBE, M.J., *Growth,* *29*, 323, 1965.

SPIEGELMAN, S., *Amer. Nat.*, *80*, 186, 1946.

STAHL, W.R., *Perspect. Biol. Med.*, *6*, 291, 1963a.

——————————, *Adv. Biol. Med. Phys.*, *9*, 355, 1963b.

TEISSIER, G., *Les Lois quantitatives de la Croissance.* Paris: Hermann, 1937.

——————————, *Biometrics,* *4*, 14, 1948.

——————————, *Physiology of Crustacea.* WATERMAN, T.H. (ed.), New York: Academic Press, *1*, 537-560, 1960.

THOMPSON, D'A.W., *On Growth and Form.* Cambridge: University Press, 2nd ed., 1942.

TOMLINSON, P.K., and ABRAMSON, N.J., *California Dept. of Fish and Game, Fish Bullatin,* No. 116, 1961.

TURING, A.M., *Phil. Trans. Roy. Soc. Lond. B.*, *237*, 37, 1952.

WADDINGTON, C.H., *Nature, 131,* 134, London, 1933.

WEISS, P.A., and J.L. KAVANAU, *Journal gen. Physiol., 41,* 1, 1957.

WEYMOUTH, F.W., H.C. McMILLIN, and W.H. RICH, *Journal exp. Biol., 8,* 228, 1931.

WHITNEY, R.J., *Journal exp. Biol., 19,* 168, 1942.

WILL, A., *Z. vergl. Physiol., 34,* 20, 1952.

WOHLSCHLAG, D.E., *Ecol., 43,* 589, 1962.

WRIGHT, S., *Journal Amer. Statist. Soc., 21,* 493, 1926.

YATES, F., *Proc. Roy. Soc. Lond. B., 137,* 479, 1950.

YONEDA, Y., and Y. YOSHIDA, *Bulletin Japan. Soc. Sci. Fisheries, 21,* 62, 467, 1955.

YOSHIDA, Y., *Bulletin Japan. Soc. Sci. Fisheries, 21,* 1007, 1956.

ZEUTHEN, E., *Compt. Rend. Lab. Carlsberg, Ser. chim., 26,* 3, 1947.

APPLICATION OF THE BERTALANFFY GROWTH EQUATION TO PROBLEMS OF FISHERIES MANAGEMENT: A REVIEW

K. RADWAY ALLEN

†*Fisheries Research Board of Canada Biological Station, Nanaimo, B.C., Canada*

INTRODUCTION

One of the most successful examples of the application of mathematical techniques to the description of the biological processes involved in the management of a natural resource is found in the field of fisheries. Successful management requires the maintenance of the resource by the balancing of the catch against the additions to the stock from reproduction (less natural mortality) and growth. In recent years mathematical models have been developed which embody biologically meaningful descriptions of each of the processes involved and combine these descriptions to build up functions which can be used to assess the yield obtainable under various conditions and to forecast the effect of changes in exploitation, or in management practices. Growth being one of the principal components of this process, it has been necessary in building up these functions to use a representation of it which is biologically satisfactory and is also in a mathematical form suitable for

*This paper was originally intended for publication in *Unity Through Diversity*, but due to a delay in the publication of the present volume it first appeared in *Journal Fisheries Research Board of Canada*, *26*, 2267- 2281, 1969.

†Present address: Division of Fisheries and Oceanography, C.S.I.R.O., P.O. Box 21, Cronolla, NSW 2230, Australia.

inclusion in more complex models.

The growth curves formed on the principles originally
suggested by Dr. Ludwig von Bertalanffy have proved to be
particularly suitable for this purpose, and this paper is
intended to describe their past use and to outline further
developments which seem likely to make them still more
widely applicable in the future.

From time immemorial, men in numerous parts of the
world have drawn an important part of their sustenance
from the fishes and other animals in the seas and fresh
waters around them. For most this time their efforts have
had little effect, except in some restricted areas, upon
the fish populations on which they preyed. In general,
men have lived in equilibrium with their environment in
this respect. Recently this situation has been changing.
Fish catches have been increasing at an ever more rapid
rate as the greater fishing power made possible by modern
technological advances has helped to meet the growing demands
of the rapidly multiplying human population. There are
now few fish stocks, subjected to more than local fisheries,
whose size and structure have not been seriously affected
by fishing. In many instances the stocks have been driven
below the level required to produce, on a sustained basis,
the maximum yield of which they are capable.

Although restrictions, based on law or custom, and
aimed at protecting fish during what seemed to be particularly vulnerable periods of their lives, have a long history
in many human communities, it is only recently that informed
opinion has seen any need for the protection of the fish
stocks of the open seas. Just 100 years ago, in 1866, a
British Royal Commission was able to report, "We advise that
all acts of Parliament which profess to regulate, or restrict,
the modes of fishing pursued in the open sea be repealed,
and that unrestricted freedom of fishing be permitted here-
after". Even later, in 1883, no less an authority than T.H.
Huxley could declare, "I believe then that the cod fishery,
the herring fishery, the pilchard fishery, the mackerel
fishery, and probably all the great sea fisheries are
inexhaustible: that is to say that nothing we do seriously
affects the number of fish. And any attempt to regulate
these fisheries seems consequently from the nature of the
case to be useless". But the fishing fleets were already

growing in size and power, and the very meeting at which
Huxley made this assertion passed a resolution calling for
an international conference for the protection of fisheries
by better regulation.

Since that time the continuous expansion of the world's
fisheries has been accompanied by increasing efforts to
regulate their operation so that the stocks can be maintained
at a productive level. To provide a foundation for these
regulations, there has been in most countries a progressive
expansion of research on the stocks upon which the fisheries
are based. Although much of this research has continued to
be devoted to the biology — food, growth, movements, and so
on — of the animals concerned, more and more attention has
been given to quantitative aspects of the studies, to the
actual sizes of the stocks, and to the measurement of the
effects upon them of the catches taken by the fisheries.
This has led to the development of a number of theoretical
approaches aimed not merely at the measurement of existing
stocks and conditions in quantitative terms, but also at
forecasting the effects of possible changes in the nature
of the fisheries themselves, and the determination of the
conditions which would allow the maximum yield to be obtained
on a sustained basis. These developments now represent one
of the most successful examples of the application of mathematical techniques to biological problems.

BASIC THEORY OF FISHING

The basic principle on which the modern theory of fishing is based was probably first formulated in words by Petersen
(1894) who stated, "For it cannot well be doubted that the
same area of sea would be able to give a quantitatively
greater profit as a constancy, when we suffered the stock of
fish to be as fully developed, as in the years before the too
eager fishing commenced, ... and then took exactly so much
as the stock could reproduce by new growth". In other words,
that, for the level of yield to be maintained, the catch
must be in equilibrium with the rate of production by the
fish stock, and for this sustained yield to be a maximum
the stock must be allowed to build up to an appropriate
level.

The first attempt at a comprehensive mathematical formulation of the processes involved in the maintenance and exploitation of fish populations seems to have been that of Baranov (1918). The essential principles of his approach were those which still underlie the modern theory of fishing. He pointed out that the net production from the fish population, with which the yield must be in equilibrium, is the resultant of the processes of growth and mortality; and, by adopting mathematical models for these processes, he was able to set up differential equations from which the yield under various conditions could be computed. Unfortunately, Baranov's work was long overlooked in most parts of the world, with the result that some time elapsed before these principles were re-enunciated and the developments began which have led to the theories of fishing most widely used at the present time. Baranov, in his analysis, also adopted as a model for the growth process simple linearity in length with equal annual increments throughout life. Although such a model may be adequate for dealing with events over a short period during the life of the fish, it is rarely a satisfactory description of the whole span of later life, from the time the fish enter the fishery until they are caught or die naturally.

The basic principles involved were re-stated in a simple mathematical form by Russell (1931) in the equation

$$S_2 = S_1 + (A + G) - (C + M) \tag{1}$$

where S_1 and S_2 are the weights of the stock at the beginning and end of the year, A is the total of the initial weights of the recruits to the physical stock during the year, G is the amount added by growth of all the individuals which survived to the end of the year, and C and M respectively are the total weights of the catch and of those fish dying naturally. He pointed out that the stock would increase or decrease during the year according as $(A + G)$ was more or less than $(C + M)$.

A further advance was made by Graham (1935) who pointed out that the difficulties which arise in the application of Russell's equation from attempting to combine changes in numbers in the population with changes in the weights of individual fish disappear if logarithmic rates are used. He showed that Russell's equation, when written in the form describing the equilibrium situations

$$C = A + G - M \tag{2}$$

is mathematically correct if C, A, G, and M are all logarithmic rates. He further showed that this enabled deductions to be made regarding the values of some of these rates if the others are known or can be approximated.

THE YIELD EQUATION

Proceeding from this basis, Beverton and Holt (1957) (see also Beverton, 1953) developed a comprehensive theory of fishing centred round the yield equation

$$Y = FRe^{-M(t_\rho{}' - t_\rho)} W_\infty \sum_{n=0}^{3} \frac{\Omega_n e^{-nk(t_\rho{}' - t_0)}}{F + M + nK} \left[1 - e^{-(F + M + nK)} \right] \tag{3}$$

In developing this model, Beverton and Holt sought for a satisfactory means of representing mathematically each of Russell's four processes: recruitment (A), natural mortality (M), fishing mortality (C), and growth (G); and they then combined these into a single expression. They stressed the interdependence of these processes, which may be either direct (e.g., the same fish cannot both be caught and die naturally) or indirect (e.g., the rate of growth may be affected by the density of the population). They emphasized the resulting need for models which would not only describe the result of each process both accurately (e.g., would give a curve of suitable shape to describe growth) and in simple mathematical form, but that could also be related in their structure to the actual mechanisms involved, so that their parameters could be considered to be biologically meaningful.

The models used for recruitment and natural and fishing mortalities are of little direct concern to us here, and need be only briefly mentioned. The fishing and natural mortality rates were expressed in logarithmic terms, and in the basic model were regarded as having constant rates, F and M respectively. Thus, the number N_t of survivors of N_0 animals at time 0, subject to both fishing and natural deaths, would be given after time t by

$$N_t = N_0 e^{-(F + M)t} \tag{4}$$

The effects of changes in F and M were also considered; in particular F was regarded as being proportional to the fishing effort when this is expressed in suitable terms.

The model adopted for recruitment was based on the concept that a given number of recruits (R) enter the fishing area at age t_ρ, but that they are not subject to capture (e.g., they are able to escape through the meshes of the net) until they reach the age t_ρ'. During this interval they are subject to natural mortality at the standard rate M, so that the actual number of recruits on which the fishery operates is given by the expression

$$R' = Re^{-M(t_\rho' - t_\rho)} \tag{5}$$

which may be recognized towards the left-hand side of the yield expression. In later parts of their paper, Beverton and Holt considered the effect of changes in the values of M, t_ρ', and t_ρ, and particularly of the situation which actually exists in most fisheries when the probability of capture increases gradually from zero to its maximum over a range of sizes or ages, and does not develop suddenly to its maximum value at a critical age, as the simple model implies.

THE GROWTH COMPONENT

Recruitment and mortality are relatively simple processes, although they may be subject to a variety of external and internal forces, and they may be represented effectively by these relatively simple mathematical models. Growth, however, is a much more complex process biologically; and its representation by a mathematical model, which, as well as fitting actual growth curves reasonably well, is also so constructed that its parameters can be regarded as biologically meaningful, is fraught with difficulty. Beverton and Holt, after considering and rejecting a number of possibilities such as linear and exponential growth, and the Gompertz and logistic curves, wrote, "The question is therefore whether a function can be found that not only gives a good and conveniently simple representation of data, but that can also be used for analytical studies of growth phenomenon.... The important question is not, however, whether a universal representation of growth in a mathematical form is possible, but whether a representation can be made that is adequate for a particular purpose, and in our opinion a function has been developed that satisfies the essential requirements of the present problem. This is the one developed by L. von Bertalanffy".

The function referred to is that described by Bertalanffy (1938, and numerous other papers). Starting from the assumption that growth is the resultant of anabolic and catabolic processes, and that these are allometrically related to the weight W of the organism, the expression is obtained

$$\frac{dW}{dt} = HW^n - kW^m \tag{6}$$

where H and k are the coefficients of anabolism and catabolism respectively. If anabolism is governed by surface processes, and catabolism by mass processes, and if growth is isometric, then $n = 2/3$ and $m = 1$, so that

$$\frac{dW}{dt} = HW^{2/3} - kW \tag{7}$$

Integrating, this leads to the growth equations

$$l_t = L_\infty (1-e^{-K(t-t_0)})^3 \text{ for length} \tag{8}$$

and

$$W_t = W_\infty (1-e^{-K(t-t_0)})^3 \text{ for weight} \tag{9}$$

where L_∞ and W_∞ are the asymptotic maximum length and weight, t_0 is the time at which the animal was theoretically at zero size, and $K = k/3$ in the original equation.

The function for growth in weight thus obtained is that used by Beverton and Holt in their yield equation, the cubed expression being expanded to give

$$W_t = W_\infty \sum_{n=0}^{3} \Omega_n e^{-nK(t-t_0)} \tag{10}$$

where Ω_n is a variable of summation having the values 1, -3, 3, -1 for $n = 0, 1, 2, 3$.

This expression also can be easily recognized as a component of the Beverton and Holt yield equation.

The derivation of the yield equation from these bases is comparatively simple. The total weight of the individuals of age t in a year-class is given, by extension from equations (4), (5), and (10), by

$$N_t W_t = R'e^{-(F+M)}(t-t_\rho') \, W \sum_{n=0}^{3} \Omega_n e^{-nK(t-t_0)} \qquad (11)$$

With an instantaneous rate of fishing mortality F, the rate at which the catch (Y_w) is being removed is given by

$$\frac{dY_w}{dt} = FN_t W_t \qquad (12)$$

which from equation (11) with some rearrangement gives

$$\frac{dY_w}{dt} = FR'W_\infty e^{(F+M)t_\rho'} \sum_{n=0}^{3} e^{nKt_0} - (F+M+nK)t \qquad (13)$$

Integrating between $t = t_\rho'$ and $t = t\lambda$, where $t\lambda$ is the maximum age at which fish are caught and $\lambda = t\lambda - t_\rho'$, and substituting for R' from equation (5), then gives the yield equation (3). As calculated, this is the yield obtainable from a single year-class over the whole of its fishable life span, but, in a steady state, this is equal to the annual yield obtainable from the entire population.

This yield equation has proved a most valuable tool in the analysis of fisheries problems, and, as Beverton and Holt showed in their original publication, it is susceptible to modification to allow for a number of additional complexities not included in the simple statement given above. Probably its most valuable application has been to estimate for a given fishery what would be the effect on the yield of changing the conditions of the fishery, particularly as regards the age at first exploitation (t_ρ') and the rate of fishing mortality (F). A particularly useful method of expressing results of this nature is by means of an isopleth diagram, first proposed by Beverton (1953), in which contours of equal yield are plotted against t_ρ' and F, so that the effect on yield of any change in either or both variables may be seen at a glance. Figure 1, for example, shows such a

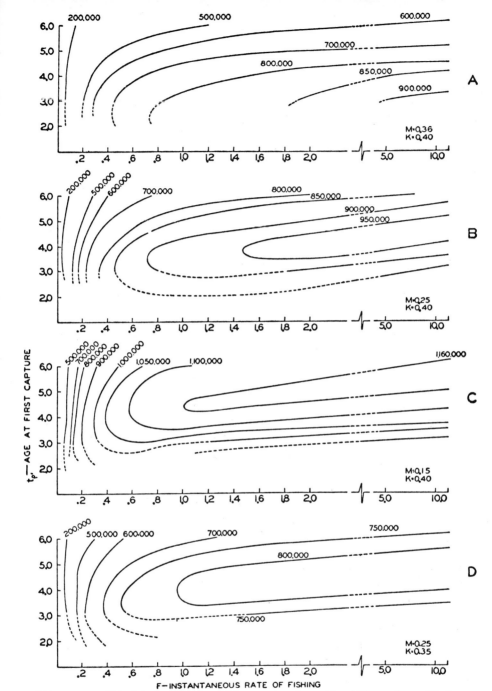

Fig. 1. Yield-isopleth diagrams for the flounder fishery of St. Mary Bay, Nova Scotia. (After Dickie and McCracken, 1955, Fig. 3) Yield contours are in units of pounds per 1 million recruits annually at age t_ρ = 3 years. Alternative diagrams are given for various possible combinations of the parameters M and K.

diagram prepared by Dickie and McCracken (1955) for a
flounder fishery in Nova Scotia. This approach has been
used by numerous other authors for various fisheries.
Application of this yield function to the analysis of
particular situations has been facilitated by the production
of tables giving values of the function for a range of
values of the principal parameters (Beverton and Holt,
1964).

APPLICABILITY OF THE BASIC YIELD EQUATION

The success of this model depends, of course, on the
accuracy with which its components fit the actual situation
and, in particular, on the suitability of the basic Bertalanffy
growth equation as a description of the growth of fishes
in general. Beverton and Holt in their original study
(1957) showed that it gave a good fit for a number of important
commercial fishes, including plaice, haddock, and cod, and
have since (1959) determined the parameters for Bertalanffy
equations to fit published data for some 50 other species
of fish, although apparently without critical examination
of the goodness of fit. The equation has also been widely
used by other workers to describe the growth of fish and
shellfish (Dickie and McCracken, 1955; Southward and Chapman,
1965).

The suitability of the simple Bertalanffy growth equation as a component of yield calculations in a particular
instance can be tested by examining the goodness of fit
of the best obtainable curve to the actual growth data.
It may also be examined more directly by comparing the
results obtainable by means of the yield function with those
produced by other methods which do not make assumptions as
to the nature of the growth curve. For example, Allen and
Forrester (1966) have shown that for the lemon sole in the
Strait of Georgia, application of the yield function indicates
that the equilibrium yield would decrease slightly if the
size limit were increased from 30 to 32 cm., although
application of a method which makes no assumptions about
growth or mortality (Allen, 1953) showed that 32 cm. was
actually the optimum size limit and that the change from
30 to 32 cm. must, therefore, produce a small increase in
yield. The discrepancy in the estimated optimum size limit
suggests that the Bertalanffy model in its simple form is not,
in this instance, a sufficiently good description of growth

during the fishable life span. A change in the natural
mortality rate with age could also contribute to this discrepancy.

Thus, failure of the assumption that the simple Bertalanffy model adequately describes growth throughout the
fishable life span may cause the Beverton and Holt yield
equation to be unsatisfactory in some instances. Despite
this, the Bertalanffy model may be applied to yield problems in other ways which involve only the much less restric-
tive assumption that the model describes growth simply in
the range of possible ages of first recruitment to the
fishable stock. Allen (1967) has, for instance, shown that
with this assumption the ratio of the ultimate equilibrium
yield (Y_2) obtainable with a new and higher size limit L_2,
to the present yield (Y_1) with a limit L_1, is given by

$$\frac{Y_2}{Y_1} = \frac{Y_2}{Y_K} \cdot \frac{Y_K}{Y_1} \qquad (14)$$

where $\quad \frac{Y_2}{Y_K} \quad \left(\frac{L_\infty - L_1}{L_\infty - L_2}\right)^{\frac{Z}{K} \cdot E'} \qquad (15)$

and L_∞ and K are the parameters of the Bertalanffy growth
equation, Z is the total instantaneous mortality rate, E'
is the proportion ultimately caught of the fish reaching
takeable size, and Y_K is the immediate catch with the
new limit. $\frac{Y_K}{Y_1}$ can be simply estimated from the size distribution in the original catches.

MORE GENERALIZED GROWTH EQUATION

The occasions on which the simple Bertalanffy model
either fails to give a good fit to the original growth data,
or yields unsatisfactory results in the yield equations, also
suggest the possibility of using a more generalized form of
the equation. Bertalanffy himself has pointed out that
although direct proportionality with the weight of the organism
may be a satisfactory measure of the catabolic component in

the basic equation (6), the position regarding the anabolic
component is much less definite. He has suggested (1964,
and elsewhere) that the equation may therefore be written
in the form

$$\frac{dW}{dt} = HW^n - k\dot{W} \tag{16}$$

where n may represent the size dependence of appropriate
metabolic rates. He has shown that n may have a wide range
of possible values, if different metabolic processes are
examined, and concludes (1964) that "We shall expect all
sorts of allometric relationships of metabolic measures and
body size — with a certain preponderance of surface or 2/3-
power functions, considering the fact that many metabolic
processes are controlled by surfaces. This is precisely
what we find. In other words, 2/3 is not a magic number;
nor is there anything sacred about the 3/4 power which more
recently has been preferred to the classical surface law".

He has reviewed the values of n as derived from studies
of metabolic rates, using oxygen consumption as an index,
and has shown that insertion of these in equation (16)
produces curves tending to correspond with the actual form
of the growth curve of the organism. He has distinguished
three principal types: 1) respiration surface-proportional,
$n = 2/3$, growth curve as in equation (8), without inflection;
2) respiration weight-proportional, $n = 1$, growth exponential,
no asymptote; 3) respiration intermediate, $2/3 < n < 1$,
growth asymptotic but with an inflection. His conclusion
that fish tend to belong to type 1 is confirmed, as a generalization, by the frequent good fit of fish growth data to
the simple model that has already been noted.

The characteristics of the growth curves derived from
equation (16) have been examined mathematically by various
authors including Richards (1959), Chapman (1960), and
Taylor (1962). Taylor, for instance, wrote the basic equation in the form

$$\frac{dW}{dt} = HS - kW \tag{17}$$

where s = surface area, and he put $s = pl^a$, $W = ql^b$ so that
n in equation (16) is equivalent to a/b in equation (17).
Here s is the "physiological surface" rather than any actual

surface of the organism. He then showed that this led to
the equation for growth in length

$$l_i^{(b-a)} = L_\infty^{(b-a)} \; 1-e^{-k(b-a) \; (t-t_0)})$$

(18)

where $K = \dfrac{k}{b}$. This length growth equation may also be writ-

ten in the form

$$l_i = L_\infty(1-e^{-K(b-a) \; (t-t_0)})^{\frac{1}{b-a}}$$

(19)

and the corresponding weight growth equation is

$$W = W_\infty(1-e^{-K(b-a) \; (t-t_0)})^{\frac{b}{b-a}}$$

(20)

substituting $a = 2$, $b = 3$ in these equations leads back to
the simple Bertalanffy equations (8) and (9).

Richards (1959) and Taylor (1962) have both examined
the influence of the parameter $[1/(b-a)]$, or its equivalent,
on the shape of the growth curve. Richards has stressed the
merits of this family of curves for the empirical fitting
of growth data, and has suggested that, at least in some
instances, the best fit may be obtained by making $(b-a)$ negative, although this requires that H and k should also be
negative if the organism is to grow in the positive direction. This, however, requires the complete abandonment of
the original concept of the basic equation as a representation of actual biological processes. It thus destroys one
of the principal reasons why the Bertalanffy growth model
was chosen as suitable for inclusion in Beverton and Holt's
overall model of the processes of fisheries production and
exploitation.

If these original concepts are to be retained, certain
limits must be placed on the values which can be considered
for b and a, and hence for $(b-a)$. The value of b, which
defines the relationship between length and weight, can be
observed directly, although it is not without some complications in its interpretation (LeCren, 1951). The value is
generally fairly close to 3.0, and would rarely be outside

the limits 2.7–3.3. The value of the exponent relating metabolic rate to weight is almost invariably less than 1.0 and,
as Bertalanffy has pointed out in the above quotation, lies
rather commonly in the vicinity of 2/3 and is rarely much
below this value. This exponent, which is n in equation
(16), is equal to a/b, so that for the above range of values
of b, the values of $(b-a)$ would range normally from zero to
1.1 and commonly from 0.9 to 1.1. Values lower than 0.9
and rather higher than 1.1 would also be expected to occur,
although rarely.

THE SHAPE OF THE GROWTH CURVE

     When $(b-a)$ is exactly equal to 1.0, the simple model
applies as we have already seen, but if $(b-a)$ is between
zero and 1.0, the resulting growth curve will be sigmoid
with a point of inflection at a size given by

$$l_i = L_\infty \left| 1 - (b-a) \right|^{\frac{1}{b-a}} \tag{21}$$

     The relative size at inflection increases as $(b-a)$
decreases. Taking $(a-b) = 0.75$ as a minimum value likely
to occur naturally, the corresponding value of l_i is
$0.158L_\infty$. The theoretical maximum value occurs when $(a-b) = 0$,
and is L_∞/e ($= .368L_\infty$). Although equation (21) is insoluble if $b-a = 0$, this result may be demonstrated by insert-
ing a very small value, such as $(a-b) = .0001$, in it.

     The curve for $(b-a) = 0$ is in fact identical with the
Gompertz growth curve

$$l_i = L_\infty e^{-be^{-K(t-t_0)}}$$

as Richards (1959) has pointed out. Thus placing $n = m$ in
equation (6) or $n = 1$ in equation (16) can be shown mathematically to lead to two growth curves of entirely different
form, the exponential, in which size increases ever more
rapidly, and the Gompertz, which is asymptotic.

     In the comparatively rare instances where $(a-b)$ is greater
than 1.0, the growth curve is not inflected, and resembles
the simple model in general form although it approaches the

asymptote more slowly as $(b-a)$ increases.

Applying similar methods to the weight growth curve, equation (20), we find that inflection occurs at the weight

$$W_i = W_\infty \left| \frac{a}{b} \right|^{\frac{b}{b-a}} \tag{22}$$

Since a/b equals n of equation (16) this becomes

$$W_\infty n^{\frac{1}{1-n}} \tag{23}$$

The usual range of values of n has been seen to be from 2/3 to 1. The corresponding range of W_i/W is 0.296-0.368.

Thus growth curves based on the more generalized Bertalanffy model and using values of the parameters in accordance with the biological basis of the model may be expected to be, for length, generally uninflected, or, rarely, with an inflection at less than 15% of the asymptotic length; and, for weight, generally inflected, with the point of inflection at about 30-38% of the asymptotic weight. These general characteristics would, in fact, apply to the growth curves of a great many species of fish.

Although the simple model has been very widely used in fisheries work, and has been fitted to numerous sets of data, there have been relatively few attempts to determine the parameters of the more generalized equation. Taylor (1962) examined published data for several species of fish using approximate trial-and-error methods. For Arctic char (data from Grainger, 1953) he found $(b-a) = 0.3$; and for rainbow trout (Hasler, 1938), 0.4. Southward and Chapman (1965) have applied more exact methods, using a computer, to data for Pacific halibut, walleye, and largemouth bass. They found that the values of the parameters varied significantly with the range of age for which the analysis was performed. For halibut the most probable value of their parameter m varied from 0.60 to 0.78. Since $(1-m)$ in their notation equals $(b-a)$ in the present paper, this corresponds to values of $(b-a)$ of 0.22-0.40. For walleye and bass, the values were respectively, m, 0.54-0.38, 1.20-0.59; $(b-a)$, 0.62-0.46, 0.41 - (-0.20).

Since Southward and Chapman also state that the exponent of the weight-length relationship (b) for halibut is about 3.2, one may estimate $a(= 3.2 - 0.22$ to 0.40) as 2.98-2.80. Thus a/b, which equals n in the basic equation (16), appears to lie between .87 and .93, which is within the range discussed earlier as being biologically reasonable.

A GENERALIZED YIELD EQUATION

If the Bertalanffy growth equation, when generalized in th[is] way, is still to be applied to problems of fisheries management, corresponding modifications must be made in the yield equation. The original equation, as proposed by Beverton and Holt, was based on the simple Bertalanffy model, and in effect assumed that the exponent $[b/(b-a)]$ in equation (2) was equal to 3. Using the integral value for this parameter made it possible to use an expansion in constructing the yield equation (3). When the generalized equation is used, without this restriction on the value of the exponent, it is necessary to replace the expansion by an integral function and the equation becomes

$$Y_w = FRe^{-M(t_\rho'-t_\rho)} W_\infty \int_{t_\rho'}^{t_\lambda} e^{-(F+M)(t-t_\rho')} \cdot$$

$$\left[1-e^{-K(t-t_0)} \right]^{\frac{b}{b-a}} \cdot dt \tag{24}$$

Fortunately, this integral can be reduced to a standard form which has been tabulated. Jones (1957) has shown that by substituting

$$y = e^{-K(t-t_0)}$$

and $\quad x = e^{-K(t_\rho'-t_0)}$

$$x_1 = e^{-K(t_\lambda-t_0)}$$

the equation becomes

$$Y_w = FRe^{-M(t_\rho{}'-t_\rho)} W_\infty e^{(F+M)(t_\rho{}'-t_0)}.$$

(25)

$$\frac{1}{K}\int\limits_{\frac{1}{K}}^{x_1} y^{\frac{F}{K}\frac{M}{}-1} (1-y)^{\frac{b}{b-a}} \cdot dy$$

and that this integral is the difference between two incomplete beta-functions. This enables us to write

$$Y_w =$$

$$FRe^{-M(t_\rho{}'-t_\rho)} W_\infty e^{(F+M)(t_\rho{}'-t_0)}$$

(26)

$$\left\{ Bx\left[\frac{F+M}{K},\frac{b}{b-a}+1\right] - Bx_1\left[\frac{F+M}{K},\frac{b}{b-a}+1\right] \right\}$$

where $Bx\left[\dfrac{F+M}{K},\dfrac{b}{b-a}+1\right]$ is the incomplete beta-function with

parameters x, $\dfrac{F+M}{K}$, and $\dfrac{b}{b-a}+1$. The values of these functions

are available in tables, thus enabling yield calculations to be made relatively simply within the limits of the tables. Extensive tables were published by Pearson (1948) but were not designed for fisheries use. Jones (1957) published a short table intended for this purpose but limited to the simple Bertalanffy equation, the only value of

$\left[\dfrac{b}{b-a}+1\right]$ given being 4.0. Wilimovsky and Wicklung (1963)

have, however, published quite extensive tables designed for fisheries purposes, using values of $\left[\dfrac{b}{b-a}+1\right]$ from 3.50

to 4.50 in intervals of 0.125.

In presenting their tables, both Jones (1957) and Wilimovsky and Wicklund (1963) have pointed out the advantage
of using the incomplete beta-function both in simplifying
the calculations and also in enabling them to be made when
growth is allometric, so that the exponent of the weight-
length relationship is not exactly 3.0. It has been shown
here, however, that the more generalized basic equation (16)
leads to both length and weight growth equations of the same
general type, which also includes the weight growth equation
derived from the simple Bertalanffy model, in which the term
$(1-e^{-k(b-a)(t-t_0)})$ has an exponent. The incomplete beta-
function technique, therefore, allows yield calculations to
be made, provided tables for the appropriate value of the
exponent are available, for all growth models based on equation (16) whatever the value of n, and whether growth is
isometric or allometric.

Thus, it can truly be stated that the mathematical
descriptions of the growth curves of animals which have
been proposed by Dr. L. von Bertalanffy have played an
important part in the development of the modern theoretical
approaches to the problems of fisheries management. In
their simplest form they are an essential component of the
most widely used function for calculating the yield obtainable from a fish population under various conditions. The
use of somewhat more complex growth curves developed from
the basic principles laid down by Bertalanffy will probably
enable the yield function to be modified to give satisfactory
results in an even wider range of situations. Some of the
directions in which these modifications may be expected to
develop have been outlined in the present paper.

REFERENCES

ALLEN, K.R., "A method for computing the optimum size limit
for a fishery". *Nature*, *172*, 210, 1953.

ALLEN, K.R., "Some quick methods for estimating the effect
on the catch of changes in the size limit". *J. Conseil
Conseil Perm. Intern. Exploration Mer*, *31*, 111-126, 1967.

ALLEN, K.R. and FORRESTER, C.F., "Appropriate size limits
for the lemon sole (*Parophrys vetulus*) in the Strait of
Georgia". *J. Fish. Res. Bd. Canada*, *23*, 511-520, 1966.

BARANOV, F.I., "On the question of the biological basis of fisheries". *Nauchn. Issled. Iktiol. Inst. Izves., 1*, 81–128, 1918.

von BERTALANFFY, L., "A quantitative theory of organic growth (inquiries on growth laws, II)". *Human Biol., 10*, 181–213, 1938.

von BERTALANFFY, L., "Basic concepts in quantitative biology of metabolism". *Helgolaender Wiss. Meeresuntersuch., 9*, 5–37, 1938.

BEVERTON, R.J.H., "Some observations on the principles of fishery regulation". *J. Conseil Conseil Perm. Intern. Exploration Mer, 19*, 56–68, 1953.

BEVERTON, R.J.H. and HOLT, S.J., "On the dynamics of exploited fish populations". *U.K. Min. Agr., Fish. Food, Fish. Invest., 19*, 1–533, 1957.

BEVERTON R.J.H. and HOLT, S.J., "A review of the lifespan and mortality rates of fish in nature, and their relation to growth and other physiological characteristics". *Ciba Found. Symp. Lifespan Animals*, 142–177, 1959.

BEVERTON R.J.H. and HOLT, SJ., "Tables of yield functions for fishery assessment". *FAO Fish. Tech. Paper, 38*, 1–49, 1964.

CHAPMAN, D.G. "Statistical problems in dynamics of exploited fisheries populations". *Proc. Fourth Berkeley Symp. Mathematical Statistics Probability*, 153–168, 1960.

DICKIE, L.M. and McCRACKEN, F.D., "Isopleth diagrams to predict equilibrium yields of a small flounder fishery". *J. Fish. Res. Bd. Canada, 12*, 187–209, 1955.

GRAHAM, M., "Modern theory of exploiting a fishery and application to North Sea trawling". *J. Conseil Conseil Perm. Intern. Exploration Mer, 10*, 264–274, 1935.

GRAINGER, E.H., "On the age, growth, migrations, reproduction potential and feeding habits of the Arctic char (*Salvelinus alpinus*) of Frobisher Bay, Baffin Island". *J. Fish. Res. Bd. Canada, 10*, 326–370, 1953.

HASLER, A.D., "Fish biology and limnology of Crater Lake, Oregon". *J. Wildlife Management, 2*, 94–103, 1938.

JONES, R., "A much simplified version of the fish yield equation". *Joint Meeting ICNAF/ICES/FAO, Lisbon. Doc. P21*, 1–8, 1957.

LeCREN, E.D., "The length–weight relationship and seasonal cycle in gonad weight and condition in the perch (*Perca fluviatilis*)". *J. Animal Ecol., 20*, 201–219, 1951.

PEARSON, K., *Tables of the Incomplete Beta-function*. Cambridge, England: University Press, 494, 1948.

PETERSEN, C.G.J., "On the biology of our flatfishes and on the decrease of our flatfish fisheries". *Rept. Dan. Biol. Sta., 4*, 1–47, 1894.

RICHARDS, F.J., "A flexible growth function for empirical use". *J. Exptl. Botany, 10*, 290–300, 1959.

RUSSELL, E.S., "Some theoretical considerations on the 'over-fishing' problem". *J. Conseil Conseil Perm. Intern. Exploration Mer, 6*, 3–20, 1931.

SOUTHWARD, G.M. and CHAPMAN, D.G., "Utilization of Pacific halibut stocks: study of Bertalanffy's growth equation". *Rept. Intern. Pacific Halibut Comm., 39*, 1–33, 1965.

TAYLOR, C.C., "Growth equations with metabolic parameters". *J. Conseil Conseil Perm. Intern. Exploration Mer, 27*, 270–286, 1962.

WILIMOVSKY, N.J. and WICKLUND, E.C., *Tables of the Incomplete Beta-function for the Calculation of Fish Population Yield*. Vancouver, B.C.: Univ. British Columbia, 291, 1963.

THE ENERGETICS OF ANIMAL GROWTH

FRIEDRICH KRUGER

Biological Institution of Helgoland, Central Hamburg-Altona, Federal Republic of Germany

INTRODUCTION

At the beginning of the last century the urea synthesis of Wöhler (1828) refuted the dogma that living matter is basically different from inanimate material. This became the starting point of modern Biochemistry which succeeded, with increasinly refined methods, in producing profound insights into the chemical structure of living matter and into its continual changes. This development continues even today.

The living organism is, however, characterized not only by its chemical elements, but also by its temporary change of form. Every organism is subject to such change; it is this process which we designate as growth. Here we are dealing with changes of dimension-phenomena which the methods of chemistry are not able to describe. The process of growth appears to us primarily as a numerical series. We can expect clarification of the regularities which are the basis of such numerical series only by mathematical description. But there is a viewpoint which to a large extent still prevails among biologists, that the extremely complex nature of vital processes does not permit a systematic mathematical treatment. As early as 1934 von Bertalanffy pointed out that "it is in principle possible, to indicate legitimacies of a statistical type for total processes which are inaccessible in the single occurrences of their analysis". Modern physics is also acquainted with phenomena which can no longer be exactly

described, but are understood through statistical legitimacies. In Biology we are concerned with such statistical
legitimacies and it is important that this fundamental knowledge of von Bertalanffy be universally recognized within
the discipline.

We are, of course, far removed from being able to
describe mathematically all biological systems. In systems
which are not close to being in a state of equilibrium
(which is the case with many "Oiko" systems, for example),
the obtaining of specific measuring values meets with maximum difficulties. Due to this there are limits to the
elaboration of mathematical relationships. With growth
data the situation is more favorable; the statistical averages are easily reproduced and the changes in the organism
are not very far removed from a state of equilibrium.

The rejection which mathematical treatment of biological
problems has encountered is in part due to unfortunate
experiences which are based on the largely indiscriminate
acceptance and application of formulations from other fields
of knowledge. In this way, the term "Parameters" came
about which have little significance and therefore can
yield no information.

A typical example of this is provided by the application,
still common today, of the Q_{10} — value for the description
of the dependence of biological processes on temperature.
Korgh (1914) had already recognized the inadequacy of the
Q_{10} value. In Biology we must attempt to find specific
methods which are supported by results from the living
organism. To this end I have myself tried to propose a
new kind of solution (Kruger 1961, 1963, 1966) which comes
essentially closer to the demands of a biological temperature function.

THE ALLOMETRIC FUNCTION

In the most widely varying fields of biological research
the mathematical reproduction of growth values as a function
of age appeared as a stimulating and important problem.
Thus people have been occupied with it for a long time and
have proposed over 100 solutions, none of which, however,
have been really satisfactory. This failure makes it understandable why one views the possibility of a solution with

some scepticism.   Basically, however, the problem had already been solved by von Bertalanffy (1934).

A further proof that the mathematical formulation of growth processes is possible presents the existence of the so-called allometrical formula.   To be sure, this does not relate the changes in size resulting in the cause of growth to age, but rather describes the relative changes in size between two growth processes of an organism proceeding at different rates.

If we designate by "X" and "Y" the dimensions of the two structures compared to one another then the mathematically simple relationship

$$y = b \cdot x'^{\alpha} \tag{1}$$

exists between them.   If one takes the log of this equation, the even simpler linear relation results:

$$\log y = \log b + \alpha \cdot \log x' \tag{1a}$$

b and α are the personifiers, which describe the relative size changes between the two structures to be compared. The exponent α is particularly meaningful here. From the equation (1a) it follows that the relative size relations of the structures of an organism are presented in a double logarithmic subdivided system of co-ordinates, by straight lines.

Snell (1891) first set up this function in a general form for the description of the relation between brain and body weight.   In specific form, i.e., for the description of the relation between metabolic rate and body surface, it was already used by Sarrus and Rameaux (1840).   In the interim this simple function has proved good in a vast number of investigations into the presentation of morphological and physiological changes in the course of growth.   The stature serves in general here as the point of reference. The application of the allometrical function is not limited to individual growth, but also allows the interspecific comparison of organisms from various systematic units, as Benedict (1938) showed for the production of metabolism in warm-blooded animals — ranging from the mouse to the elephant.

The relative changes in size are expressed by the exponent α. If this has the value 1.0, then an isometric growth is present, the size relationship is constant and is given by b. Values under 1.0 indicate that x becomes smaller in relationship to y. α-values above 1.0 indicate that x increases faster than y. In both of the last cases b presents a factor of proportionality. Also the length relationship of weight of an organism is given by the allometrical formula.

The application of the allometrical function to metabolism shows that the concept of "dimension" used here also includes physiological measuring sizes, like changes in the chemical composition or in energy transformation.

The extensive reliability of the allometrical growth relation gives the right to use it as the basis for further ideas. The explanation of the two inserted Parameters was thus far not clear, so that they represented pure numerical values. In the following the attempt will be made to give a meaningful explanation at least for the exponent α of the metabolic measurements.

THE GROWTH AS A FUNCTION OF THE TIME

The allometrical function describes the relative changes of the dimensions of a growing organism with the exclusion of the time factor. Growth, however, by definition represents a change of dimension of the organism as a function of time. The mathematical solution to this relation is considered to be extremely important. I would like to forego mention of the history of the problem here. Von Bertalanffy's merit (1934) remains as that of having given the first really useful solution and having guided it to a success through his numerous publications. By this means he created a more general interest in this central biological problem and his formulation also escaped the danger of being quickly forgotten, as was the fate of Pütter's (1920) very similar growth formula.

Basically the Bertalanffy function allows animal growth data to be rendered in very close approximation as a function of time. It found practical application only in Fishing Biology and, in contrast, remained unnoticed in the domesticated animal science and in medicine. With

insignificant adjustment it could also have been established in these latter cases as von Bertalanffy showed
(1938) in the example of the mouse, the rat and the human
being.

The Bertalanffy function (for which I prefer Beverton
and Holt's (1957) way of expression), reads as follows:

$$\ell_\tau = L_{max} \cdot \left[1 - \ell^{-k[\tau - \tau_0]} \right] \tag{2}$$

The parameters are: L_{max} = Maximum size; k = velocity constant; τ_0 = cumulative time value. I designate the age with
τ in order to make a distinction with the temperature symbol τ: ℓ_τ = length in the age τ.

The possibility of comprehending the animal growth
from the beginning on the basis of a uniform mathematical
function indicates that in the entire animal kingdom it
depends on identical principles.

The Bertalanffy function is distinguished by the fact
that, similar to the course of events in Physics, it was
developed by proceeding from concrete notions on the nature
of growth. A specific suggestion for the presentation of
growth data will be discussed further on. The fundamental
conception of the Bertalanffy function is the idea that in
the organism, besides the processes which form new living
matter, oppositely directed processes constantly occur
which decompose a part of the substance on hand.

THE ANABOLISM — CATABOLISM SKETCH

It was already recognized in previous centuries that
organic growth does not just depend on the accumulation of
new substance, but that at the same time a part of the
formed matter always disappears. (Cl. Bernard, 1885). In
connection with von Bertalanffy I am labelling the processes of synthesis as anabolism and those of decomposition
as catabolism. We can approach the nature of the growth
process if we also consider, in a mathematical formulation,
the participation of the two oppositely acting processes.

We obtain information about the catabolic process by
letting an animal starve. The synthesis is then stopped

and the processes of decomposition become measurable as a loss in weight. It has been discovered that in starving animals the losses in weight are approximately proportional to the weight existing for the time being. Also, the elimination of nitrogen from the starving organism proceeds in simple relationship to the weight. That is easily understood because in the decomposition of living matter as much nitrogen is liberated as corresponds to its protein content.

For approximation we can assume the catabolic processes as being proportional to the weight. The value for the allometrical exponent is thus equal in this case to 1.0. Since this exponent is not usually written in the mathematical formulation the mathematical expression for catabolism would be:

$$\text{Catabolism} = k \cdot w \tag{3a}$$

if we designate the weight with w.

The relationships are different with anabolism. It creates the demand for material and energy necessary for growth. From innumerable measurements we know that, disregarding a few exceptions, the oxygen usage and, parallel to it, the heat emission, do not proceed proportional to the mass but are in exponential relation to the weight. Formerly it was assumed that the production of energy was causally related to the surface development of the organism. In this case the value 2/3 or 0.66 could be inserted for the exponent α. A strict surface proportionality appears to be only rarely fulfilled. We therefore want to formulate the equation for the processes of synthesis very generally:

$$\text{Anabolism} = a \cdot w^{\alpha} \tag{3b}$$

The increase in weight now represents the difference between these two oppositely acting sizes and von Bertalanffy consequently formulates the temporal growth as

$$\frac{dw}{d\tau} = a \cdot w^{\alpha} - k \cdot w \tag{3c}$$

If one puts in this equation, in place of the weight, the third power of the length, and integrates, one obtains the Bertalanffy formula, equation (2). The favorable suitability of the growth function derived in this way must be valued as the basic confirmation of the mathematical equation.

A few years ago (1962) the author derived a new growth function from a given example. In this case he used the graphic analysis which is a well known means in Physics for explaining unknown functional connections. Only later did I discover that Zucker (1941) had already found in principle the same formula for the representation of the growth in weight of the rat. It seems noteworthy that two writers independent of one another arrived at the same formulation of growth on basically different grounds.

The values calculated according to the new formula agree as to the point of inflection of the growth curve almost exactly with those values which are obtained from the Bertalanffy function. The new function was purely descriptively found. The mathematical analysis showed that it also contains the Bertalanffy equation. The new growth formula reads:

$$y_x = \frac{D_{max}}{\dfrac{1}{N^{x+\xi}}} \tag{4}$$

Besides some other favorable characteristics, the new function offers the advantage of existing in a very simple mathematical relation to the allometrical function which is given by the two equations:

$$\alpha = \frac{\log N_1}{\log N_2} \qquad\qquad 1 = \frac{D_1 max}{D_2 max^\alpha} \tag{5a and b}$$

Here the meaning of the exponent α is of chief interest. It represents the relationship of the logarithms of the velocity v, constants of the two growth processes compared with one another. As the designation indicates, with the log N we are dealing with a parameter for the rate of growth which has a constant value for the whole length of time covered by the formula. Also the exponent α represents a parameter, independent of time.

The rate constant can describe a retarded growth for parts of the organism. Besides, the new function in the reciprocal age value of the exponent contains a part which supposes for all parts of the organism a rate of growth which decreases with age.

The rate constant log N — it enters into all calculations and evaluations as a logarithm — for the growth in
weight is identical for all growth processes which proceed
proportional to the mass. If we then take the Bertalanffy
equation as a basis, it (this rate constant) also proves
correct for catabolism. Likewise the value of log N for
the surface growth agrees with all growth processes which
proceed proportional to the surface area.

The interpretation of the exponent α given by the new
growth function is very important.

We again take the Bertalanffy equation (3) as our basis
and divide it by w. The result is then

$$\frac{dw}{w \cdot d\tau} = a \cdot w^{(\alpha-1)} - k \tag{6}$$

On the right side only $w^{(\alpha-1)}$ remains as a variable. α
thus represents the exponent of anabolism. The relation
formulated mathematically here is easily understood. In
the linear, graphic representation per unit of weight the
catabolism appears as a parallel to the abscissa and each
deviation of our metabolic curve from the horizontal course
is based on the anabolism which is not proportional by
weight.

If we therefore determine α for the relation between
metabolic rate and weight, this value then holds for the
allometrical relation between anabolism and catabolism.
This seemed to provide the foundation for quantitatively
determining the share of anabolism and catabolism in the
total respiration. In the calculation of an example, however, unbelievably low values for the catabolism resulted
which were apparently caused only by insignificant variations from the theoretical values.

ANABOLISM AND CONVERSION

This failure in mathematical evaluation forced a more
exact intellectual analysis of the Bertalanffy equation (3)
In it, corresponding to the definition, the differential
quotient represents a very small magnitude. Therefore one
can also write:

$$a \cdot w^{\alpha} \simeq k \cdot w \qquad \qquad (7)$$

Pütter (1920) applies these two quantities directly. Now one can easily understand that it is not possible to achieve equality in the whole range with the product k·w with some value for the factor α. This only becomes possible if we put an exponential part in place of a.

Let us remember now the experimental foundations of the equation! The expression for the catabolism: k·w represents an expression for the loss in weight of a starving organism, that is, for the changes in volume. The exponential term $a \cdot w^{\alpha}$ — the expression for anabolism — can also be reproduced in heat units; with it we are concerned with an energetic value. On both sides of the equation exist basically different units of measurement. That is of course inadmissible. We can only reach an approximate equality if we insert into the expression for anabolism an exponential term that quantitatively renders the relations between anabolism and conversion, that is to say, the relationship between energy production and built-in substance.

Under the condition assumed in equation (7), that no increase occurs, the exponent of this part would be = $(1-\alpha)$. Then we find on the left side the exponent 1.0 as on the right side and the matter decomposed by catabolism would be similar to the matter formed by anabolism.

In fish the value for α, according to bibliographical data, remains uniform at about 0.8 and the value for $(1-\alpha)$ would accordingly be about 0.2. In a growing organism, however, a higher value is to be expected, since, in addition to the replacement for the catabolic loss of substance, excess material must be formed for growth.

If we now try to formulate an equation based on the anabolism-catabolism concept for growth, we would arrive at the formulation:

$$\frac{dw}{d\tau} = a \cdot w^{\alpha} \cdot c \cdot w^{\gamma} - k \cdot w^{\kappa} \qquad \qquad (8)$$

Corresponding to the writing of the allometrical function I use Latin letters for the factors and Greek symbols for the symbols used by von Bertalanffy. (a and α for anabolism#, c and γ for conversion and k and κ for catabolism). For the case

$$\frac{dw}{d\tau} = 0$$

c would be equal to k and α would have the value 1.

My theoretical considerations had progressed up to this point when by chance I got hold of the results of an investigation, existing in print, of a Dr. T.J. Pandian, in a thesis from the University of Madras (India). This author determined calorimetrically with two fish, namely the *Ophiocephalus striatus* and the *Megalops cyprinoides*, food consumption and absorption and the mixing in of matter in such a wide range of weight that an allometrical evaluation is possible. Fish are particularly suited for the clarification of fundamental growth problems because they go through a growth which after the larva stage exhibits no instability. Furthermore, we have at our disposal very good experimental foundations because of the practical interest in the growth of fish.

Indeed there is already a series of investigations into the consumption of food in the growth of fish (e.g. Winberg 1956, Ivlev 1961, Paloheimo and Dickie 1965/66); however, the evaluations of earlier writers did not lead to such clearly visible connections as does Pandian's research, which related all measurements to the weight of the fish. Pandian determined in detail the food taken in by the fish and the matter given off as excrement. The difference of these two quantities gives the amount of food actually absorbed by the fish. In addition he determined the growth.

Of the consumed food only a certain portion is used for the synthesis of substance belonging to the body, a process which is usually termed "conversion". The unconverted part — numerically it is the difference between absorbed and converted matter — is apparently used up in the metabolic process, i.e. oxydized and eliminated in the form of CO_2, and H_2O and excrements.

Table 1 presents the factors and exponents calculated from the results of determining food consumption, food absorption, conversion and consumption. From the figures of the table the exponents for the consumption and conversion are of main interest. The single values are published in the work still existing in print (Pandian, 1967).

TABLE 1. Parameters of the allometric function ($y = b \cdot w^{\alpha}$) for the relationship of food consumption, food absorption, consumption and conversion to body weight. Calculated according to the result of experiments by Pandian (1967).

	Megalops		*Ophiocephalus*	
	Exponent	Factor	Exponent	Factor
Food-consumption	0.71	0.085	0.76	0.057
Food-absorption	0.70	0.081	0.77	0.050
Consumption	0.77 (α)	0.045	0.88 (α)	0.025
Conversion	0.54 (γ)	0.040	0.55 (γ)	0.028

The exponent for the consumption of substance (α) equals
0.77 for the *Megalops* and 0.88 for the *Ophiocephalus*. The
latter value appears somewhat too high. At least according
to quantity, however, it still agrees with the amount of the
exponent for the oxygen usage of fish which lies rather
uniformly at 0.8 according to Winberg (1956).

In comparison, the exponents for the conversion are
essentially lower. They resulted in both types with close
agreement at 0.54 and 0.55 respectively. Other authors
(Winberg, Ivlev, etc.) found values of 0.8 for the exponent
in the quantitative working of the problem of food utilization in fish. They therefore concluded with a parallel
between energetic metabolism and conversion. This interpretation is, however, not applicable, since the exponent α
for the oxygen usage was based on the weight, the conversion,
however, on the food consumption. The value of the exponent
for the conversion — based on the weight — is obtainable by
multiplying the exponent for the food consumption, which
Pandian found to be 0.76 and 0.71 respectively, with the
exponent for the relationship between conversion and food
consumption. If we assume in this case that the exponent
for the relation: food consumption/conversion is 0.8, then
a value of 0.61 or 0.57 results for the relationship of conversion to weight. These values convincingly confirm the
figures of Pandian.

The exponents for food consumption and food absorption
are practically identical, which indicates that both processes proceed parallel to one another. Thus the percentage
of the unabsorbed food is identical in all the size groups.

On the other hand, the conversion proceeds neither
parallel to the food consumption nor to the oxygen usage,
but exhibits its own allometrical relation to weight. The
value of the exponent for conversion is lower than the
exponent for food consumption and lower than the value of
the exponent for the oxydizing consumption of substance.
The experiments on the food conversion confirm, therefore,
the conclusion drawn from theoretical considerations that
we must insert in the Bertalanffy equation, in place of the
factor, a further exponential term on the part of anabolism.
This would express the energetic relations between the
energy-producing oxidation processes and the synthesis of
the body substance.

If we want to formulate this relation more exactly, we obtain:

$$\log konv = \log k + \delta \cdot \log anab.$$

We insert the given allometrical relation to weight for log anab:

$$\log anab = \log a + \alpha \cdot \log w$$

and obtain:

$$\log konv = \log k + \delta \cdot (\log a + \alpha \cdot \log w)$$
$$= \log k + \delta \cdot \log a + \alpha \cdot \delta \cdot \log w$$

Both of the first parts of the right side contain only constant quantities; we group them together under c:

$$\log konv = C + \alpha \cdot \delta \cdot \log w$$

After this we can also determine the exponent for the relation between anabolism and catabolism. The conversion exponent based on the weight was γ, thus is:

$$\alpha \cdot \delta = \gamma$$
$$\delta = \frac{\gamma}{\alpha}$$

For *Ophiocephalus* δ is calculated to be

$$\frac{0.549}{0.879} = 0.625$$

and for *Megalops*

$$\frac{0.543}{0.770} = 0.705.$$

Remarkably enough both exponents for the allometrical relation between anabolism and conversion lie in the dimension of the surface exponents. With the narrow experimental basis, on which for the present our mathematical evaluations are based, we must content ourselves with the establishment of dimensional relations.

THE ENERGETIC RELATIONS BETWEEN ANABOLISM AND CATABOLISM

It seems to me that the previous mathematical explanations of experimental findings have given the principle prerequisites for a closer look at the energetic relations between anabolism, catabolism and conversion in animal growth. In so doing we must make a few simplifying assumptions in order to be able to more clearly recognize the basic relations.

1. We assume the chemical composition of living matter as being homogeneous. The relatively constant results of chemical analysis justify this assumption. From this it follows that in the catabolic decomposition of living matter amounts of energy were liberated which are proportional to the weight.

2. Hence it follows inversely that in the oxydation of living matter proportional amounts to the oxygen usage are oxydized. This assumption is confirmed by the finding of Pandian that the exponent for the consumption of substance is identical with the exponent for the oxygen usage. Furthermore, this assumption is confirmed by the old experiments of Rubner (1894) on the relationship of the oxygen consumption to the loss of heat in mammals.

3. We have become acquainted above with a value of the respiratory measurements as an expression for the quantitative relations between anabolism and catabolism. Now we can also consider it as an expression for its energetic relation.

4. The substrata of the organism, necessary for the obtaining of energy, are parts of living matter and must therefore be first built into their structure. Because the substrata represent substances belonging to the body they are also understood through our growth formulations.

5. The incorporation of the consumed food into the body substance requires a certain expenditure of energy. The part allotted to purely chemical conversion must be small since the animal absorbs his chemical elements as such with the food. Therefore, we can ignore the

such with the food. Therefore, we can ignore the demand for
energy, necessary for the chemical transformations. The
essential portion of energy required in the synthesis of
body substance results out of concentration and transportation
work as well as out of the energy which is required for the
synthesis and the maintenance of the organic structure.
Thus it is essentially a question of a physical demand for
energy.

If we assume now, as did von Bertalanffy, that the
decomposition of body substance takes place proportional
to the mass, then it is to be accepted that the liberated
energy in this case serves the maintenance of the living
state — or more exactly expressed, the maintenance of the
living structure. For the starving animal only his own
body substance is at his disposal for this démand for energy.
Related to the unit of weight, this demand for energy would
be a constant quantity.

This material used up by catabolism must be again
replaced, by the intake of food. By way of the body liquids
the cells obtain the necessary substances. Hereby, however,
it is not sufficient that replacement material be equivalent
in amount of energy with disposal material, for this must
still be first incorporated into the living matter, for
which an additional demand for energy is necessary. Thus
for the loss in substance through catabolism an intake of
a larger amount of food material than is decomposed is a
requisite. Only a part of it is converted to substance
belonging to the body; the remaining part is oxydized, and
the liberated energy is used for the synthesis of the organic
structure.

The necessary energy for this, which we can designate
as "structure-energy", is, however, distinguished by the
fact that it can not be recovered again in the later oxydation, for the organic substance yields only the amount
of energy corresponding to the chemical composition. Also
the non-growing organism must be fed a greater amount than
that corresponding to its loss through catabolism.

Without a doubt anabolism and catabolism are not two
processes which occur independently of one another. On the
contrary, it is to be assumed that they are tied together
in such a way that through anabolism the substance which

was decomposed by catabolism is for the time being replaced.
In a growing organism the part necessary for the reproduction
of substance is added. The differential quotient of equation
(4) describes mathematically the interceding regulation of
the rate of growth:

$$\frac{dw}{w \cdot d\tau} = \frac{\ln N}{\tau^2} \tag{9}$$

If w and τ are given in the differential quotient a decrease
of w leads to an increase of ln N, i.e., to an increase in
the rate of growth until the relation of the differential
quotient is fulfilled. The increased rate of growth is
obtained by a heightening of the anabolic processes.

    We must therefore, at this point in the relation between
anabolism and catabolism, accept regulation mechanisms about
whose modes of action we can not as yet make any statements.
The one possibility of thought would be that in the growing
organism, dimensions corresponding to definite age values
are co-ordinated as theoretical values. The very exact
genetic propagation of the cause of growth could speak for
such a regulative mechanism. The other possibility would
be that the mechanism which regulates the relations between
anabolism and catabolism determines the course of growth.
With regard to the effective regulation mechanisms, it is
still not possible to decide whether it is a question of
the feed-back mechanisms or of steady states in von Bertalanffy's sense.

    The explanation of the relations between anabolism and
catabolism given here seems to me to provide an interesting
viewpoint for the comprehension of pathological growth.
This would be based on a disturbance of the regulation
mechanisms between anabolism and catabolism. Under these
conditions both elementary processes of growth proceed
independently of one another. Through anabolism there
occurs under these conditions an unlimited increase of the
living substance. The lactic acid appearing in pathological
growth comes presumably from the catabolic processes and
one could suppose that the lactic acid, or one of its preliminary stages, represents a link in the regulation chain
between anabolism and catabolism. In the balancing out of
these two processes the lactic acid would find no further
application and would be eliminated. It seems to me that

much speaks for the fact that the catabolic processes in
the organism proceed anoxybioxically throughout, and that
the oxydation processes are to be adjoined to anabolism.
The energies liberated by it would be conducted to the places
of consumption by carrying substances rich in energy. Muscle
metabolism appears to me to be an informative example of this
process.

After these theoretical digressions I would like to
return to the quantitative relations between consumption
and conversion. An interesting mathematical consequence
results in this case: namely, if we place the proportion
of the anabolic expenditure of energy with the converted
amount of substance in relation to one another and calculate
the expenditure of energy for the synthesis of the unit of
weight of living matter

$$a \cdot w^{\alpha} : c \cdot w^{\gamma} = x : w$$

then it follows

$$x = \frac{a}{c} \cdot w^{(1+\alpha-\gamma)} \tag{10}$$

Since γ is smaller than α we obtain an exponent which is
higher than 1.0. That means that the expenditure of energy
for the unit of weight of converted substance becomes higher
with increasing size. In this we find one of the causes for
the delimitation of animal growth. This connection becomes
clear if we convince ourselves that with the increasing size
of an organism the transportation capacities become greater
and the energetic charge of the surfaces, through which the
substances must pass, grows. If it is permissible to extrapolate this relation between the expenditure of energy and
the size of the organism, the expenditure of energy would
then be equal to 0 for $w = 0$, (that is, for the first formation of an organism). Since, moreover, according to the
growth function (equation #4) the rate of growth at this
time is infinite, the first formation of an organism would
be comparable to the crystallization process which follows
without addition of energy.

THE STRUCTURAL ENERGY

The foregoing analyses of the growth process have led
to an important constituent of the energetics of the living

organism: the structural energy. In principle, the presence
of such a performance for the maintenance of the organic
structure was already known; it was covered by the "cell
work" of von Bertalanffy (1951). Thus far its arrangement
as to size was incomprehensible. Now a way seems to have
been found which at least makes the value of the exponent
of the structural energy accessible. We obtain this by
mathematically constructing the proportions in the non-
growing organism corresponding to the ideas put forward on
page 652. For *Ophiocelphalus* a value of 0.12 would result,
for *Megalops* 0.23. We also arrive at values of the same
magnitude on the basis of the experimental findings if,
namely, we relate the substance synthesized in fish to the
used up substance:

$$\frac{a \cdot w^{\alpha}}{c \cdot w^{\gamma}} = \frac{a}{c} \cdot w^{(\alpha - \gamma)} \tag{11}$$

The exponent of the structural energy according to this
calculation would have the value 0.33 for *Ophiocephalus* and
0.23 for *Megalops*. While the agreement is remarkably good
in the latter case, the values for *Ophiocephalus* differ more
considerably. Probably, however, the exponent of consumption as calculated from the experiment values is in this
case not quite correct.

These lines of thought, along with the introduction
of the concept of structural energy, also allow the interpretation of the curves which von Bertalanffy recently (1964)
published. These curves, according to the experiments of a
student Racine, designate the allometrical relation of the
metabolism of the rat to its weight. It is striking that
the curves mount very sharply up to a weight of about 120 g
almost at an angle of 45°, which would correspond to an
α-value of about 0.9. Above this weight the oxygen usage
increases slowly, dependent on the weight. The angle of
increase of the regression lines is here only equal to
about 30°, corresponding to an α-value of about 0.35. I
would like to trace the instability occurring at a weight
of about 120 g back to the retardation of growth which
results in the rat at about this weight, coinciding with
the beginning of puberty. Von Bertalanffy recognized this
retardation in growth as early as 1938, and it also appeared
in my evaluations of rat growth (1966 and 1967).

Now the exponent α contains two components. The first
part is the structural energy which belongs to the preservation

of the given organization. One can designate this part as
the metabolism of preservation. Its exponent is very low,
as we saw, and not too far removed from a weight proportin-
ality. The second component is the growth metabolism which
yields the energy for the synthesis of new substances.
Both exponents add up to that of the total metabolism. By
a decreased rate of growth, as is the case for the rat after
puberty, the exponent becomes smaller and approaches the
low value of the exponent for the structural energy.

This explanation appears to provide a key for the low
α-value, which Locker (1961) found for the activity metabolism and which also appears in Racine's curves in a similar way. If we measure the activity metabolism of animal existing body substance is then used for the performance.
This must be again supplemented. Thus a fluctuation of the
relationship between growth and maintenance metabolism
results in favour of the latter part. This fluctuation is
expressed by the lower α-value for the activity metabolism.
I would like to confine myself to these basic considerations
as long as more thorough quantitative analyses on the basis
of experimental data cannot be carried out.

THE PROBLEM OF ENTROPY

The proof and the quantitative comprehension of structural energy seem to me to be extraordinarily significant
for the understanding of the energetic relationships in the
organism. Above all, physicists have been concerned with the
problem of what role entropy plays in the vital process.
This question is of interest for the physicists because the
concept of entropy is adjoined to the concept of probable
and improbable conditions. Considered from this point of
view the organism represents a system of an extremely
improbable order and on the basis of this definition would
be a system with a high, negative entropy. It seems to me,
however, that one cannot equate the ordinal conditions of
living matter with physical and chemical orders.

In the literature the arrangement prevailing in crys-
tals is often compared to animal structures. The crystal
structure is, however, energetically preferred at the moment
of its origin and thus the more probable condition. The
crystal structure remains in its static state until it
passes over again to the state of disorder under suitable
conditions, i.e., with the addition of energy. The condition

of order in the organism is, however, only maintained with
the constant addition of energy.

Entropy is difficult to understand as a concept; thus
people have tried to explain it with model representations.
Maxwell's demon (which separates the fast molecules from
the slow ones), has become the most well known. Apart from
the fact that this separation can not be performed without
an expenditure of energy, as Meixner (1960) emphasizes, the
demon also produces a temperature drop which can be energetically utilized anew. The organic order is, however,
characterized by the fact that it cannot be energetically
utilized at all or at best to a minimal degree. For this
reason Maxwell's model cannot be used for the explanation
of the organic states of order.

The situation in the organism is better visualized by
the picture chosen by von Weizsäcker (1948) of balls lying
disorderly on a hill. These balls roll down the slope and
form a circular figure at the bottom as a less probable
state. The formation of this order requires an expenditure
of energy which is furnished by the original height potential. Weizsäcker's picture represents only a static order;
the situation in the organism is better characterized if
we carry the balls up to the top of the hill again and let
them fall repeatedly to form the circular figure at the
bottom.

The essential feature of von Weizsäcker's idea is the
expenditure of energy required in order to create the
improbable arrangement. The energy expended in producing
the arrangement can in no way be further utilized: it
becomes positive entropy.

Also the installation of chemical elements into the
structure of the living organism necessitates a certain
expenditure of energy — the structural energy — that cannot
be further utilized by the organism and b ecomes unregulated
thermal movement or entropy. The organism uses a portion
of the negative entropy which it receives with its food
(Schrödinger, 1964) for the installation into the elements
of its body substance. It uses the other part for the
performance of work; the structural energy, however, degrades
to positive entropy without energetic efficiency.

The chemical and physical efficiencies sell naturally
under the formation of entropy. We can apply physical-chemical

formulations to them. It still remains to be seen whether
the statistical equation for the general description of
entropy is also applicable for structural energy, since the
arrangement in the organism is linked with the positive
formation of entropy.

In connection with the problem of entropy the question
occurs as to whether the energy period of the organism differs basically from the situation in inanimate nature. It
is mainly a question of whether or not there are processes
in the organism which contradict the second axiom of Thermodynamics. The question arose when people recognized the
arrangement of living matter as indicative of a higher negative entropy. According to the above ideas, however, this
is not the case. The maintenance of the organic structure
continuously consumes free energy which is degraded to
entropy. The phenomenon of life thus represents a struggle,
carried out with a considerable expenditure of energy,
against the purely physical tendency toward disorder. The
vital process should, therefore, not conflict with the second
principle and there is no reason to grant it a special position energywise.

The differentiation between physical entropy and structural entropy is very important for the explanation of
energy proportions in the organism. If we attempt, for
example, to determine the energetic efficiency of the muscle
activity, we obtain values of about 30% for the efficiency
of energy contained in the oxydized substration. But we
must bear in mind that the occurring entropy is composed of
the loss of energy during the conversion of free chemical
energy into mechanical work and the structural energy, which
takes no part in the performance and becomes entropy without
any mechanical equivalent. From this it can be concluded
that the efficiency of the actual contractile mechanism is
higher than our balance measurements indicate.

FINAL REMARKS

We are standing at the beginning of a development which
demands to an increasing degree the introduction of mathematical methods even in the field of biology. Only in this way
will it be possible to comprehend the relationships, more
and more difficult to survey and for which experimental
research only yields us isolated numerical values. This

development will be favored by the recent construction of electronic calculation aids, which have allowed the solution of even very complicated equations with a negligible loss of time.

The use of computers, which afford a solution for even the most complicated problems, includes, however, certain dangers. The agreement between found and computed numbers usually serves as the criterion for the correctness of chosen equations. But one has to keep in mind that the insertion of a few parameters allows the reproduction of very complicated curve patterns and also — above all — that mathematical models which are based on quite a different principle can yield practically the same curve. It is not to be disputed that such solutions are valuable in special cases. But they only signify an advance for biological research if they lead to the discovery of generally valid principles.

Von Bertalanffy adopted the method of proceeding from a very simple and clearly arranged, but basically sound, equation. This strikes me as being more promising since it offers the possibility of supplementing it with progressive knowledge or of correction. The fundamental formulations of Thermodynamics also proceed from very simple mathematical definitions resulting from experimental observation. Only with this presupposition do they offer a strong point for further evaluation.

Hess (1965) stated in a discussion that the concept of anabolism/catabolism was difficult to grasp. Without doubt these two fundamental processes are so closely interwoven in metabolic activity that chemically they are difficult to separate. Moreover, the structural problem enters into the anabolism/catabolism pattern which is impossible to solve with chemical methods. There is no doubt as to the existence of anabolic and catabolic processes in the vital process, and we would be committing a fundamental error not to separate them in the empirical balance of the mathematical equation.

The concept of anabolism and catabolism as the elementary processes of growth in von Bertalanffy's formulation also proved to be a worthy basis for the ideas under discussion, after one introduces conversion as an additional part. In this way it was possible to gain deeper insight

into the energetics of living matter. But it is probable
that even the present formulation can only be viewed as an
approximate solution. We proceeded from the mathematical
necessity that the sum of the exponents of anabolism and
conversion must be approximately equal to 1.0 if the catabolism has this exponent. We saw, however, that through
growth the value of the sum is higher than 1.0. One could
conclude from that, that catabolism is not in simple proportion either, but rather in exponential relation to the
mass. Since, in any case, the exponent of catabolism is
assumed as being small, one can ignore it at first. Nevertheless, the curves for the weight loss of starving animals
exhibit a bend, so that the simple mass proportionality of
catabolism presumably represents only a first approximation.

A few other equations have been used for the mathematical formulation of growth processes, but I do not wish to
deal with them at present. The highly differentiated proposal of Weiss and Kavanaugh (1957) is frequently cited in
recent literature. It remains indisputable that the equation encompasses lines of thought which should be considered in a more thorough analysis of growth processes.
For the present, however, it seems to depend less on
experimental results and more on *a priori* considerations
and therefore displays a strongly hypothetical character.
This is especially so as concerns Murray's growth curve
(1926) which is used by the authors. The course of this
function's curve deviates considerably from real growth
curves and does not allow evaluation in such a wide range
as tried by the authors. Such inappropriate terms of an
equation necessitate additional parameters which compensate
for the deviations from the real course of the curve and
thus complicate the solutions.

The only example which to my knowledge the authors
worked out represents the growth in weight of the hen. It
requires the insertion of 14 parameters which were empirically found by trial and error. Unfortunately the graphic
representation does not clearly show the degree of agreement between calculated and measured values. In any case,
application of the Bertalanffy function, or of my proposal,
would have yielded satisfactory results. Since the parameters can be calculated from the measuring data in a purely
mathematical way with both formulae, the calculation loss
would be incomparably smaller. Also, the mathematical
evaluation of experimental defect-settlements appears to have
been tentatively certified with too few findings by Weiss

and Kavanaugh.

In most recent times Paloheimo and Dickie (1965/66) have again undertaken to set up a growth function. They both subject experimentally found connections to their equation. But these are only approximately fulfilled. Thus they formulate the conversion proportional to the food absorption and this again parallel to the oxygen usage. Both provisions are, however, not fulfilled according to the evaluations of Pandian. It must be stressed here that Pandian's results are not contrary to the experiments on which Paloheimo and Dickie base their equation. The representation of curves, as yielded by the growth data, is mathematically soluble through the use of a sufficient number of parameters. Of course, the goal remains to insert as few parameters as possible. But the setting up of a growth model is first and foremost a biological problem, and the biologist has a series of demands to place upon the mathematical solution. One such demand is that the solution must not be limited to a special case but must have as wide as possible an area of validity.

If we want to aim at progress in the mathematical handling of biological phenomena, then a second essential demand is that the parameters of applied formulations show relations to other functions. Only when this condition is fulfilled, will it be possible to employ mathematical procedures for the investigation of biological relationships. For this reason even pure correlation calculations, which lead to purely mathematical parameters, promise only limited information.

In the case of the growth formulation the connection to the allometrical function presents a demand to be unconditionally fulfilled. Since length and weight of an organism are also allometrically related, all formulations, which are confined to either of these dimensions, are unsuited for a more exact analysis of the growth process.

The fundamental significance arising from the discovery of two functions is shown by the ideas of this paper. My proposal for a growth function (#4) allows for the first time the realization of a very simple and clearly visible relation between a growth function and the allometric formula.

The explanation of the parameters — in particular of the allometric exponent — derived from this basis, forms the foundation of my ideas.

Also in other cases such formulations should be preferred that can be mathematically related to growth functions. This is no utopian demand. With the use of my temperature function the calculated parameter yielded quite obvious connections to the allometric function. This fact spurs me on to deal more closely with the problem of growth mathematics.

Perhaps I can indicate at this point a viewpoint that arises from the definition of structural energy. In the allometric representation of the rate constants from my temperature function a strikingly lower, negative exponent resulted which applies to the structural energy in the exponential order of magnitude. It is conceivable that this low exponent in the temperature function reflects the fluctuation between anabolic and catabolic processes during growth; i.e., it must also find expression in a temperature function, meaningful to biology.

The organism represents a steadily changing system through the phenomenon of age. It is therefore expected that age also enters into the mathematical description of other phenomena of life as a parameter. Although the mathematical relationships of the parameter in the temperature function are not yet fully comprehensible, they offer a starting point for future solutions.

The analysis of growth processes on such a simple basis, e.g., the Bertalanffy equation, appears to many, perhaps, as an oversimplifcation of an extremely complex happening. As opposed to this one should point out that this equation is based on two very successful mathematical formulations of growth processes and does not require the introduction of hypothetical equations. The more complicated the formulation of a process, the greater the danger of introducing an error. We have seen how even the use of a simple mathematical expression, such as in the allometric function, can result in error.

Without doubt the complete mathematical analysis of even the smallest and simplest organism could remain an insoluble problem. But, apparently, even today the analysis of individual processes is able to give important information on the basis of the allometric function.

In such a complex system as the organism the quantitative analysis of partial processes is already a substantial gain. This can be compared to the theory of heredity which owes its fundamental discoveries to the simple quantitative relations found by Mendel. Also here it was a matter of extremely complex processes which had appeared fully obscure up until Mendel's time.

It is, however, utopian to assume that such a partial analysis is possible intellectually, without the use of mathematical procedures. As already recognized by Janisch (1927), most quantitative relations in living beings can only be represented by exponential functions. The mental processing of these represents considerable difficulties. To explain the co-operation of various exponential functions is a problem which can only be solved with pencil and paper, using the mathematical formulation.

The discovery of quantitative relations which can be clearly formulated between a series of fundamental manifestations of organic life shows that even in the field of Biology we can only gain deeper insight into the vital process through mathematical methods — and exclusively through them. The mathematical treatment of problems is becoming, to an increasing degree, ... important aid even in biology — also important as a medium for new experimental questioning.

We are still at the beginning of this field. Our equations and solutions are doubtless in need of further correction. For a mass of findings must be gathered in this new field of endeavour, today's biology, and mistakes will occur. We will have to make allowance for such roundabout ways until Biomathematics has achieved its place in the science of life.

REFERENCES

BENEDICT, F.G., *Vital Energetics*, Publ. Carnegie Institution of Washington, 503, 1938.

BERNARD, C., *Lecons sur les phénomènes de la vie*. Paris, 1885.

von BERTALANFFY, L., "Untersuchungen über die Gesetzlichkeit des Wachstums". I."Allgemeine Grundlagen der Theorie." *Arch. Entw. Mech.*, *131*, 613-653, 1934.

von BERTALANFFY, L., "A quantitative theory of organic growth", *Human Biol.*, *10*, 181–213, 1938.

— *Theoretische Biologie*, *2*, Stoffwechsel, Wachstum.   2nd ed., Francke, Bern, 1951.

— *Biophysik des Fliessgleichgewichts*, translated by: W.H. WESTPHAL.   Vieweg, Braunschweig, 1953.

— "Principles and the theory of growth", in: NOVINSKY, W.W. (ed.), *Fundamental Aspects of Normal and Malignant Growth*, Elsevier, Amsterdam, 1960.

— "Basic concepts in quantitative biology of metabolism". *Helgol. wiss. Meeresnunters.*, *9*, 5–37, 1964.

BEVERTON, R.J.H. and HOLT, S.J., "On the dynamics of exploited fish populations". *Fish. Invest.*, *19*(2), 1–533, London, 1957.

HESS, B., "Diskussionsbemerkung zum Vortrag Krüger", (II. intern. Symp. quantit. Biol. Stoffwechsels), *Helgol. wiss. Meeresunters.*, *14*, 1966.

IVLEV, V.S., *Experimental Ecology of the Feeding of Fishes*, Yale Univ. Press, New Haven, 1961.

JANISCH, E., "Das Exponentialgesetz als Grundlage einer vergleichenden Biologie", *Abh. Theor. org. Ent.*, *2*, 1927.

KRÜGER, F., "Über die mathematische Darstellung des tierischen Wachstums", *Naturwissenschaften*, *49*, 454, 1962.

— "Über den Exponenten der Temperaturfunktion biologischer Vorgänge und deren Grössenabhängigkeit", *Biol. Zbl.*, *80*, 721–750, 1961.

— "Neuere mathematische Formulierungen der biologischen Temperaturfunktion und des Wachstums", *Helgol. wiss. Meeresunters.*, *9*, 108–124, 1964.

— "Zur mathematischen Struktur der lebenden Substanz dargelegt am Problem der biologischen Temperatur- und Wachstumsfunktion", *Helgol. wiss. Meeresunters.*, *14*, 1966.

— "Zur mathematischen Wiedergabe des Rattenwachstums", *Zool. Anz. Suppl.*, *30*, 1967.

LOCKER, A., "Das Problem der Abhängigkeit des Stoffwechsels von der Körpergrösse", *Naturwissenschaften*, *48*, 445-449, 1961.

MEIXNER, J., Neuere Entwicklungen der Thermodynamik. Arbeits-gemeinsch. Forschg. Nord-Rhein-Westfalen, Heft 72, 1960.

MURRAY, H.A., "Physical ontogeny". 3. "Weight and growth as function of age", *J. gen. Physiol.*, *9*, 39, 39, 1925.

PALOHEIMO, J.E. and DICKIE, L.M., "Food and growth of fishes". I. "A growth curve derived from experimental data". *J. Fish. Res. Bd. Canada*, *22*, 521-542, 1965.

— II. "Effects of food and temperature on the relation between metabolism and body size". Ibid. *23*, 869-908, 1966.

— III. "Relations among food, body size, and growth efficiency' Ibid., *23*, 1209-1248, 1966.

PANDIAN, T.J., Intake, digestion, absorption and conversion of food in the fishes *Megalops cyprinoides* and *Ophiocephalus striatus*. *Marine Biol.*, *1*, 16-32, 1967.

PÜTTER, A., Wachstumsähnlichkeiten. *Pflügers Arch. ges. Physiol.*, *180*, 298-340, 1920.

RUBNER, M., "Die Quelle der tierischen Würme", *Z. Biol.*, *30*, 73, 1894.

RAMEAUX, M. and SARRUS, P.F., *Bull. Acad. Méd.*, Paris, *3* 1094-1100, 1837/39.

SCHRÖDINGER, E., *Was ist Leben?* Francke, Bern, 1964.

SNELL, O. "Die Abhängigkeit des Hirngewichts von dem Kör-pergewicht und den geistigen Fähigkeiten". *Arch. Psychiatrie*, *23*, 436-446, 1891.

WEISS, P. and KAVANAU, J.L., "A model of growth and growth control in mathematical terms", *J. gen. Physiol.*, *41*, 1-47, 1957.

von WEIZSÄCKER, C.F., *Die Geschichte der Natur*. Stuttgart, 1948.

WINBERG, G.G., "Rate of metabolism and food requirements of fishes", Transl. *Fish. Res. Bd. Canada*, No. 194, 1956.

ZUCKER, L. and ZUCKER, Th.F., "A simple time weight relation observed in well nourished rats", *J. gen Physiol.*, *25*, 445-463, 1941.

THE PROBLEM OF THE OSCILLATING
COMPONENT OF THE HUMAN GROWTH CURVE

JOACHIM-HERMANN SCHARF*†

Director, Anatomical Institute of the Martin-Luther University, Halle-Wittenberg in Halle, German Democratic Republic

Ludwig von Bertalanffy, as is well known, has successfully analyzed and interpreted the growth processes of organisms as has no other scientist before him. His chief publications appeared in 1942, 1957, 1960, and 1964. One problem, however, has not yet been satisfactorily solved, namely, the representation of the growth process for a living individual (or a collection of individuals) of a species over its life span, by means of a single analytical expression. This should be achieved without forcibly eliminating discontinuities in the curve, and should include causal analysis of

---

*With appreciated assistance given by a research commission of the State Ministry for University Education, German Democratic Republic. Numerical calculation: Mrs. Ruth Pieper (Table Calculator), leading medical-technical assistant at the Anatomical Institute in Halle, and Miss Friedegund Hüther (Digit Calculator for Programs ZRAI), mathematical-technical assistant at the Institute for Numerical Mathematics in Halle. Illustrations: academic draftsman Hellmut Helwin.

†Home address: DDR-4002 Halle, Schlieszfach 84, Germany.

well-known oscillations, which are additively superimposed upon a continuous and ideally monotonic growth function.

Scharf was able to show on the basis of investigations (Scharf and colleagues, 1965ff) that the variations of body weight in rats are regularly influenced in an artificial microclimate by the diversions of O_2 metabolism. These diversions, in turn, depend regularly on the oscillations in a given temperature of the surroundings. In these experiments the room temperature was varied according to schedule withint the 56 days (exactly 8 weeks) so that two year cycles expired: i.e., two cold (winter) and two warm (summer) intervals expired, of sine shape. The body weight reacted in such a way that a temperature minimum resulted in a weight minimum, and vice versa.

In order to avoid a fallacious conclusion, a simultaneous system of differential equations of the 9th order was set up and solved for three dependent functions with coupling in the first differential quotient (coupling of speed). With arbitrary integration of T (t) ['C], the values V_{O_2} (t) and g (t) resulted by necessity, and the integrals fitted exactly with the test results.

DIFFERENTIAL EQUATIONS AND INTEGRALS IN CONSISTENT FORM FOR THE DESCRIPTION OF HUMAN GROWTH OVER GREATER INTERVALS OF TIME.

In order then to gain a more extensive control, a search was carried out for other publications on the subject. In the well-known text book by Martin and Saller (1959) there is a table on page 862, in which measured values for children and juveniles are given (altogether data on 822 persons were compiled by Daffner [1897]).The dates cited there are mean values of measurements, which in this case were considered in April and October. On the other hand, the single values were not indicated by Daffner, but rather the extreme ordinates on each point of support, with which, of course, nothing can be done. Daffner's mean values are fully presented in Plate 1. In the first place, the exponential trend of longitudinal growth of the "experimentees" was determined according to the approved algorithm of Prony (cited from Whittaker

and Robinson; see also Willers, 1957; Scharf, 1966). By
differential calculation (see Formula 1) the first differences were determined about the total interval of time,
$11 \leq t \leq 20$ years

$$\Delta^1_{i+0.5} = y_{i+1} - y_i \tag{1}$$

replaced line by line and the linear system of equations
established from them by Gaussian transformation.

$$\alpha_0 \Sigma \Delta^1_{i+0.5} \Delta^1_{i+0.5} + \alpha_1 \Sigma \Delta^1_{i+0.5} \Delta^1_{i+1.5} +$$

$$\alpha_2 \Sigma \Delta^1_{i+0.5} \Delta^1_{i+2.5} + \Sigma \Delta^1_{i+0.5} \Delta^1_{i+3.5} \qquad = 0$$

$$\alpha_0 \Sigma \Delta^1_{i+0.5} \Delta^1_{i+1.5} + \alpha_1 \Sigma \Delta^1_{i+1.5} \Delta^1_{i+1.5} +$$

$$\alpha_2 \Sigma \Delta^1_{i+1.5} \Delta^1_{i+2.5} + \Sigma \Delta^1_{i+1.5} \Delta^1_{i+3.5} \qquad = 0 \tag{2}$$

$$\alpha_0 \Sigma \Delta^1_{i+0.5} \Delta^1_{i+2.5} + \alpha_1 \Sigma \Delta^1_{i+1.5} \Delta^1_{i+2.5} +$$

$$\alpha_2 \Sigma \Delta^1_{i+2.5} \Delta^1_{i+2.5} + \Sigma \Delta^1_{i+2.5} \Delta^1_{i+3.5} \qquad = 0$$

The unknown values α_i were calculated and they are,
therefore, the coefficients of the characteristic equivalent equation of the third degree.

$$\xi^3 + \alpha_2 \xi^2 + \alpha_1 \xi + \alpha_0 = 0 \tag{3}$$

where roots are $|\xi_i| = e^{-\gamma_i}$, insofar as ξ_i is real and
$|\xi_i| < 1$. With the Δ inserted from the measuring values of
Daffner in (2), the constants become

$$\alpha_0 = -0.6513264574$$

$$\alpha_1 = -0.8351691422$$

$$\alpha_2 = +0.7898491876$$

and this α_i inserted in (3) yields the following, by solving the cubic equation:

$$\xi_1 = + 0.9111923125$$

$$\xi_2 = - 0.9431422937$$

$$\xi_3 = - 0.7578992064$$

The exponential time constants are the following, according to McLaurin's development

$$\gamma_1 = \ln |\xi_1| = - 0.09300130354$$

$$\gamma_2 = \ln |\xi_2| = - 0.05853811412$$

$$\gamma_3 = \ln |\xi_3| = - 0.27720487534$$

in which a half-year is conceived of as the unit of time.

By means of (3+1)- dimensional calculation of the regression, the growth function resulted for the interval $11 \le t \le 20$ years.*

$$L(t) = - 182.785 + 3173.213e^{-0.2772t} - 4235.943e^{-0.09300t} + 3227.743e^{-0.05854t} \tag{4}$$

This function fits the measuring values optimally, as the multiple measuring of the determination with n = 27 amounts to the accompanying points B = 99.88%. All terms in (4) are also significant ($t_i > 16.8214$). The function (4) can certainly not be extra-polarized from the validity range (Plate 1). (4) can be taken as a particular integral of the linear differential equation with constant coefficients:

$$\frac{d^4L}{dt^4} + 0.428744293 \frac{d^3L}{dt^3} + 0.04745158629 \frac{d^2L}{dt^2} + 0.001509136861 \frac{dL}{dt} = 0 \tag{5}$$

which produce a connection between the rate of growth (L'), growth acceleration (L''), the change in the growth acceleration (L''') and the change of the change in growth acceleration (L''''). This differential equation is also valid for the growth of the human body outside the given

---

*The calculation was continously carried out to 9 digits; in order to minimize the error in rounding off the constants are noted here in abbreviated form.

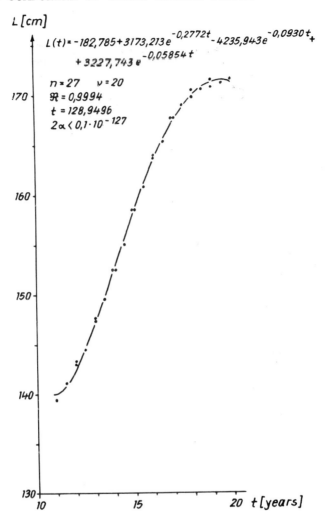

$$L(t) = -182{,}785 + 3173{,}213\,e^{-0{,}2772t} - 4235{,}943\,e^{-0{,}0930t} + 3227{,}743\,e^{-0{,}05854t}$$

$n = 27 \quad \nu = 20$
$\mathfrak{R} = 0{,}9994$
$t = 128{,}9496$
$2\alpha < 0{,}1 \cdot 10^{-127}$

Plate 1: Purely real integral to the differential equation (5). Particular integration by regression calculation for $11 \leq t \leq 20$ years. Between this graph and the preceding points the differences in Plate 5 have been formed. Values according to Daffner. (1897, p. 83)

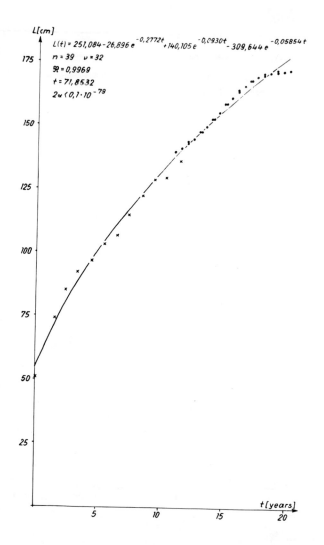

Plate 2: Purely real integral to the differential equation.
Particular integral by regression calculation (5)
for $0 \leq t \leq 20$ years. In the interval portion
$14.4 \leq t \leq 20$ years, the curve no longer fits the
points, because the values L (t > 20) were not
included. Values according to Daffner. (1897,
p. 78 and 83)

interval $11 \leq t \leq 20$ years. Insofar, as only the clearly essential trend is observed. In another table Daffner again gives measurements of the height of children of $0 \leq t \leq 11.42$ years. If one inserts these together with the values used for (4) one comes to an expression

$$L(t) = 251.084 - 26.896e^{-0.2772t} +$$
$$140.105e^{-0.09300t} - 309.644e^{-0.05854t} \tag{6}$$

which is valid for $0 \leq t \leq 20$ years, and which is fulfilled by the data above with B = 99.28% (Plate 2). In this way the common validity of (5) for Homo sapiens is proven. For t < 20 years only correspondingly reliable values of measurements have to be alleged. If one chooses one year as a physiological unit of time, then the exponential time constants because of

$$\Delta T = h^{-1} = (\Delta t)^{-1} \text{ in } h = 0.5 \text{ years}$$

become

$$\gamma_1 = 2 \ln |\xi_1| = -0.18600260708$$

$$\gamma_2 = 2 \ln |\xi_2| = -0.11707622823$$

$$\gamma_3 = 2 \ln |\xi_3| = -0.55440975068$$

which is equal to the solutions of the differential equation

$$\frac{d^4L}{dt^4} + 0.857488586 \frac{d^3L}{dt^3} + 0.1898063452 \frac{d^2L}{dt^2} +$$
$$0.01207309488 \frac{dL}{dt} = 0 \tag{7}$$

Instead of (4) one gets for $11 \leq t \leq 20$ years the integral

$$L(t) = 149.570 + 20751.085e^{-0.5544t} -$$
$$1998.752e^{-0.1860t} + 734.583e^{-0.1171t} \tag{8}$$

which with B = 99.70% satisfies equally well the values of measurement (Plate 3). If one combines all Daffner's dates (as in (6)), the result for $0 \leq t \leq 20$ years is adjustments of worth (Plate 4) with B = 99.66%.

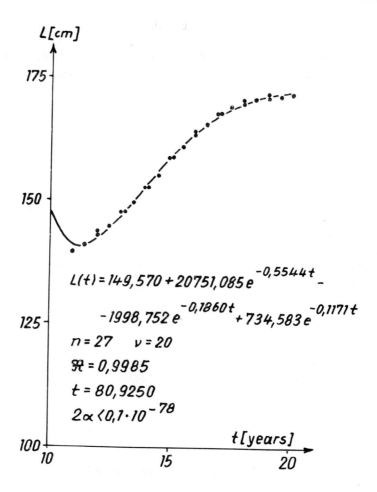

Plate 3: Purely real integral to the differential equation
          (7). Particular integral ascertained by the
          regression calculation for 11 ≤ t ≤ 20 years.
          This integral is somewhat less suited for this
          limited interval than the one in Plate 1, as was
          seen from the comparison of the t-values. Data
          according to Daffner. (1897, p. 83)

$$L(t) = 205.527 - 52.301e^{-0.5544t} +$$

$$275.344e^{-0.1860t} - 377.193e^{-0.1171t} \tag{9}$$

The differential equation (7) is therefore universally
applicable, insofar as one needs the clearly essential
trend.

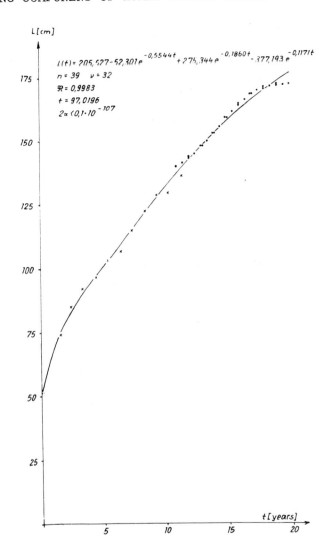

Plate 4:   Purely real integral to the differential equation (7). Particular integral ascertained by
the regression calculation for $0 \leq t \leq 20$ years.
The graph fits better on the whole than the one
in Plate 2 (compare the t-values!), but just as
there the greatest variations are in the ordi-
nates to $14.5 \leq t' \leq 20$ years, because no $L(t \leq 20)$
were included. Data according to Daffner (1897,
p. 78 and 83).

THE PERIODICITY OF HUMAN GROWTH CURVES

If one denotes Martin and Saller's (1959) shared
average values of measurement from Daffner with $\mathcal{L}_i$ and
the functional values from (4) in the points of support
t_i with L_i, then one can separate, according to the series
of measurements, the included oscillating components.

$$\mathcal{L}_i - L_i = D_i \qquad\qquad\qquad (10)$$

These differences D_i (t_i) are presented in Plate 5.

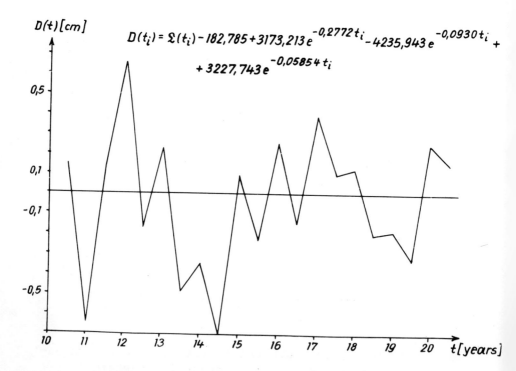

$$D(t_i) = \mathcal{L}(t_i) - 182{,}785 + 3173{,}213\,e^{-0{,}2772\,t_i} - 4235{,}943\,e^{-0{,}0930\,t_i} +$$
$$+ 3227{,}743\,e^{-0{,}05854\,t_i}$$

Plate 5: Graphic presentation of the differences between
the points from Daffner (1897, p. 83) and the
graph of Plate 1. The discrete differences are
bounded provisionally by straight lines, in order
to clarify the amplitudes. The point D (10.5) =
D (20.5) has been extrapolated. For the Fourier-
analysis, D (10.5) = D (0) = D (2π) = D (20.5),
so that Δt = 0.5 is transformed to $D_t = 10^{-1}\pi = 18°$.

With respect for the following Fourier analysis by means of double convolution according to Runge (see Zurmühl 1963), the divisibility by 4 of the N ordinates assumed (N = 4P), must now be decided, which voluntary action would falsify less the series of measurements. According to the cancellation of three differences (10) or the extrapolation of one value (4). The series of measurements with n = 27 single points of Daffner is founded (Plate 1) only on 19 discrete points of time t_i. After an estimation of the possibility of errors it was decided to extrapolate a point D(t = 10.5), so that the number became N = 20, thus (0.5 N) - 1 = 9.

The Fourier analysis lead to the polynomial

$$D(t) + a_0 + \sum_{k=1}^{9} (a_k \cos k\omega t + b_k \sin k\omega t) + a_{10} \cos 10\omega t \qquad (11)$$

in which

$$c_k = + \sqrt{a_k^2 + b_k^2} \qquad (12)$$

The result is the spectrum of the nine first harmonics. (Plate 6) As one can see, the 2nd harmonic dominates (= first superposed harmonic), which corresponds to the known fact that pre- and post-puberty growth are different. Otherwise the long period of τ_2 = 5 years has no real meaning. The next greatest amplitude points to the 6th harmonic, which corresponds to a period length τ_6 = 1.66 years, therefore does not permit the hypothesis of a year's periodicity of the human body growth. The same is valid for the other harmonics, which contribute essentially to the evaluation. The 10th harmonic, which corresponds to τ_{10} = 1 year, cannot bear weight in the preceding formulation according to (11) and (12), since for it only the cosines-constant a_{10} is the result, whereas b_{10} = 0 disappears. But according to the Fourier-analysis (11) it was shown that $| a_{10} | > |a_i|$ for i = 1...9.

In order to be able to comprehend the periodicity of D(t) more clearly, this function was further presented for the discrete values (of Plate 5), in polar coordinates. The strong distortion of the star in the form of an "8" makes clear the over-balance of the 2nd harmonic; on the other hand it clearly reveals the year periodicity, which

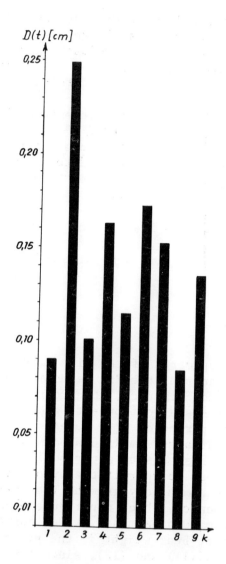

Plate 6:   Spectrum of the (0.5 N) – 1 = 9 harmonics as a
           clear result of the Fourier analysis of the pro-
           visionary graph from Plate 5. The trigonometric
           polynomial is now steady and continuously dif-
           ferentiable; it runs exactly through the preced-
           ing points $D(t_i)$. It surpasses the 2nd harmonic,
           but a period length of one year is not demon-
           strable.

is only disturbed once in the position t = 11. In order to be able to present negative D_1 also, the constant C = 1 was added to all differences (Plate 7).

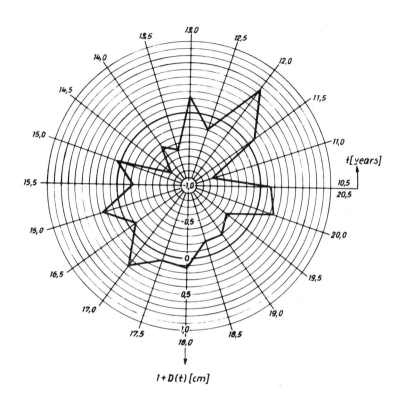

Plate 7: Graph presented on Plate 5 in polar coordinates. In order also to present negative D (t_i) all D^* (t_i) = D (t_i) + 1 was designed. The predominance of the 2nd harmonic is clearly recognizable in the distortion but also the period for k = 10 of a 1-year period. The full circle is divided 20^{-1}x360° = 18°.

From the graphic presentations (Plates 5 and 7) a period with τ = 1 year appears to be directly visible. However, when restricted to the dates imparted by Daffner (1897) with the Fourier analysis there is no clear proof when 9 harmonics are included. Therefore, another way was tried. If one includes the differences $\Delta^1_{i+5.5}$ which have been replaced by five lines, then a (5+1)-dimensional difference equation system is established, which according to the Gaussian transformation is determined in matrix spelling:

$$(\Sigma\Delta_j^1 \ \Delta_k^1)\begin{pmatrix} \alpha_0 \\ \vdots \\ \alpha_4 \end{pmatrix} = \begin{pmatrix} \Sigma\Delta_{i+5.5}^1 & \Delta_{i+0.5}^1 \\ \vdots & \vdots \\ \Sigma\Delta_{i+5.5}^1 & \Delta_{i+4.5}^1 \end{pmatrix} \quad \begin{matrix} (i=0,1,2....\mu) \\ \\ (j,k=i+0.5,i+1.5...i+4.5) \end{matrix}$$

13

It is diagonally symmetrical, positively definite as well as being regular in line and column (= nonsingular). The solution, according to the unknown quantities α_i gave:

$$\begin{aligned}
\alpha_0 &= 0.2951554190 \\
\alpha_1 &= - \ 0.1718965673 \\
\alpha_2 &= 0.3348551531 \\
\alpha_3 &= - \ 0.6444091262 \\
\alpha_4 &= - \ 0.7311506874
\end{aligned}$$

With these constants the characteristic equation of degree 5

$$\xi^5 + \alpha_4\xi^4 + \alpha_3\xi^3 + \alpha_2\xi^2 + \alpha_1\xi + \alpha_0 = 0 \tag{14}$$

was analogously established (3) and solved according to the combined Bombelli-Newton-Horner-Bairstow proceedings. The result was the following roots:

$$\begin{aligned}
\xi_1 &= 0.9355282447 \\
\xi_{2.3} &= - \ 0.08582706966 \pm i \ 0.5974152808 \\
\xi_{4.5} &= 0.9191665357 \pm i \ 0.1457238207
\end{aligned}$$

So the exponential time constants become:

$$\begin{aligned}
\gamma_1 &= 2 \ \ln|\xi_1| = - \ 0.1332878832 \text{ (because h = 0.5, } h^{-1}=2) \\
\gamma_{2.3} &= - \ 1.009856236 \pm i \ 2.856217358 \\
\gamma_{4.5} &= - \ 0.1437519567 \pm i \ 1.399031458
\end{aligned}$$

The conjugate complex roots were, according to

$$\gamma_{i,j} = r_{i,j} \pm i\omega_m$$

$$r_{i,j} = (2h)^{-1} \ln (a^2 + b^2) \begin{pmatrix} \text{when } \xi_{i,j} = a \pm ib; \\ i,j = 2,3;\ 4,5 \end{pmatrix} \quad (15a)$$

$$\pm i\omega_m = h^{-1} \arctan (ba^{-1}) \qquad [m = 1,2] \qquad (15b)$$

brought to the preceding form, which was useful for further calculation. The result of Daffner's measurements in a half-year interval was the interval $h = \Delta t = 0.5$. According to the calculation of the integration constants A_i (with $i = 0,1,. . .,5$) by the $(5 + 1)$ = dimensional linear regression the result is the curve*

$$L(t) = A_0 + A_1 e^{\gamma \cdot t} + e^{\gamma_2,3t} (A_2 \cos \omega_1 t + A_3 \sin \omega_1 t) +$$
$$e^{\gamma_4,5t} (A_4 \cos \omega_2 t + A_5 \sin \omega_2 t) \qquad (16)$$

of Plate 8, which fits the points well, but with a certainty measure of $B = 99.12\%$ is inferior to the function (4). The function (4) is in any case according to the comparison of the non-linear correlation coefficients R by means of Z- transformation according to Fisher (z_i = Artanh R_i) is better suited with a significance of $2\alpha < 0.001$. The result of this is that this method does not lead much further. Nevertheless, it is striking that $\omega_1 = 2.856217358$ comes very near to the value of $9\omega = 2.827433388$ from the Fourier analysis, and therefore leads to the significant 9th harmonic from Plate 3. On the other hand $\omega_2 = 1.399031458$ differs quite significantly from $4\omega = 1.256637061$. The 4th harmonic in Plate 6 is significant, since it ranges in the amount from c_4 to 3rd position. The formula is not able to demonstrate an annual period.

Thus, an attempt still remains with the formulation of Whittaker and Robinson (1926; cf. Whittaker and Robinson, 1965; Willers, 1957; Stumpff, 1927, 1937) to

---

*
(16) is the integral of the linear differential equation

$$\frac{d^6L}{dt^6} + 2.4405 \frac{d^5L}{dt^5} + 12.0439 \frac{d^4L}{dt^4} + 8.1979 \frac{d^3L}{dt^3} +$$

$$\qquad (16a)$$

$$19.0374 \frac{d^2L}{dt^2} + 2.4196 \frac{dL}{dt} = 0$$

ascertain unknown period lengths, which are not integrally proportional to each other. For the preceding case
the equation

$$\Delta_{i+4.5} + \Delta_{i+0.5} + \alpha_1 \Delta_{i+3.5} + \alpha_1 \Delta_{i+1.5} + \alpha_2 \Delta_{i+2.5} = 0 \qquad (17)$$

was laid as a basis, which in the final analysis leads to
a function with purely imaginary exponents. While (17),
according to the formulation of Gauss, is determined in
such a way that the α_i fulfill the minimum square demand,
the result is the linear equation system:

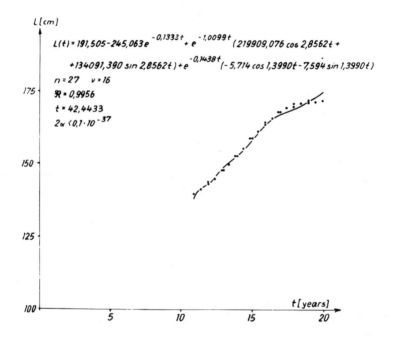

Plate 8:   Integral from a purely real term and two con-
           jugate complex parts of the differential equa-
           tion (16a). For about two-thirds of the graph
           a good result in aplitude but nothing more in
           the last third. A period of 1 year is not demon-
           strable. Particular integral for $11 \leq t \leq 20$
           years by regression calculation.

$$\alpha_1 \left[\sum \Delta^1_{i+3.5} \Delta^1_{i+3.5} + 2\sum \Delta^1_{i+1.5}\Delta^1_{i+3.5} + \sum \Delta^1_{i+1.5} \Delta^1_{i+1.5} \right] +$$

$$\alpha_2 \left[\sum \Delta^1_{i+2.5} \Delta^1_{i+3.5} \quad \sum \Delta^1_{i+1.5} \Delta^1_{i+2.5} \right] = \tag{18a}$$

$$- \left[\sum \Delta^1_{i+3.5} \Delta^1_{i+4.5} + \sum \Delta^1_{i+1.5} \Delta^1_{i+4.5} + \sum \Delta^1_{i+0.5} \Delta^1_{i+3.5} + \sum \Delta^1_{i+0.5} \Delta^1_{i+1.5} \right]$$

$$\alpha_1 \left[\sum \Delta^1_{i+1.5} \Delta^1_{i+2.5} + \sum \Delta^1_{i+2.5} \Delta^1_{i+3.5} \right] + \alpha_2 \sum \Delta^1_{i+2.5} \Delta^1_{i+2.5} =$$

$$- \sum \Delta^1_{i+0.5} \Delta^1_{i+2.5} + \sum \Delta^1_{i+2.5} \Delta^1_{i+4.5} \tag{18b}$$

By resolution according to the α_i one gains the constants of the characteristic equation of degree 4:

$$\xi^4 + \alpha_1 \xi^3 + \alpha_2\xi^2 + \alpha_1\xi + 1 = 0 \tag{19}$$

therefore of a reciprocal (symmetrical) equation, which according to division by ξ^2 and substitution of

$$\lambda = \xi + \xi^{-1} \tag{20}$$

goes over to the square equation

$$\lambda^2 + \alpha_1 \lambda + \alpha_2 - 2 = 0 \tag{21}$$

As soon as both roots λ_i are known, the ξ_i from

$$\xi^2_{1.2} - \lambda_1\xi_{1.2} + 1 = 0$$
$$\xi_{3.4} - \lambda_2\xi_{3.4} + 1 = 0 \tag{22}$$

can be ascertained.

In the preceding case the equation system (18) had the solutions

$$\alpha_1 = -0.09317119441$$

$$\alpha_2 = -1.720515614$$

so that (19) after reduction to (21) gave the roots

$$\lambda_1 = -1.8828406986$$

$$\lambda_2 = +1.9760118930$$

which according to insertions in (22) leads to the two conjugate complex root pairs of (19):

$$\xi_{1,2} = -0.9414203493 \pm i\, 0.3372352175$$

$$\xi_{3,4} = 0.9880059465 \pm i\, 0.1544155377$$

The common integral of the deduced linear differential equation by the transformation under consideration of the constants previously calculated

$$\frac{d^4 L}{dt^4} + 31.40272381 \frac{d^2 L}{dt^2} + 3.009955629\; L(t) = 0 \qquad (23)$$

is given by

$$y = A_1 e^{\gamma_1 it} + A_2 e^{-\gamma_1 it} + A_3 e^{\gamma_2 it} + A_4 e^{-\gamma_2 it} \qquad (24)$$

in which

$$\gamma_{1,2} = \pm i\, 5.595233985 \text{ becomes } \gamma_{3,4} = \pm i\, 0.3099952798,$$

in which in (23) the transformation to the graphic width h = 1 year is already taken into consideration. One comes to the same result by a logarithm of ξ_i according to (15a,b). The real part - right to the smallest error - results in r = 1 and with this $(2h)^{-1} \ln(r) = 0$, the question is according to the evaluation of purely imaginary exponents, which result from (15b), when one considers that

$$\xi_1 = e^{\gamma_1 ih}, \; \xi_2 = e^{-\gamma_1 ih} \; \xi_3 = e^{\gamma_2 ih} \; \xi_4 = e^{-\gamma_2 ih} \qquad (25a)$$

and

$$\xi_1 = \xi_2^{-1} \; \xi_3 = \xi_4^{-1} \qquad (25b)$$

they are calculated with

$$h = \Delta t = 0.5$$

See Table 1.

If one shortens the results of the very exact calculation to a sensible index, then two periods are formed
from the material of Daffner: one period of 1.12 years
and a second of 20.26 years' duration. The first is,
therefore, about the year period with the season variations of the longitudinal growth of the human. The result is therefore sensible, since it is in harmony with
experiences, but is relatively inexact because of the few
supporting positions.

As a control, between every two adjacent differences
D_i (Plate 5) the arithmetical mean was formed (the extra-
polar ordinate $D_{10.5}$ of the evaluation (11) was not
needed):

$$D_{i+0.25} = 0.5 \ (D_i + D_{i+0.5}) \quad [h = 0.25 \text{ years}] \tag{26}$$

so that instead of the 19 original dates of Daffner (1897),
the N = 37 ordinates now were available. By emitting D_{20},
N = 4 and P = 36, so that a Fourier analysis can again be
applied, in which the number of harmonics becomes
(0.5 N) − 1 = 17. According to (12) the spectrum was then
calculated, which is presented in Plate 9. Because
h = 0.25, the angular frequency becomes

$$\omega = (4)(2\pi)(N^{-1}) = 0.6981317012 \text{ rad.}$$

so that the 9th harmonic with

$$9\omega = 2\pi$$

has the period length τ_9 = 1 year. As is directly apparent
from Plate 9, the long time period with k = 2 again predominates, which corresponds to a period length of 4.5
years, the 9th harmonic follows directly, which − as already
was carried out − reflects exactly the year's cycle of
growth and in position 3 stands the wave k = 3 with a
three year periodicity. Like the 4th harmonic, all harmonics
with k ≥ 10 also do not contribute essentially to the evaluation, which on account of the interpolation according to
(26) is self-evident for all k ≥ 10.

TABLE I

Roots	$\tan\phi = b\,a^{-1}$	Quad-rant	$\phi(°)$	$\phi\pi/180$ (rad)	$h^{-1}\mathrm{arc}\phi = \omega$	$\tau = 2\pi\omega^{-1}$ yrs.
$\xi_{1,2}$	-0.3582195963	II	160.2914824	2.797614131	5.595228262	1.122954241
$\xi_{3,4}$	$+0.1562900893$	I	8.882902086	0.1550358885	0.310071777	20.26364788

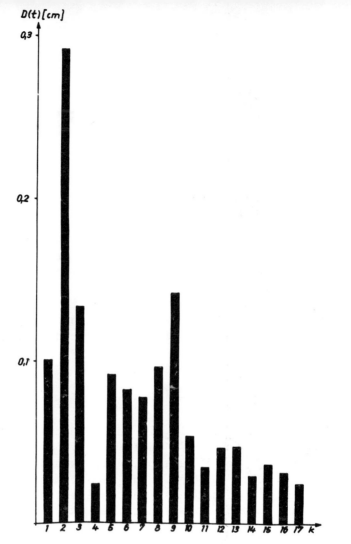

Plate 9: Spectrum of the harmonic for 36 included ordinates
according to the Fourier analysis. From the curve
in Plate 5 after omitting the extrapolation point
D(10.5) = D(20.5) in the interval $11 \leq t \leq 20$
years, the equidistant ordinates in the period
$h = \Delta t = 0.25$ were concluded. The total interval
was then put $T = 2\pi$, which leads to $D_t = 36^{-1}$ x
$360° = 10°$. Thus it is only D(20) itself which
does not go into the formulation. This formulation yields unequivocally interpreted and absolutely clear results: as in Plate 6, the 2nd harmonic predominates then follows 9th, which on
account of $\Delta t = 10°$ with (9x)(10°) = 2π leads to
X = 4h = 1 year. The 3rd harmonic, moreover,
contributes essentially to the formulation, which
proves a 3-year cycle. The 3 harmonics embrace
42.1% of the divergences, the other 14 together
57.9%

If one now adds (4) to the trigonometric polynomial (in which only the significant harmonics $k = 2, 3, 9$ are included), one comes, with $C_0 = A_0 + a_0$, to

$$\Lambda(t) = C_0 + A_1 e^{-\gamma_1 t} + A_2 e^{-\gamma_2 t} + A_3 e^{-\gamma_3 t} +$$

$$\sum_{k=1}^{3} (a_k \cos k\omega t + b_k \sin k\omega t) \qquad (27)$$

if one puts $t_{11} = t_{20} = 2\pi$. The graph of this function, which reflects the oscillations of human growth satisfactorily, shows the oscillations indistinctly in a strong reduction as a result of low amplitudes. It was not worthwhile to illustrate. On the other hand, if one chooses for the graphic presentation the purely harmonic portion in strong extension in the direction of ordinates, then the oscillating becomes clear. The Fourier portion of (27) is symbolized by

$$F(t) = \Lambda(t) - C_0 - A_1 e^{-\gamma_1 t} - A_2 e^{-\gamma_2 t} - A_3 e^{-\gamma_3 t} \qquad (28)$$

and is presented in Plate 10. If sufficient measuring values were known, then (27) could easily be formulated by a simple conversion of a_k, b_k, which would satisfy the legitimate demand $t_0 = 2\pi = 0$. But measurements on the oscillating growth of infants, the smallest children and small children have obviously not been carried out till now.

DISCUSSION

The analytical experiments show that, from the date material of Daffner (1897), a year's periodicity of the human growth is demonstrable only in the insertion of a considerable requirement of numerical mathematics. This is partly due to the fact that the seasonal variations of growth are relatively small, but mostly to the fact that a measurement interval of six months is a very rough choice. There is no doubt that increase in human growth is greater between April and October than in the winter period of the year. It is also certain that growth amplitude before and during puberty is greater in means than in juveniles after the seventeenth year (of a three year periodicity), and that there is an influence of season (after the termination of growth) on the stature. It can therefore be supposed that the rhythmical changes of growth acceleration are caused in the main by the seasonal environmental temperature, although it is certain that this is not the only cause. It would demand a more exact analysis to measure in shorter time intervals, in which it is recommended to raise measuring values in the same population in every month. Regular meteorological measurements would have to run parallel, which causes no difficulties in the duration registration of the most important variables by a meteorological use.

For future measurements, however, the realization of the demand for equidistance of the supporting position apart from the smaller interval of h = 1 month is required. A more certain declaration on the problems of rhythms is then only possible, if the date material admits an analysis according to Fourier, and this is the most simple and most certain in the age of the computer, if the interval is constant.

CONCLUSION

By using the measuring values of Daffner (1897) on altogether 1697 infants, children, and juveniles in the range of $0 \leq t \leq 20$ years, the differential equation is set up for human growth and a particular integral is applied, which describes the aperiodical growth process for the preceding time interval in a closed analytical expression. For juveniles in the age group of $11 \leq t \leq 20$ years - the collection measured by Daffner embraces 822 persons - it is proven moreover by the Fourier analysis and purely imaginary regression calculation that a season-conditioned oscillation overlaps the aperiodical growth, whose shortest and most surely comprehended period length amounts to one year. Besides this period, lengths of 3, 4.5, and 5 years were found.

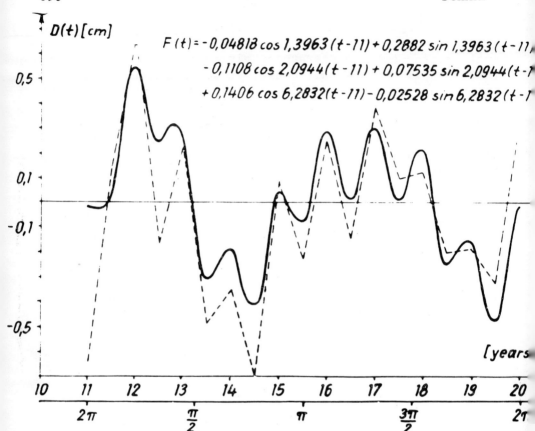

$$F(t) = -0,04813 \cos 1,3963\,(t-11) + 0,2882 \sin 1,3963\,(t-11,$$
$$- 0,1108 \cos 2,0944\,(t-11) + 0,07535 \sin 2,0944\,(t-1$$
$$+ 0,1406 \cos 6,2832\,(t-11) - 0,02528 \sin 6,2832\,(t-1$$

Plate 10: Harmonic function to Plate 9, in which only the 3 significant harmonics ($k = 2$, 3, 9) have been included for the Fourier-synthesis. If one adds the trigonometric polynomial presented here for the graph of Plate 1, then the result is an increase of adaption value.

$R = 0.9998$ $n = 27$ $\cdot \nu = 13$

$t = 166.7644$

$2\alpha < 0.1 \times 10^{-126}$

The fact that the possibility of error does not also decrease despite the increased t-value opposite Plate 1, lies in the loss of further degrees of freedom because the number of the parameters has increased. (Dotted graph: Differences from Plate 5).

REFERENCES

von BERTALANFFY, L., "Theoretische Biologie", *Stoff-wechsel, Wachstum*, Berlin: Borntraeger, 1942.

von BERTALANFFY, L., Wachstum. In: *KÜKENTHALs Handbuch der Zoologie, 8*, 4(6). Berlin: W. de Gruyter, 1957.

von BERTALANFFY, L., Principles and theory of growth. In: NOWINSKI, W.W. (ed.) *Fundamental aspects of normal and malignant growth*, 137-259, Amsterdam: Elsevier, 1960.

von BERTALANFFY, L., "Basic concepts in quantitative biology of metabolism". *Helgol. Wiss. Meeresunters., 9*, 5-38, 1964.

BLUME, H., "Theorie und Praxis der Periodogrammanalyse von Registrierkurven, die im wesentlichen aus nichtpersistenten Wellenzügen bestehen", *Z. angew. Math. Mech., 25/27*, 113-118, 1947.

BLUME, H., "Nachweis der Eindeutigkeit der Schwingweg- und Beschleunigungsaufzeichnung stoszartig verlaufender Vorgänge durch geeignete Analyse", *Z. angew. Math. Mech., 25/27*, 174-176, 1947.

DAFFNER, F., *Das Wachstum des Menschen - Anthropologische Studie*, Leipzig: Engelmann, 1897.

MARTIN, R. and SALLER, K., *Lehrbuch der Anthropologie*. 3rd ed., *2*, Stuttgart: G. Fischer, 1959.

SCHARF, J.H., "Zur Regressionsrechnung in der Morphologie: Funktionelle Anatomie und mathematische Funktion". *Verh. anat. Ges., 60*, 481-499, 1965.

SCHARF, J.H., "Wachstums- und Abklingfunktionen als Beispiele mehrgliedriger Exponentialfunktionen". *Morph. Jb., 108*, 283-343, 1966.

SCHARF, J.H., "Analysis von Schwingungsvorgängen bei funktionell-anatomischen Fragestellungen". *Verh. andt. Ges., 61*, 1966. 609-629, 1966.

SCHARF, J.H., MARZOTKO, D., SCHMIDT, R., BRÜCKMANN, P. and MAISSER, P., "Weitere Untersuchungen über Gasstoffwechsel und Körpergewicht bei weiszen Ratten im chronischen Versuch

bei Verabreichung von Alloxan, p-Hydroxypropiophenon, Dijodtyrosin sowie Methylthiouracil einzeln und in Kombination".
Endokrinologie, 47, 237-254, 1965.

SCHARF, J.H., MARZOTKO, D., SCHMIDT, R. and HAMMER, R.,
"Die kurzzeitige Komponente der Gasstoffwechselregelung
als Funktion der kurzzeitigen Oscillationen der Umgebungs-
temperatur". *Endokrinologie, 48*, 303-314, 1965.

SCHARF, J.H., MARZOTKO, D., SCHMIDT, R. and THIELE, R.,
"Abhängigkeit des Gasstoffwechsels vom Körpergewicht und
vom Futterverbrauch während antithyreoidaler und contra-
insulärer Behandlung bei weiszen Ratten. *Endokrinologie,
49*, 235-252, 1966.

SCHARF, J.H., SCHMIDT, R. and MARZOTKO, D., "Zur Frage der
Vermaschung des Zwischenhirn-Hypophysenvorderlappen-Schild-
drüsen-Systems mit anderen Regelkreisen bei der weiszen
Ratte auf Grund einer multiplen Konkordanzanalyse". *Biol.
Rdsch., 3*, 193-198, 1965.

SCHARF, J.H., SCHMIDT, S., KAMINSKI, K. and MARZOTKO, D.,
"Vergleich zwischen der Wirkung von Thyroxin, Trijodthyro-
nin sowie Dijodtyrosin mit und ohne Methylthiouracilzugabe
auf Gasstoffwechsel und Körpergewicht bei der weiszen Ratte".
Endokrinologie, 46, 22-57, 1964.

SCHARF, J.H., SCHMIDT, S. and MARZOTKO, D., "Zur Biokyber-
netik des Gasstoffwechsels und des Körpergewichts weiszer
Ratten in Abhängigkeit von der Zeit und von einigen Klima-
faktoren", *Endokrinologie, 46*, 139-156, 1964.

STUMPFF, K., *Analyse periodischer Vorgänge"*. Ein Abrisz der
Periodographie mit besonderer Berücksichtigung moderner
Methoden". (*Sammlung geophysikalischer Schriften, 6*)
Berlin: Borntraeger, 1927.

STUMPFF, K., *Grundlagen und Methoden der Periodenforschung*,
Berlin: Springer, 1937.

WHITTAKER, Sir E. and ROBINSON, G., *The Calculus of Observations. A Treatise on Numerical Mathematics*, 4th ed., 10th
reprint, London-Glasgow; Blackie & Son Ltd., 1965.

WILLERS, Fr.A., *Elementar-Mathematik, ein Vorkurs zur
Höheren Mathematik*, 7th ed., Dresden-Leipzig: Steinkopff,
1956.

WILLERS, Fr.A., *Methoden der praktischen Analysis*, 2nd ed., Berlin: W. de Gruyter, 1950.

ZURMÜHL, R., *Matrizen und ihre technischen Anwendungen*, 3rd ed., Berlin-Göttingen-Heidelberg: Springer, 1961.

ZURMÜHL, R., *Praktische Mathematik für Ingenieure und Physiker*, 4th ed., Berlin-Göttingen-Heidelberg: Springer, 1963.

ZWANZIG, W., "Persistenzuntersuchungen zur 27-tägigen Variation der Intensität der kosmischen Strahlung", *Math.-nat. Inaug. Diss.*, Halle, 1964.

FLUORESCENCE CYTOCHEMISTRY
OF NUCLEIC ACIDS

ITS MODERN STATE AND PROSPECTS

M.N. MEISSEL AND A.V. ZELENIN

Institute of Molecular Biology,
USSR Academy of Sciences,
Moscow, U.S.S.R.

INTRODUCTION

In the development of modern cytology an increasingly more important part is played by special methods of microscopy, which make it possible not only to study the peculiarities of the structural organization of the cell, but also to obtain information on the chemical nature and physico-chemical and functional state of cellular structures and the cell as a whole. These methods include fluorescence microscopy which has afforded and continues to afford ever new possibilities for a fine analysis of the chemical anatomy, physiology, and pathology of the cell. A prominent role in fluorescence microscopy and cytochemistry is played by cytochemistry of nucleic acids in view of the great importance of these biopolymers in the vital activity of any cell and the very apt and fine approaches to their study offered by fluorescence microscopy.

The basic contribution to the development of fluorescence cytochemistry of nucleic acids, and thereby to fluorescence microscopy in general, was made by Professor L. von Bertalanffy who substantiated the use of acridine orange, a fluorescent dye, for studying nucleic acids, especially ribonucleic acids, in cells and successfully used the methods he had devised in studying

phenomena of malignant transformation and in recognising
cancer cells.

It is not surprising that so outstanding a figure in
theoretical biology as L. von Bertalanffy should devote
considerable time and attention to cytochemistry of
nucleic acids. In his review, "Acridine Orange
Fluorescence in Cell Physiology, Cytochemistry and
Medicine" (1963), he recalls the impression which his
acquaintance with the possibilities of fluorescence microscopy in Professor Höfler's laboratory in Vienna in 1943
produced on him. It was precisely under this impression
that he decided to try fluorescence microscopy and
fluorochrome acridine orange in studying the behaviour of
nucleic acids in malignant growth. These studies proved
of fundamental importance to cytology and cytochemistry
and led to the elaboration of a practically important
fluorescence-microscopy method of detecting cancer cells
now widely used in clinical practice.

We deem it appropriate, while acknowledging Professor
L. von Bertalanffy's outstanding contributions to the
development of the general theory of biology, also to
devote some attention to his interest in fluorescence
cytochemistry of nucleic acids, which has led to considerable scientific and practical results. We should like to
examine as briefly as possible some of the historical and
modern aspects of fluorescence cytochemistry of nucleic
acids. In doing this we shall cite a number of studies
carried out in the Soviet Union and scarcely known in the
West.

ON THE HISTORY OF FLUORESCENCE MICROSCOPY*

The history of the origin and development of
fluorescence microscopy was described many times by
various researchers (Haitinger, 1938; Loos, 1936/1939
Ellinger, 1940; Meissel, 1947; Strugger, 1949; Bräutigan,
1949; Bräutigan and Grabner, 1949). However, it is
necessary to emphasize the importance of Köhler's observations (1904) which revealed the possibility of

---

*(The following abbreviations are used: AO -
acridine orange; DNA - deoxyribonucleic acid; RNA -
ribonucleic acid; DNP - deoxyribonucleoprotein; RNP -
ribonucleoprotein.)

registering fluorescence under the microscope, the construction by him and Siedentopf of the fluorescence microscope in 1908, the manufacture of the first fluorescence
microscope (Reichert, 1911), and the first experiments in
vital fluorescence microscopy of chlorophyll and cyano-
phyll performed with this microscope in 1911 by M. Tswet,
a prominent botanist and initiator of the chromotographic
method.   A very important contribution was made by
Haitinger, who introduced "staining" of objects by fluorochromes, i.e., fluorescent dyes (see Haitinger, 1934 and
1938).   Precisely because of this, fluorescence microscopy
began to develop as a promising method of biological
research.   Among the fluorochromes, Bukatsch and Haitinger
(1940) and, independent of them, Struggar (1940) discovered acridine orange, a fluorescent dye, which has
played, especially as the result of the studies of L. von
Bertalanffy and Bickis (1956), Schümmelfelder et al.(1957),
and Armstrong (1956), a very important role in fluorescence microscopy, mainly in fluorescence cytochemistry
of nucleic acids.   The elaboration of immunofluorescence
methods by Coons (Coons et al., 1941, 1942; Coons and
Kaplan, 1950; Weller and Coons, 1954) was a major event in
the history of fluorescence cytochemistry and formed the
basis for the independent branch of fluorescence cytochemistry.

Ample new opportunities have presented themselves to
fluorescence microscopy through the development of
apparatus and elaboration of precise methods of quantitative evaluation of the fluorescence intensity of micro-
objects (microfluorimetry) and registration of the spectra
of excitation and emission (microspectrofluorimetry).   Of
essential importance in this regard are the studies of
Mellors and Silver (1951).   The possibilities of fluorescence microscopy have considerably increased since the
elaboration by Brumberg (Brumberg, 1956; Brumberg et al
1958, 1961, 1962) of apparatus and methods of studying the
fluorescence of microscopic objects in the ultraviolet
spectral region (excitation and recording of fluorescence
is carried out in the u.v. region).

Such are some of the important stages in the
development of fluorescence microscopy.

History of Fluorescence Cytochemistry of Nucleic Acids

The modern conceptions of the possibilities of studying nucleic acids with the aid of fluorescence cytochemistry
have formed as the result of the studies conducted in different directions by a large group of researchers.

Already in the early studies of Bukatsch and Haitinger
(1940), Strugger (1940), and Bukatsch (1940, 1941) it was
established that acridine orange (A)), a fluorescent dye,
possesses a number of interesting properties. It easily
penetrates into the cells and, what is particularly interesting, into the nuclei of living cells, giving a dull-green
fluorescence to the cytoplasm and a bright-green fluorescence to the nuclei. Accumulating in the vacuoles of a
living plant cell, it begins to fluoresce bright red.

In injured and dying cells the fluorescence colour
shifts to the longer spectral region becoming, instead of
green yellow, orange and red. This applies primarily to
plant cells, but also to animal cells which are rich in
RNA (Strugger 1940, 1941; Kölbel, 1947; Schümmelfeder,
1950). The physico-chemical bases of such fluorescence
metachromasia have been investigated especially by Höfler
(1949) and Zanker (1952, 1959). It was found that the
fluorescence colour of AO solutions changes in accordance
with the concentration of the substance (so-called concentration effect): in greatly diluted solutions AO
molecules dissociate (the fluorescence colour is green),
while in more concentrated solutions associations of
molecules arise and fluoresce red.

In 1951, Meissel published data he had obtained jointly
with Korchagin, demonstrating the different character of
fluorescence of acridine orange complexes with DNA and RNA
and corresponding nucleoproteins *in vitro*. The DNA and
RNA, like the DNP and RNP isolated from microorganisms,
formed with AO solutions of the same concentration complexes fluorescing green in the cases of DNA and DNP, and
red in the cases of RNA and RNP. It followed that the
character of complexes formation depended on the type of
nucleic acid (Meissel, 1951; Meissel, Kondratieva and
Pomoshnikova, 1951; Meissel and Korchagin, 1952). The
numerous studies conducted since then and employing different physical approaches, spectrofluorimetry in the
first place, confirmed and ascertained these observations
and made it possible to describe these complexes in detail

(Peacocke and Skerrett, 1956; Steiner and Beers, 1957;
Bradley and Wolf, 1959; Lerman, 1961, 1963, 1964; Luzzati
et al., 1961; Stone and Bradley, 1961; Boyle et al., 1962;
Weil and Calvin, 1963; Borisova et al., 1963; Borisova and
Tumerman, 1964, 1965; Kiselev et al., 1964; Gersch and
Jordan, 1965). The data obtained in the experiments *in
vitro* have made it possible to give a cytochemical interpretation of the fluorescence microscopy pictures. In some
of the studies the fluorochroming with acridine orange,
aimed at revealing nucleic acids, was carried out on living
cells and on cells that had survived.

Studies containing principles of differential cytochemistry of nucleic acids on fixed preparations appeared in
1956-1957 (L. von Bertalanffy and Bickis, 1956; Armstrong,
1956; Armstrong and Niven, 1957; Schümmelfeder et al., 1957).
The simplicity and reliability of the method attracted wide
circles of researchers working on theoretical problems of
cytology, as well as on cytodiagnosis of malignant tumors.
We have already made repeated mention of L. von Bertalanffy's
principal role in these studies.

The use of microspectrofluorimetric methods in determining the functional activity of DNP and describing the
secondary structure of nucleic acids was an important stage
in the development of fluorescence cytochemistry of nucleic
acids. The most significant study in this field was that
of Rigler (1966).

The use of acridine orange was paralleled by development in other branches of fluorescence cytochemistry of
nucleic acids. The first to be mentioned in this connection
was the fluorescence variant of Feulgen's test proposed in
1959 by Kasten (Kasten et al., 1959).

*Study of Nucleic Acids by Treating Fixed Cells with Acridine
Orange*

The very first researchers who treated fixed cell preparations or tissue sections with AO solutions noticed that
the cytoplasm, especially its basophilic regions, fixed
this fluorochrome and acquired a red fluorescence. Gössner
(1949) and a number of other authors held that under these
conditions AO was bound by RNA. Reliable proof of the ribonucleic nature of the cytoplasmic component producing red
fluorescence in complex with AO was furnished by L. von
Bertalanffy and Bickis (1956). In a very accurate study they

showed that the RNA eliminated from the cells by ribonuclease
is precisely the substrate which in a characteristic manner
combines with AO. The green fluorescence of the nuclei was
identified as a result of acridine orange forming a complex
with DNA. Armstrong (1956) and Schümmelfeder (1957, 1958)
arrived at the same conclusions.

In the numerous studies carried out later, these ideas
were essentially confirmed and made somewhat more precise.
It was shown that the red fluorescence of the preparation
was the result of AO combining with the single stranded
regions of the nucleic acids (RNA, single stranded or
denatured DNA), while the green or yellow-green fluorescence
was the result of AO combining with double stranded nucleic
acids (native DNA, double stranded regions of RNA).

An important part in the development of these ideas
was played by the studies of the nucleic acid - AO interaction (as well as the interaction of nucleic acids with
other acridine derivatives) *in vitro*.

In this article we cannot possibly set forth the
results of the various studies and will therefore confine
ourselves to inferences and a general description of the AO
complexes with nucleic acids differing in structural order,
as they appear on the basis of numerous studies summed up
by Borisova and Tumerman (1964) and Rigler (1966).

Two types of AO complexes with nucleic acids have been
described. The complex of one type (Complex II of Steiner
and Beers) arises on interaction of AO with double stranded
DNA or double stranded regions of RNA with a 4:1 or smaller
ratio of the number of nucleotides to the number of AO
molecules. The complex of this type is characterised 1)
by an absorption maximum at 502-504nm, 2) by green fluorescence with a maximum at 530nm, and 3) by fluorescence
yield and fluorescent lifetime 2-2.5 times higher than
that of acridine orange in diluted solutions when the dye
is in monomeric form.

The most widespread point of view (Lerman, 1961, 1963,
1964; Luzzati et al., 1961) is that a complex of this type
forms as a result of intercalation of AO molecules between
pairs of nucleic acid bases, the dimethyl amino groups
of the dye contacting the negatively charged phosphate groups
of both strands of nucleic acid molecules. With such an

arrangement, the distances between the separate AO molecules are big enough to prevent their interaction and production of associated forms.

Recently, however, another model was suggested to explain the interaction between AO and double stranded DNA; according to this model the dye is located in a narrow longitudinal groove in the molecule of the latter (Gursky, 1966).

An AO complex with single stranded RNA or single stranded regions of DNA and denatured DNA forms according to another type (Complex I of Steiner and Beers). In this case AO molecules can combine with the phosphate group of almost every nucleotide unit the molecules of the dye so closely approaching each other as to form dimers.

A complex of this type considerably differs from the preceding one. It is characterized by the following properties: 1) an absorption maximum at 475nm, 2) red fluorescence with the maximum at 640nm, and 3) a certain decrease in the fluorescence yield and a sharp (tenfold) increase in the fluorescence lifetime of the AO molecule dimers compared with the monomer molecular form in solution.

It has been established that the RNA whose molecules, being single stranded, have in various regions helix links (for example, ribosomal RNA) are characterized by two bands of absorption and fluorescence, each band being typical for single-stranded and double-stranded nucleic acids.

These data have made it possible to work out methods of determining the relative number of helix and random coil regions in a molecule of nucleic acid. In one of such methods for this determination the ratio between the fluorescence intensities at 590nm and 530nm is used; this ratio is a function of the AO:P ratio and it increases with the decrease in the structural organisation of the nucleic acids (Rigler, 1966).

Simultaneously with and independently of these investigations, several studies of AO complexes with nucleic acids were carried out by Borisova and Tumerman; these studies employed various optic methods, including investigations of such characteristics of fluorescence as fluorescent lifetime (Borisova and Tumerman, 1964, 1965). It was confirmed that AO in concentrations not exceeding 5×10^{-6} moles forms complexes with native double-stranded DNA only in monomeric form, while with denatured single-stranded DNA it forms dimers. In the former case the quantum yield was 0.88 and the fluorescent lifetime was 5×10^{-9} seconds, in the latter case 0.26 and $(19 \pm 1) \times 10^{-9}$ seconds, respectively. The fluorescent lifetime proved a very fine index of the ratio of helix and random coil regions in the nucleic acid molecules. All the experiments in producing AO complexes with nucleic acid molecules were conducted *in vitro*. The average fluorescent lifetime was determined on a phase fluorometer (Borisov and Tumerman, 1959). The experiments showed, as was already mentioned, that the fluorescent lifetime of the dimers of AO molecules formed in complexing with single-stranded denatured DNA, when measured in the red spectral region, was four times that of the monomeric complexes. A highly sensitive, quantitative method for studying the secondary structure of nucleic acids was elaborated on the basis of fluoreometric tau measurements. By this method it is possible to discover 3-5 percent of random coil regions in the nucleic acid molecules. Investigation of transfer RNA by this method established the degree of their spiralization to be 78 percent. Studies of the action of ribonuclease on transfer nucleic acids showed that the enzyme primarily attacks the single-stranded regions of these nucleic acids. The same method served to discover in the DNA molecules, exposed to ultraviolet irradiation, regions in which dimerisation of AO molecules (so-called "locally denatured regions") and linkage between complementary strands of macromolecules occur (Borisova, Kiselev and Tumerman, 1963; Borisova et al., 1964; Kiselev et al., 1964; Zavilgelski et al., 1964). The use of the principles of these methods for studying cytological preparations and elaboration for this purpose of a special microtaumeter would be of considerable interest.

Some new approaches for the investigation of the interaction of acridine orange with nucleic acids have been recently developed by Pritchard, Blake and Peacocke (1966).

Fluorescence microscopy of nucleic acids on fixed preparations fluorochromed with acridine orange is now very widely used in the most diverse studies.

Four basic trends in the use of these methods may be outlined:

a) Differential revealment of nucleic acids in histological preparations during routine work. Very many examples
of such work may be cited. In our laboratory (Zelenin,
1967), in particular, fluorescence microscopy is employed
whenever it is necessary to make, if one may put it that way,
a primary examination of a preparation for nucleic acids.
Other cytochemical methods, particularly staining with
methyl green-pyronin, or toluidine blue, are used in cases of
doubt and when it is necessary to obtain additional information. Fluorescence microscopy is especially desirable when
it is necessary to reveal nucleic acids present in cells
either in small amounts or in a low concentration. Such
study makes it possible to form a tentative idea of secondary
structure of nucleic acid.

b) The use of fluorescence cytochemical studies of
nucleic acids for cancer cytodiagnosis. An important role in
developing the studies in this direction was played by L.
von Bertalanffy, his son Felix Bertalanffy and their associates (L. von Bertalanffy et al., 1956; L. von Bertalanffy,
1959; L. von Bertalanffy and F. Bertalanffy, 1960). They
worked out scientifically substantiated and thoroughly
tested methods of treating preparations for the purpose of
obtaining stable, reproducible results, and showed on extensive and diverse material the merits of acridine fluorochroming for both research and cancer cytodiagnosis. Living
and actively proliferating cancer cells are, in most cases,
known to be rich in ribonucleic acid. That is why in fluorescence microscopy, even at slight magnification, they are
immediately discovered because of their red fluorescence.
But, as L. von Bertalanffy justly asserts, this is only a
warning signal. To identify such a cell, it is necessary
to establish its nucleo-cytoplasmic relation, the structure
of the nucleus, and the state of the nucleolus. Only the
complex of the features of the structural organization of
the cell, deviating from normal, warrants diagnosing it as
a cancer cell. Fluorochroming with acridine orange makes
it possible sufficiently clearly to reveal all the cytological peculiarities of the examined cell.

A somewhat different approach was made by Meissel and
Gutkina (1953) who, for the purpose of detection of cancer
cells, proposed supravital fluorochroming with an acridine
orange solution (1:25000). In this concentration, acridine
orange combines much more actively with the ribonucleic

acids of the cytoplasm and the nuclei of tumors than of
normal cells and imparts a diffuse orange or bright-red
fluorescence to the cytoplasm of cancer cells. This may
be due to a more easily irreversible alteration of the
RNP of cancer cells by the AO solution in such a relatively high concentration with liberation of reactive
phosphate groups and also to a well-known RNA increase
in these cells. The nuclei of cancer cells usually
fluoresce yellow or yellow-orange, the nucleoli, bright-
orange. By these fluorescence peculiarities and the
characteristic structural pathology of the nucleus supra-
vitally florochromed cancer cells sharply differ from
normal cells and may be easily identified. The advantage of supravital fluorochroming is a much better preservation of the fine structural features of the cytoplasm (delicate vacuolisation and fine lipid inclusions)
and the nucleus (state of the nuclear envelope, the
chromatin structures and the nucleolus). The shortcoming
of this method is that the preparation must be made, treated
and studied soon after the material in question has been
obtained.

Both methods have been widely tested on a large
number of healthy people and patients and have yielded
very good results (concerning the use of Bertalanffy's
method see F. Bertalanffy, 1960, 1961, 1962; L. von Bertalanffy, 1963, 1964; Sani et al., 1963). In the Soviet
Union fluorescence cytodiagnosis is successfully used
on a large scale in its different methodological variants
and modifications (see Derazhne, 1962; Zheleznov, 1956,
1964; Svindler, 1964; Makarenko, 1962; Stupko and
Brusiyanikova, 1960; Khokhlov and Opaleva, 1958).

c) The use of fluorescence microscopy for studying
the secondary structure of nucleic acids in the cell.

We have already mentioned the fact that the fluorochroming of cells with acridine orange makes it possible not
only to reveal nucleic acids in them, but also to judge of
their secondary structure. Such information may be,
to a certain extent, obtained by visual examination of the
fluorescence. But the fine partial changes in the secondary
structure of nucleic acid are of the greatest interest.
Such data may be obtained only by spectral methods of
investigation. Until recently, such data with regard to
nucleic acids and nucleoproteins were rare (see, in particular

Nash and Plaut, 1964). This gap was recently filled by
Rigler's first-class study carried out in Professor Caspersson's Institute in Sweden.

To conduct such studies Caspersson, Lomakka, and Rigler
(1965) built a recording microspectrofluorimeter which made
it possible to study the structural characteristics of nucleic
acids on cytologic preparations. With the aid of this and a
number of other apparati and specially devised methods of
fixation, blocking of active protein groups, and staining
with AO, Rigler has shown that practically all the information
obtained by many authors as regards the acridine orange
complexes with nucleic acids and nucleoproteins *in vitro*
is also correct with respect to these substances and compounds
found in the undestroyed cell. According to Rigler, native
(double-stranded) DNA produces in a complex with AO green
fluorescence with a maximum of 530 nm. In denatured DNA and
ribonucleic acids the emission maximum shifts towards the
red. The spectral characteristic of absorption and emission
by nucleoproteins in nucleoprotein-AO complexes somewhat
changes in accordance with the binding strength of the
proteins with the nucleic acids. There is clear competition
for the binding sites with nucleic acids between AO and the
protein amino groups. Experiments have shown that upon
weakening of this interaction, which occurs at a neutral pH,
or upon blocking of the protein amino groups the emission
spectra of nucleoprotein-AO complexes come close to those
of the complexes of the corresponding nucleic acids with AO.
It follows that in these cases, as in those with free nucleic
acids, the ratio between the fluorescence intensities at
590:530nm may be used for determining the relative amounts
of helix and random coil regions in nucleic acids which
form part of nucleoproteins (Rigler, 1966). This, in its
turn, makes it possible, as we have already noted, to judge
not only of the state of the secondary structure of nucleic
acids, but also of its changes in accordance with the
stages of development, functional state of the cells and
cases of cell pathology. Rigler's study (1966), to which
we are referring, contains several interesting examples of
molecular changes in nucleic acids and nucleo-proteins
under different conditions of cell activity. Thus the
action of phytohemagglutinin on the human lymphocyte leads
within 5 minutes to a very sharp increase in the binding
of acridine orange by DNP phosphate groups unaccompanied
by any increase in DNA. This effect seems to be due to
the liberation of reactive DNP phosphate groups (Killander

and Rigler, 1965) apparently in connection with the dissoci-
ation of DNA-histone complex, which leads to activation of
the genetic mechanisms of the cells. On the contrary, on
maturation of the male sex cells a swift decrease in free
AO-binding phosphate groups is observed; this characterizes
the transition of the cells to a genetically inactive stage
(Gledhill et al., 1966). The authors assume, and not without
reason, that the liberation of reactive phosphate groups
leads to activation of the DNA molecule and creates favorable
conditions for its matrical functioning. The methodological
approaches are also of some importance to judging the degree
of nativity and denaturation processes arising in cell
nucleoproteins in different pathological processes and under
external influence.

We do not doubt that the objective quantitative methods
of studying and evaluating the functional state of DNA and
the degree of its nativity in cells, offered by fluorescence
cytochemistry, build a bridge between cytology and molecular
biology. The results obtained by these methods are, it must
be supposed, a very promising beginning of a new trend in the
formation of molecular cytology.

d) Acridine orange in quantitative cytochemistry of
nucleic acids. Of late the attention of researchers has been
increasingly attracted by quantitative fluorescence cytochemistry, i.e., the complex of methods of revealing the
amount of substances in the cell by their own fluorescence
or by the fluorescence of the fluorochrome combined with them.

In 1963, Agroskin showed that the fluorescence methods
of determining the amount of substance in a cell possess
certain advantages over the absorption methods. The main
advantage is that the registration of the fluorescence
intensities of a substance in a cell does not depend on
the differences in its distribution, which makes unnecessary
the use of such complicated methods of study as the two-
wavelength cytophotometry and scanning. This characteristic
of quantitative fluorescence cytochemistry is also noted
by other authors (Barsky and Ivanov, 1964; Sandritter, 1964).

The results obtained by Rigler (1966) warrant the
assumption that, if preparations are fluorochromed under
appropriate conditions, the amount of acridine orange combined with nucleic acid is directly proportional to the
amount of the nucleic acid phosphate groups. This attests

that the amount of nucleic acid can be judged by the fluorescence intensities of the monomeric (green) or dimeric
(red) fluorescence of acridine orange. Of course, such a
conclusion must be drawn with great caution. In particular,
when judging the amount of cell RNA on the basis of the
intensity of red fluorescence of AO complexes, it is
necessary not only to carry out all the procedures recommended by Rigler (special fixation methods, acetylation of
protein amino groups, etc.), but also to be sure that in
the cells being compared it is only the content of nucleic
acid which changes but not its secondary structure. Fluorochroming with acridine orange offers a possibility of
determining, in certain cases, the amount of DNA in a cell
by the intensity of the green fluorescence of its complexes
with AO. However, we do not consider this possibility
faultless primarily because green fluorescence is also
possessed by complexes of acridine orange with double-
stranded regions of RNA. Moreover, there are other sufficiently simple and reliable methods of revealing the
amount of DNA in the cell, including the fluorescence
method (for the latter see below).

Vital and Supravital Fluorochroming with Acridine Orange

Numerous studies have been devoted to those problems.
Wittekind's (1964) and Stockinger's (1964) good reviews
free us from the necessity of examining in detail the studies
conducted in this field. We shall but add somewhat to the
information contained in these reviews by citing the works
published in Russian and usually not mentioned, and shall
touch upon some general propositions.

Cytochemical interpretation of microscopical pictures
arising in living cells as a result of their treatment with
so-called vital stains always presents considerable difficulties. Nor is vital fluorochroming with acridine orange
an exception.

However, some sufficiently accurate information on this
problem is available. On the basis of an analysis of
literary data and our own experience, it may be confidently
stated that supravital fluorochroming of cells with acridine
orange makes possible a reliable study of the localisation
and morphology of nuclear nucleoproteins. By this method
the minutest nucleoids of bacteria containing DNA in a high
concentration are easily revealed; the sizes of these

nucleoids often approach the limit of the resolving power
of the microscope (Schuller, 1952, 1954; Krieg, 1953,
1954; Meissel and Mirolyubova, 1959). The nuclei of yeast
organisms, which all stained with difficulty by ordinary
cytological methods, are very easily revealed by vital and
supravital fluorochroming (Strugger, 1943; Meissel and
Zavarzina, 1947; Meissel, 1950). In vital and supravital
fluorochroming, acridine dyes — aurophosphin and coriphosphin O — combine with the mitochondria of the yeast
cells and impart an orange fluorescence to them (Meissel
and Zavarzina, 1947; Meissel, 1950). It is possible that
in this case the fluorochromes form complexes with the
nucleic acids of the mitochondria. An analogous accumulation of coriphosphin O was described in the case of
mitochondria (sarcosomes) of the heart muscle.

The action of acridine orange may give rise to reversible alterations of nuclear nucleoproteins in the cells
of tissue cultures. It has been demonstrated that fluorochroming of cells in tissue cultures with highly-diluted
AO solutions may be really vital, the fluorochromed cells
retaining their ability to multiply (Meissel, Larionov
and Kondratieva, 1951; Meissel, Kondratieva and Pomoshnikova, 1951). Supravital fluorochroming of suspensions of
cells from hemopoietic organs was successfully used in the
study of early pathological alterations of nuclear and
cytoplasmic nuceloproteins resulting from ionising radiation and chlorethylamines (Meissel and Sondak, 1955, 1956;
Meissel et al., 1958; Meissel et al., 1960; Meissel and
Gutkina, 1961; Meissel and Manteufel, 1963; Kondratieva,
1956; Breivis, 1958; Yarmonenko, 1959). A peculiar injury
to the nuclear nucleoproteins consisting in their separation into two fractions, one weakly fluorescent, green
coloured fraction and one fluorescing with a brilliant,
whitish light, were for the first time discovered in these
experiments; this alteration must apparently be regarded
as a manifestation of DNP deproteinization (Meissel,
Kondratieva and Yemelianov, 1951; Meissel et al., 1960).
Mention should be made of the numerous studies devoted to
elucidating the action of various antimetabolites, anti-
biotics, drugs, viruses, and toxins on the cell; these
studies made use of vital and supravital fluorochroming
aimed at revealing alterations in the state of nuclear
nucleoproteins.

Interpretation of cytoplasmic pictures is a matter
of much greater complexity.

The very first studies in fluorescence microscopy of living cells established that the AO which penetrates into them accumulates in various regions of the cytoplasm in the form of cytoplasmic granules with a bright-red fluorescence. Described for the first time apparently by Vonkennel and Wiedemann in 1944, these granules were subsequently discovered in practically all animal cells treated by this fluorochrome *in vivo*.

The point of view that the red granules were a complex of acridine orange with cytoplasmic RNA prevailed for a rather long time. This point of view was based on the well-known fact of red fluorescence of complexes of acridine orange with RNA *in vitro* or in fixed cell preparations.

But the detailed studies of the nature of the red cytoplasmic granules conducted in recent years have brought a change in this point of view. It was experimentally demonstrated that the red cytoplasmic granules were lyso-somes and lysosomelike structures of the living cell, which had accumulated considerable amounts of acridine orange. This conclusion was drawn in consequence of the studies conducted in two directions. On the one hand, Robbins and his co-authors (Robbins et al., 1964) succeeded in identi-fying the red granules with cytoplasmic structures con-taining acid phosphatase and in discovering considerable changes as a result of prolonged treatment of lysosome cell structures with acridine orange. On the other hand, Zelenin and Lyapunova (1964) managed to isolate from the hepatic tissue homogenate of animals, injected large doses of acridine orange, a fraction enriched to the utmost with red granules. Electron microscopy of these granules carried out by the negative-contrast method discovered an ultra-structure in them typical of lysosomes and lysosomelike structures (Zelenin et al., 1965). It was suggested that it was possible to use fluorescence microscopy for intra-vital studies of the lysosome structures of the living cell (Allison and Young, 1964; Zelenin, 1965). The possi-bilities of this method are discussed in greater detail in a special article (Zelenin, 1966). Here we deem it necessary but to mention that fluorescence microscopy of the lyso-somes of the living cell stained with acridine orange is superior to the microscopy using other vital dyes, neutral red in the first place; an appropriate, brief fluorochroming of cells with acridine orange very fully reveals the lyso-some structures and at the same time does not in any way noticeably alter them.

The establishment of the lysosome nature of the cytoplasmic granules does not do away with the question of
cytochemical interpretation of their red fluorescence.
The aggregate of facts warrants the assertion that RNA is
absent from the granules discovered in cells treated with
acridine orange for short periods of time (one minute)
(see Zelenin, 1965, 1967). The most credible assumption
is that the red fluorescence arises as the result of
absorption of acridine orange by the hydrolases of the
lysosomes. Incidentally, no direct proof of this assertion
is available. As for the granules discovered in cells
treated with acridine orange for a long period of time,
it is impossible to deny the presence of RNA in them, as
it is known in the case of the so-called krinoms (Chlopin,
1927; Schmidt, 1962).

A totally different situation arises when living cells
are fluorochromed with such a concentration of acridine
orange and under such conditions that, as a result of the
fluorochroming, the cells die (or are severely injured)
and begin to bind acridine orange like fixed cells. The
red fluorescence of the cytoplasm arising in such cases
is not particularly difficult to interpret; it is apparently
associated with cytoplasmic RNA. Under some conditions it
may yield interesting results, namely, when the fluorochromed cells differ in resistance to acridine orange.
In this case supravital fluorochroming of cells with high
concentrations of acridine orange may prove a very valuable
method of revealing various types of cells.

Fluorescence Variants of Feulgen's Test

Another important part of fluorescence cytochemistry
of nucleic acids is associated with the use of the fluorescence variant of Feulgen's test. In 1959, Kasten and his
co-authors showed the possibility of preparing Schiff's
reagent by replacing the basic fuchsin with a fluorocrhome.
They demonstrated the possibility of performing with the
aid of such fluorescence Schiff-type reagent all the histochemical tests in which this reagent has long been used,
Feulgen's test in the first place. The peculiarity of
this new test is that it combines the high and now indisputable specificity of Feulgen's test with the extra-
ordinary sensitivity of the fluorescence methods. The
foregoing largely determines the most obvious fields where

this method can be used: revelation of DNA where it is
present in very small amounts or in very low concentration.
Literature contains several felicitous examples of the use
of this method with the aforesaid aim, particularly to
reveal DNA in the so-called Feulgen-negative nuclei of
plant cells, in the mitochondrialike organoids of a number
of protista, etc.

The use of the fluorescence variant of Feulgen's test
assumes particular importance in revealing the amount of
DNA in cells. We have already mentioned the advantages
of the fluorescence methods over the absorption ones in
determining the amount of substance in a cell.

Of course, the use of any test in quantitative fluorescence cytochemistry requires observance of a number of
essential conditions. We shall discuss some of them in
relation to Feulgen's fluorescence test:

(1) The connection of the fluorochrome with the tested
substrate must be strictly quantitative. With regard to
Feulgen's test, it has been demonstrated by numerous studies
conducted with the classical (non-fluorescence) variant of
this test that this condition is observable.

(2) Absence of fluorochrome dimerisation. In most of
the studies using Feulgen's fluorescence test, no appropriate
attention has been devoted to this question so that the
danger of such errors is quite real. However, it can be
eliminated. Recently Khachaturov and Smirnova (1966) worked
out in our laboratory a method of preparing the Schiff-type
reagent by using rivanol (3,9-diamino-7-ethoxyacridine).
These authors' studies have shown that neither this reagent,
nor rivanol itself, possess any marked tendency to dimerisation.

(3) Absence of fluorescence reabsorption by the dye.
According to Zanotti and Prenna (Zanotti, 1964; Zanotti
and Prenna, 1964) such a danger does exist, but it may be
avoided by using a variant of Schiff's reagent whose fluorescence is excited in the ultraviolet part of the spectrum,
while emission occurs in the visible part. Such, in particular, is Schiff's reagent proposed by Prenna, Zanotti,
et al. and prepared from 2-(p-aminophenyl)-6-methyl-2,6-
dibenzothiazole (Prenna and de Paoli, 1963; Zanotti and
Prenna, 1964).

(4) Absence of fading of the fluorochromed preparation under the influence of exciting light. According to Prenna and his co-authors (Prenna et al., 1962, 1964; Prenna and Zannotti, 1964) such a phenomenon always occurs and develops during the first 2-3 seconds after the beginning of the study. Prenna (1966*) therefore believes it necessary to measure the fluorescence intensity only in the first seconds after the beginning of irradiation of the preparation, which they did by means of oscilloscopic technique. The author considers the measurements made at later periods unreliable. It is not unthinkable, however, that he somewhat exaggerates the danger of such errors. For example, Khachaturov and Smirnova (1966) obtained quite reproducible results by making measurements at later periods after the beginning of irradiation of the preparation.

Of course, the true criterion of applicability of the new cytochemical method is the coincidence of its results with those obtained by other (control) methods. Such data with regard to Feulgen's fluorescence test are found in the studies conducted by Prenna and his co-authors (1964). Khachaturov and Smirnova (1966) also convincingly demonstrated the applicability of the method of cytofluorimetria of the fluorescence variant of Feulgen's test in quantitative cytochemistry of DNA. And, although very few such studies have as yet been made, a good future may safely be predicted for this method.

We have considered but a few of the most widespread fluorescence cytochemistry methods of studying nucleic acids. However, this does not in any way mean that we regard the establishment and development of other fluorescence cytochemistry tests for nucleic acids as having no prospects. Several publications have reported the possibility of conducting such studies. The use of other acridine derivatives, besides acridine orange, as well as other dyes and chemical substances, for example, indium trichloride with its subsequent revealment by means of 8-hydroxyquinoline, are suggested for fluorescence cytochemistry of nucleic acids (Aldrige, 1961; Keeble and Jay, 1962; Young and Smith, 1963). A detailed study may show all these tests to be useful. In our opinion, however, the establishment of a reliable quantitative fluorescence microscopy method of revealing RNA (besides the method

---

*Personal communication.

based on the fluorescence of acridine orange) would make a
rather important contribution to the development of fluorescence cytochemistry of nucleic acids.

When Ludwig von Bertalanffy published his article on
fluorescence microscopy of cytoplasmic basophilia about 15
years ago, there was practically no fluorescence cytochemistry of nucleic acids. We hope that we have succeeded
in tracing the development of this branch of cytochemistry,
showing its increased importance and outlining the range
of problems with which researchers are faced.

CONCLUSION

This article has dealt with the development of one of
the most promising trends in studying the cell, namely,
fluorescence cytochemistry of nucleic acids. This trend
owes its origin, firstly, to the discovery of the ability
of acridine orange to produce fluorescence metachromasia,
secondly, to elucidation of the nature of this metachromasia and, thirdly, to the establishment of an affinity
of this fluorescent dye for nucleic acids.

The establishment of two facts should be considered
important stages in the development of this field: a) DNA
and DNP, on the one hand, and RNA and RNP, on the other,
in different manners combine *in vitro* with acridine orange,
and this affects the fluorescence spectra of the forming
complexes, and b) this regularity occurs on fluorochroming
of cells; i.e., takes effect not only in experiments *in
vitro*, but also *in situ*.

The subsequent studies were aimed at elucidating the
physical regularities of interaction of acridine dye molecules with nucleic acids differing in structural order,
on the one hand, and at a strict substantiation of the use
of acridine orange for cytochemical studies on the other.
The former trend has resulted in a system of ideas concerning the mechanism of binding acridine orange by nucleic
acids, differing in the secondary structural order, and
in the elaboration, on this basis, of fine fluorescence
methods of revealing the degree of chain ordering of the
secondary structure of nucleic acid. The latter, cytochemical, trend has made it possible to substantiate the
principles of using acridine orange for studying the state
of cell nucleoproteins and the alterations in them in

different pathological conditions, especially for revealing cancer cells and intracellular localisation of virus accumulations.

Very encouraging results have of late been obtained in the use of fluorescence methods for a fine and accurate determination of the degree of chain ordering of nucleic acids both *in vitro* and in cells (in nucleoproteins) in accordance with the stages of development, in different functional states, and under conditions of pathology.

Fluorescence cytochemistry methods are promising also for studying the quantitative content of DNA in the cells; they have a number of incontestable advantages over the absorption cytophotometric methods. It is very important to work out fluorescence methods of quantitative determination of RNA in the cells.

Thus there are serious reasons to believe that fluorescence cytochemistry in general, and with regard to nucleic acids in particular, will become an important trend in the development of cytological studies on the molecular level.

ADDENDUM

Owing to circumstances over which the authors had no control, more than three years elapsed from the time the article was written until it was prepared for the press; during this period fluorescence microscopy in general, and fluorescence cytochemistry of nucleic acids in particular, continued to develop intensively. Some of the achievements of recent years are reflected in the reviews of Kasten (1967) and West (1969). However, some important aspects of fluorescence cytochemistry have been omitted, which has necessitated the writing of this addendum.

To begin with, it seems expedient to dwell on some new achievements in the use of AO, i.e., on the sphere of fluorescence cytochemistry that was developed in the studies of Ludwig von Bertalanffy. It is appropriate to note that 1971 marked the 15th anniversary of the appearance of this author's basic work in this field (von Bertalanffy and Bickis, 1956).

Our article has already mentioned the main studies in
the use of cytospectrofluorimetry of AO-treated preparations
to determine the functional activity of cell DNP (Rigler's
method). These studies were successfully continued during
the subsequent years at Professor Caspersson's Institute,
as well as in some other laboratories. They confirmed the
applicability of this method to a number of other objects,
such as erythrocytes of birds stimulated as a result of
hybridisation with HeLa cells (Bolund et al., 1969) and
when treated with saline solutions and phytohemagglutinin
in vitro (Ringertz, 1969; Ringertz, Bolund, 1969), human
lymphocytes stimulated as a result of vaccination (Killander,
Rigler, 1969) or an autoimmune disease (Lideman et al.,
1969), etc. At the same time some questions concerning
the use of Rigler's method are still not quite clear.
Unclear, in particular, is the significance of the Rigler-
proposed procedure of preliminary acetylation of the
preparations. The information on this question is contradictory even in Rigler's own studies (cf. Rigler, 1966;
Killander, Rigler, 1969). Insufficiently definite is also
the situation with the so-called α-coefficient suggested
in Rigler's initial studies for determining the relative
amounts of helix and random coil regions in DNA. In their
last studies even the Swedish authors have abandoned its
use and in determining the activity of DNP confine themselves to measuring the intensity of green fluorescence
alone — I_{530} (Bolund et al., 1969; Darzynkiewicz et al.,
1969).

Some doubts also arise concerning the use of AO in
studying the processes of thermal denaturation of DNA on
a fixed histological preparation. This method was also
elaborated at Caspersson's Institute and has enabled its
authors to reveal important differences in the melting
point of DNA of resting and stimulated cells (Rigler et
al., 1969). It should be noted, however, that in its
present state this method makes it possible to reveal the
melting point of DNA not in separate cells, but in homogenous cell populations, which makes the study biochemical
in its approach rather than cytological, and is, at the
same time, less sensitive than the former. As a whole,
however, the complex of methods elaborated by Rigler et
al. is already in its present state very valuable for cytochemical studies of the functional activity of DNP directly
on the cytological preparation. An extensive employment

of these methods in the very nearest future may be boldly
predicted.

Another important trend in using AO to study the
properties of nuclear DNP was started in the works of Roschlau
(1965). The method suggested by this author is based on
treatment of the preparations with hydrochloric acid, but
after the hydrolysis the preparations are not stained by
the Feulgen method, but are treated with AO. The fluorescence microscopic picture varies with the conditions
of the hydrolysis. In a typical Feulgen hydrolysis the DNP
of all cells acquires a red fluorescence. At the same time,
with a milder hydrolysis (1 min. in N/I hydrochloric acid
at 37 and 60°C) the picture turns out to be differentiated,
the DNP of some cells retaining a green fluorescence and
that of other cells acquiring a red fluorescence. According to Roschlau, such fluorescence characterises in the
main degenerating cells, while, according to Meissel et
al. (1969), cells damaged by ionizing radiation also have
such fluorescence. Of some interest are Roschlau's observations that, when stained by this method, red fluorescence
is exhibited by mitotic chromosomes, heterochromatic parts
of interphase nuclei, and nuclei of cancer cells. The
mechanism of Roschlau's reaction has not been explained yet,
but the facts already obtained warrant the assumption that
this method offers an interesting approach to studying the
properties of nuclear DNP.

Completing the review of the recent studies in using AO
to investigate the properties of nuclear DNP, it is necessary
to mention the studies of authors who employed the method
of determining the polarization of fluorescence of AO in
investigating the structure of chromosomes (MacInnes and
Uretz, 1966, 1967, 1968).

Another important division of fluorescence cytochemistry
of nucleic acids is connected with the use of different
variants of Schiff-type fluorescence reagents. The possibility
of using a fluorescence variant of Feulgen's test for qualitative and quantitative studies of DNA has been additionally
confirmed in recent years (Ruch, 1966; Fossati-Tallard, 1967;
Rosonov and Kudrjavtzev, 1967; Böhm and Sprenger, 1968;
Prenna and de Paoli, 1968; Gecile, 1969; Prenna, 1969; Khavkin
et al., 1970; Nitsch et al., 1970). At the same time it
became obvious that a number of questions concerning the use
of fluorescence variants of Feulgen's test were still insufficiently clear.

It is usually regarded as an axiom that the different
Schiff-type reagents are just as specific as the classical
reagent prepared with basic fuchsin. The correctness of
this point of view was questioned by Stoward (1967) who
added the prefix 'pseudo' to these reagents and arrived
at the conclusion that they combine with DNA by an entirely
different mechanism than is the case in Feulgen's classical
test.

Stoward's point of view is not as yet widely recognised.
However, it is already necessary to attend to some debatable
questions concerning the specificity of the fluorescence
variants of Feulgen's test. Thus Barsky et al. (1970) have,
on the basis of fluorimetric studies of preparations treated
with rivanol-SO_2, arrived at the conclusion that the amount
of DNA per set of chromosomes in the cells of the loach
blastula and the hepatocytes of the post-embryonal tissue
of the same organism was inconstant. At the same time
Brodsky et al. (1970) have, by more trivial methods of
absorption ultraviolet and Feulgen cytophotometry, found
in the same object a strictly diploid amount of DNA in the
cells of both embryonal and definitive tissues. Mention
must also be made of the data furnished by Khachaturov
(1968) who holds that under certain conditions of hydrolysis in Feulgen's test rivanol-SO_2 may combine not with
DNA but with RNA. This makes particularly rigid demands
of the hydrolysis in the fluorescence variant of Feulgen's
test.

Incidentally, some of the doubts in the specificity
of Feulgen's test fall away as a result of Böhm and Sprenger's
studies (1968) which have shown that when green light is
used as a source of excitation, the product of Feulgen's
usual test also acquires a clear red fluorescence. This
fluorescence is intensive enough to be used in qualitative
and quantitative studies, whereas the question of specificity is transferred to that of Feulgen's classical test.
At the same time Böhm and Sprenger's studies compel us
once more to take into account the considerable fading
of the fluorescence microscopic preparations in the course
of their measurement, which may serve as a source of
serious errors.

As was already mentioned, Khachaturov had shown
(1968) that, under certain conditions of fixing the preparation and of its hydrolysis, the Schiff-type reagent

can specifically combine with RNA. The quantitative character of this reaction was demonstrated *in vitro* (Sherudilo
and Khachaturov, 1969). According to these authors, the
obtained data make it possible to use their method for a
specific revealment of RNA and a determination of its
amount in cell structures.

The literature of recent years contains a number of
publications suggesting new methods of fluorescence microscopic revelation of nucleic acids.

In the first place mention should be made of using
fluorescent alkylating agents (quinacrine mustard and
similar substances). It has been shown that these compounds
make it possible to reveal the heterochromatic parts in
plant, animal and human chromosomes (Caspersson et al.,
1968; Caspersson et al., 1969; Caspersson et al., 1970;
Vosa, 1970), as well as in interphase nuclei (Natarjian,
1969), and by the intensity of the fluorescence produced
by them to discriminate the different human chromosomes
(Caspersson et al., 1970).

New possibilities for fluorescence microscopic studies
of cell nucleoproteins are offered by the use of the anti-
biotic olibomycin, by the mechanism of its action related to actinomycin D. This antiobiotic is quited brightly
fluorescent and imparts a yellow-green luminosity to nuclear
and cytoplasmic nucleoproteins (Zelenin et al., 1967). Of
indubitable interest to fluorescence cytochemistry of
nucleic acids is the information on the specific combination
of ethidium bromide with nucleic acids and nucleoproteins
in vitro, as well as on histological preparations (Brittman,
1969; Ringertz, 1969; Sela, 1969; Wahl et al., 1970).

Other fluorescence tests for nucleic acids have been
described, including the use of fluorochrome-labelled
DNAse (Benjaminson et al., 1968), salicylhydrazides to
reveal aldehyde groups (Stoward, 1967), a derivative of
europium (Dyer and Mori, 1969), and pseudoisocyanil chloride
(Sterba, 1963) as fluorochromes for DNA, fluorescence-
labelled specific antibodies for double-stranded DNA to
reveal its secondary structure (Schwartz and Stoller, 1969),
etc. The possibilities of these methods are not quite
clear as yet, but we may expect that their further development and wider employment will prove useful in the near
or more remote future.

In conclusion, several general considerations are offered. As in cytochemistry as a whole, the tendency toward quantitative studies is also increasing in fluorescence cytochemistry of nucleic acids. At the same time separate questions of methods of microfluorimetry are discussed and some conditions for obtaining reliable results by means of fluorimetry are formulated in single studies and usually in an incidental manner. A systematic and fundamental study of this question is an urgent task of fluorescence cytochemistry, including primarily fluorescence cytochemistry of nucleic acids.

The authors are greatly indebted to David A Myshne for the translation of their paper from Russian.

BIBLIOGRAPHY

AGROSKIN, L.S., *Cytologia,* (Leningrad), *5, 473, 1963.

ALDRIGE, G., *J. Histom. Cytochem., 9*, 620, 1961.

ALLISSON, A.C. and YOUNG, M.R., *Life Sciences, 3*, 1407, 1964.

ARMSTRONG, J.A., *Exp. Cell Res., 11*, 640, 1956.

ARMSTRONG, J.A. and NIVEN, J.S.F., *Nature, 180*, 1335, 1957.

BARSKY, V.E., GINDILIS, V.M. and KHACHATUROV, E.N., *Ontogenez* (Moscow), *1*, 482, 1970.

BARSKY, V.E. and IVANOV, V.B., "Electron and Fluorescence Microscopy of the Cell", Suppl. 1 to *Cytologia* (Leningrad), *6*, 157, 163, 1964.

BENJAMINSON, M.A., HUNTER, D.B. and KATZ, I.J., *Science, 160*, 1359, 1968.

BERTALANFFY, F.D., *Can. Med. Assoc. J., 83*, 211, 1960.

BERTALANFFY, F.D., *Mikrosopie* (Vienna), *15*, 67, 1960.

BERTALANFFY, F.D., *Cancer Research, 21*, 422, 1961.

BERTALANFFY, F.D., *Ann. N.Y. Acad. Sci.*, *93*, 715, 1962.

von BERTALANFFY, L., *Klin. Wochschr.*, *37*, 469, 1959.

von BERTALANFFY, L., *Acta Cytol.*, *3*, 367, 1959.

von BERTALANFFY, L., *Protoplasma*, *57*, 51, 1963.

von BERTALANFFY, L., Ber. über 1. Tagung dtsch. Gesell.
f. angewandte Zytologie, Ernst-Adolf. München: Mueller
Verlag, 177-183, 1963.   •

von BERTALANFFY, L., *Acta Un. Int. Cancr.*, *20*, 1329, 1964.

von BERTALANFFY, L. and BERTALANFFY, F.D., *Naturwissenschaften*, *47*, 165, 1960.

von BERTALANFFY, L. and BERTALANFFY, F.D., *Ann. N.Y. Acad.
Sci.*, *84*, 225, 1960.

von BERTALANFFY, L. and BERTALANFFY, F.D., *Acta Cytol.*, *4*,
298, 1960.

von BERTALANFFY, L. and BICKIS, I., *J. Histochem. Cytochem.*,
4, 481, 1956.

von BERTALANFFY, L. MASIN, F. and MASIN, M., *Science* (N.Y.),
124, 1024, 1956.

von BERTALANFFY, L., MASIN, F. and MASIN, M., *Cancer* (N.Y.),
11, 158, 1958.

BÖHM, N. and SPRENGER, E., *Histochemie*, *16*, 100, 1968.

BOLUND, L., RINGERTZ, N.R. and HARRIS, H., *J. Cell Sci.*, *4*,
71, 1969.

BOLUND, L., DARZYNKIEWICZ, Z. and RINGERTZ, N.R., *Exptl.
Cell Res.*, *56*, 406, 1969.

BORISOV, A.J. and TUMERMAN, L.A., *Izvestiya Akademii Nauk
SSSR, Ser. Phys.* (Moscow), *23*, 97, 1959.

BORISOVA, O.F., KISELEV, L.L. and TUMERMAN, L.A., *Doklady
Akademii Nauk SSSR* (Moscow), *152*, 1001, 1963.

BORISOVA, O.F., KISELEV, L.L., SUROVAYA, A.N. and TUMERMAN, L.A., *Doklady Akademii Nauk SSSR* (Moscow), *159*, 1154, 1964.

BORISOVA, O.F. and TUMERMAN, L.A., *Biofizika, 9*, 537, 1964.

BORISOVA, O.F. and TUMERMAN, L.A., *Biofizika* (Moscow), *9*, 32, 1965.

BOYLE, R.E., NELSON, S.S., DOLLISH, F.R. and OLSEN, M.J., *Arch. Biochem. Biophys.*, *96*, 47, 1962.

BRADLEY, D.F. and WOLF, M.K., *Proceed. Nat. Acad. Sci. U.S.A.*, *45*, 944, 1959.

BRÄUTIGAM, F., "Beiträge Zur Fluoreszenzmikroskopie". Vienna: Georg Fromme, 7-12, 1949.

BRÄUTIGAM, F. and GRABNER, F., "Beiträge Zur Fluoreszenz-mikroskopie". Vienna: Georg Fromme, 25-36, 1949.

BREIVIS, P.V., *Arkhiv Patologii* (Moscow), *20*, 39, 1958.

BRITMAN, R., *J. Mol. Biol.*, *46*, 251, 1969.

BRODSKY, V.J., BUKHALOV, I.B., NETCHAEVA, N.V., URYVAEVA, I.V. and CHERNOROTOVA, G.E., *Ontogenez* (Moscow), *1*, 558, 1970.

BRUMBERG, E.M., *Zhurnal Obshchei Biologii, 17*, 401, 1956.

BRUMBERG, E.M. and BARSKY, J.Y., *Zhurnal Obshchei Biologii* (Moscow), *22*, 459, 1961.

BRUMBERG, E.M., MEISSEL, M.N., BARSKY, J.Y. and BUCHMAN, M.P., *Zhurnal Obshchei Biologii* (Moscow), *19*, 99, 1958.

BRUMBERG, E.M., MEISSEL, M.N., BARSKY, J.Y., ZELENIN, A.V. and LIAPUNOVA, E.A., *Doklady Akademii Nauk SSSR* (Moscow), *141*, 723, 1961.

BRUMBERG, E.M., MEISSEL, M.N., GRIGORJEVA, T.A., BARSKY,J.Y. and GUTKINA, A.V., *Ann. Histochem.* (Paris), *Suppl. 2*, 135, 1962.

BUKATSCH, F., *Ztschr. ges. Naturwiss.*, *3/4*, 90, 1940.

BUKATSCH, F., *Ztschr. ges. Naturwiss.*, *9/10*, 288, 1941.

BUKATSCH, F. and HAITINGER, M., *Protoplasma*, *34*, 515, 1940.

CASPERSSON, T., FABER, S., FOLEY, G.E., KUDYNOWSKI, J., MODEST, E.J., SIMONSSON, E., WAGH, U. and ZECH, L., *Exptl. Cell Res.*, *49*, 219, 1968.

CASPERSSON, T., LOMAKKA, G. and RIGLER, R. Jr., *Acta Histochem.*, Suppl. VI, 462, 1965.

CASPERSSON, T., ZECH, L., MODEST, E.J., FOLEY, G.E., WAGH, U. and SIMONSSON, E., *Exptl. Cell Res.*, *58*, 128 and 141, 1969.

CASPERSSON, T., ZECH, L., JOHANSSON, C. and MODEST, E.J., *Chromosoma*, *30*, 215, 1970.

CHLOPIN, N.G., *Arch. exp. Zellforschung*, *4*, 462, 1927.

COONS, A.H., CREECH, H.J. and JONES, R.N., *Proc. Soc. Exp. Biol.* (N.Y.), *47*, 200, 1941.

COONS, A.H., CREECH, H.J., JONES, R.N. and BERLINER, E., *J. Immunol.*, *45*, 159, 1942.

COONS, A.H. and KAPLAN, M.H., *J. Exper. Med.*, *91*, 1, 1950.

DARZYNKIEWISZ, Z., BOLUND, L. and RINGERTZ, N.R., *Exptl. Cell Res.*, *56*, 418, 1969.

DERAZHNE, A.B., *Akusherstvo i Gynecologiya*, *N3*, 21, 1962.

DERAZHNE, A.B., *Eighth Intern. Cancer Congress, Abstracts* (Moscow), 530, 1962.

DYEK, D.L. and MORI, K., *J. Histochem. Cytochem.*, *17*, 755, 1969.

ELLINGER, P., *Biological Reviews*, *15*, 323, 1940.

FOSSATI-TALLARD, J., *Ztschr. wiss. Mikr.*, *68*, 1, 1967.

GECILE, D., *C. r. Acad. Sci.*, *268*, 348, 1969.

GERSCH, N.F. and JORDAN, D.O., *J. Mol. Biol.*, *13*, 138, 1965.

GLEDHILL, B.L., GLEDHILL, M.P., RIGLER, R. Jr. and RINGERTZ, N.R., *Exp. Cell Res.*, *41*, 652, 1966.

GÖSSNER, W., *Verh. dtsch. Ges. Path.* (33. Tagung, Kiel), 102, 1949.

GURSKY, G.V., *Biofisika*, 11, 737, 1966.

HAITINGER, M., *Handb. Biolog. Arbeitsmeth.* Abt. II, Teil 3, 3307, 1934.

HAITINGER, M., *Die Grundlagen der Fluoreszenzmikroskopie und ihre Anwendung in der Histologie und Chemie*, Leipzig: Akad. Verl., 1938.

HÖFLER, K., "Beiträge Zur Fluoreszenz-Mikroskopie". BRÄUTIGAM, F. and GRABNER, A. (eds.), Vienna: Georg Fromme, 46-70, 1949.

KASTEN, F.H., *Intern. Rev. Cytology*, *21*, 141, 1967.

KASTEN, F.H., BURTON, V. and GLOVER, P., *Nature*, *184*, 1797, 1959.

KEEBLE, S. and JAY, R.F., *Nature*, *193*, 695, 1962.

KHACHATUROV, E.N., *Izvestiya Akademii Nauk*, *Ser. Biol.* (Moscow), *No. 3*, 353, 1968.

KHACHATUROV, E.N. and SMIRNOVA, E.A., *Izvestiya Akademii Nauk*, *Ser. Biol.* (Moscow), *6*, 900, 1966.

KHAVKIN, T.N., KUDRJAVTZEV, B.N., BERLIN, L.B. and KUDRJAVTZEVA, M.B., *Cytologia* (Leningrad), *12*, 1209, 1970.

KHOKHLOV, A.B. and OPALEVA, E.F., *Akusherstvo i Ginekologiya* (Moscow), *N6*, 67, 1958.

KILLANDER, D. and RIGLER, R., Jr., *Exp. Cell. Res.*, *39*, 701, 1965.

KILLANDER, D. and RIGLER, R., Jr., *Exp. Cell Res.*, *54*, 163, 1969.

KISGLEV, L.L., FROLOVA, L.J., BORISOVA, O.F. and KUKHANOVA, M.K., *Biokhimya* (Moscow), *29*, 116, 1964.

KÖHLER, A., *Z. wiss. Mikrosk.*, *21*, 129, 1904.

KÖLBEL, H., *Ztschr. f. Naturforsch.*, *28*, 381, 1947.

KONDRATIEVA, T.M., *Doklady Akademii Nauk SSSR*, *111*, 89, 1956.

KRIEG, A., *Naturwissenschaften*, *40* (1953), 414; *Ztschr. Hyg. Infekt. Krankh.*, *138*, 357, 530; *139*(1953), 61, 65.

KRIEG, A. *Ztschr. Naturforsch.*, *9*, 342, 1954; *Naturwissenschaften*, *41*, 19, 1954.

LERMAN, L.S., *J. Mol. Biol.*, *3*, 18, 1961.

LERMAN, L.S., *Proc. Nat. Acad. Sci. U.S.*, *49*, 94, 1963.

LERMAN, L.S., *J. Mol. Biol.*, *10*, 367, 1964.

LIEDEMAN, R.R., PRILIPKO, L.L., KOLJASKINA, G.I., BODANOVA, E.D. and CHALENKO, I.M., *Zhurnal Nevropatologii* (Moscow), *69*, 1397, 1969.

LOOS, W., *Zeiss-Nachr.*, *2*, 319, 1936/1939.

LUZZATI, V., MASSON, F. and LERMAN, L.S., *J. Mol. Biol.*, *3*, 634, 1961.

MacINNES, J.W. and URETZ, R.B., *Science*, *151*, 689, 1966.

MacINNES, J.W. and URETZ, R.B., *J. Cell Biol.*, *33*, 597, 1967.

MacINNES, J.W. and URETZ, R.B., *J. Cell Biol.*, *38*, 426, 1968.

MAKARENKO, J.A., *Eigth Intern. Cancer Congress, Abstracts*, 529, 1962.

MEISSEL, M.N., *Mikrobiologiya*, *16*, 527, 1947.

MEISSEL, M.N., *"Functional Morphology of Yeast Organism"*, Moscow: Ac. Sci. Publishing House, 1950.

MEISSEL, M.N., *Izvestiya Akademii Nauk SSSR, Ser. Phys.* (Mosco *15*, 788, 1951.

MEISSEL, M.N., BRUMBERG, E.M., KONDRATIEVA, T.M. and BARSKY, J.Y., in: *The Initial Effects of Ionizing Radiations on Cells.*

HARRIS, P.J.C. (ed.). New York: Academic Press, 107-126, 1960.

MEISSEL, M.N. and GUTKINA, A., *Doklady Akad. Nauk SSSR* (Moscow), *91*, 647, 1953.

MEISSEL, M.N. and GUTKINA, A., *Izvestiya Akademii Nauk SSSR, Ser. Biol.* (Moscow), *N5*, 693, 1961.

MEISSEL, M.N., KONDRATIEVA, T.M. and EMELIYANOV, K.N., *Doklady Akademii Nauk SSSR* (Moscow), *81*, 1047, 1951.

MEISSEL, M.N., KONDRATIEVA, T.M. and POMOSHCHNIKOVA, N.A., *Zhurnal Obshchei Biologii* (Moscow), *12*, 312, 1951.

MEISSEL, M.N., KONDRATIEVA, T.M., SONDAK, V.A. and GUTKINA, A.V., *Radiation Res.*, *9*, 151, 1958.

MEISSEL, M.N. and KORCHAGIN, V.B., *Bull. Exp. Biol. i. Mediz* (Moscow), *33*, 49, 1952.

MEISSEL, M.N., LARIONOV, L.F. and KONDRATIEVA, T.M., *Doklady Akademii Nauk SSSR* (Moscow), *76*, 723, 1951.

MEISSEL, M.N. and MANTEIFEL, V.M., *Izvestiya Akademii Nauk SSSR, Ser. Biol.* (Moscow), *N8*, 871, 1963.

MEISSEL, M.N., MANTEIFEL, V.M. and DOLGORUKOVA, N.I., *Izvestiya Akademii Nauk, Ser. Biol.* (Moscow), No. 5, 767, 1969.

MEISSEL, M.N. and MIROLYUBOVA, L.V., *Izvestiya Akademii Nauk SSSR, Ser. Biol.* (Moscow), No. 6, 865, 1959.

MEISSEL, M.N. and SONDAK, V.A., *Doklady Akademii Nauk, Ser. Biol.* (Moscow), *105*, 1221, 1955.

MEISSEL, M.N. and SONDAK, V.A., *Biofizika* (Moscow), *1*, 263, 1956.

MEISSEL, M.N. and ZAVARZINA, N.B., *Mikrobiologiya* (Moscow), *16*, 394, 1947.

MELLORS, M.C. and SILVER, R., *Science, 114*, 356, 1951.

NASH, D. and PLAUT, W., *Proceed. Nat. Acad. Sci., U.S.A.*, *51*, 731, 1964.

NATARJIAN, A.T., *Chromosoma, 28*, 48, 1969.

NITSCH, B., MURKEN, J.D. and BRUCK, H.J., *Histochemie, 23,* 254, 1970.

PEACOCKE, A.R. and SKERRETT, J.N.H., *Trans. Faraday Soc.,* 261-279, 1956.

PRENNA, G., *Cytologia* (Leningrad), *11*, 264, 1969.

PRENNA, G., BIANCHI, U.A. and ZANOTTI, L., *Rivista Istochim. Norm. e Patol., 10*, 389, 1964.

PRENNA, G. and de PAOLI, A.M., *Rivista Istochim. Norm. e Patol., 10*, 185, 1963.

PRENNA, G. and de PAOLI, A.M., *Rivista Istochim. Norm. e Patol., 14*, 169, 1968.

PRENNA, G., PIVA, N. and ZANOTTI, L., *Rivista Istochim. e Patol., 8*, 427, 1962.

PRENNA, G. and ZANOTTI, L., in: *Second Intern. Congress of Histo- and Cytochem., Abstracts.* SCHIEBLER, J.H., PEARSE, A.G.E. and WOLF, H.H. (eds.). Berlin: Springer-Verlag, 1964.

PRENNA, G., BIANCHI, U.A. and ZANOTTI, L., *Rivista Istochem. Norm. e Patol., 10*, 539, 1964.

PRITCHARD, N.Y., BLAKE, A. and PEACOCKE, A.R., *Nature, 212,* 1360, 1966.

REICHERT, K., *Phys. Zeitschr., 22/23*, 1010, 1911.

RIGLER, R., Jr., "Microfluorometric Characterization of Intracellular Nucleic Acids and Nucleoproteins by Acridine Orange". *Acta Physiol. Scandinav., 67*, 267, 1966.

RIGLER, R., Jr., KILLANDER, D., BOLUND, L. and RINGERTZ, N.R., *Exptl. Cell Res., 55*, 215, 1969.

RINGERTZ, N.R., in: *Handbook of Molecular Cytology.* LIMA-DE-FA A. (ed.). Amsterdam: North-Holland, 656, 1969.

RINGERTZ, N.R. and BOLUND, L., *Exptl. Cell Res., 55*, 205, 1969

ROBBINS, E., MARCUS, P.J. and GONATOS, N.K., *J. Cell Biol.*, *21*, 49, 1964.

ROSANOV, U.M. and KUDRJAVTZEV, B.N., *Cytologia* (Leningrad), *9*, 365, 1967.

ROSCHLAU, G., *Histochemie*, *5*, 396, 1965.

RUCH, F., in: *Introduction to Quantitative Cytochemistry*. WIED G.L., (ed.). New York: Academic Press, 281, 1966.

SANDRITTER, W., *Acta Cytologica*, *8*, 165, 1964.

SANI, C., CITTI, U. and CARAMAZZA, G., *La Microscopia di Fluorescenza nella Citodiagnosi del Canres*. Bologna: Capelli, 1963.

SCHMIDT, W., *Z. Zellforsch.*, *58*, 573, 1962.

SCHULLER, R., *Naturwissenschaften*, *39*, 90, 1952.

SCHULLER, R., *Arch. Protistenkunde*, *99*, 227, 1954.

SCHÜMMELFEDER, N., *Virchows Arch. Exer. Path.*, *318*, 119, 1950.

SCHÜMMELFEDER, N., EBSCHNER, K.J. and KROGH, E., *Naturwissenschaften*, *44*, 467, 1957.

SCHÜMMELFEDER, N., EBSCHNER, K.J. and KROGH, E., *Histochemie*, *1*, 1, 1958.

SCHWARTZ, T.F. and STOLLER, B.D., *Biochem. and Biophys. Res. Communs.*, *35*, 115, 1969.

SELA, J., *Biochim. et Biophys. Acta*, *190*, 216, 1969.

SHERUDILO, A.I. and KHACHATUROV, F.N., *Izvestiya Akademii Nauk, Ser. Biol.* (Moscow), *No. 1*, 154, 1969.

STEINER, R.F. and BEERS, R.F., Jr., *Science*, *127*, 335, 1957.

STERBA, G., *Acta Biol. et Med. Germ.*, *10*, 694, 1963.

STOCKINGER, L., "Vitalfärbung und Vitalfluorochromierung tierischer Zellen". *Protoplasmatologia: Handbuch der Protoplasmaforschung, II, D. 1.* Vienna: Springer Verlag, 1964.

STONE, A.L. and BRADLEY, D.F., *J. Amer. Chem. Soc., 83*, 3627, 1961.

STOWARD, P.J., *J. Royal Microscop. Soc., 82*, 237, 1967.

STOWARD, P.J., *J. Royal Microscop. Soc., 82*, 247, 1967.

STRUGGER, S., *Jena. Ztschr. f. Naturw., 73*, 97, 1940.

STRUGGER, S., Dtsch. Tierärztl. Wschr., 49,525, 1941.

STRUGGER, S., *Flora, 137*, 73, 1943.

STRUGGER, S., *Fluoreszenzmikroskopie und Mikrobiologie.* Hanover: M. et H. Schaper Verlag, 1949.

STUPKO, A.J. and BRUSIYANIKOVA, L.N., *Voprosy Onkologii* (Moscow), *6*, 66, 1960.

SVINDLER, E.A., *Voprosy Onkologii* (Moscow), *10*, 86, 1964.

TSWETT, M., *Ber. Dtsch. Bot. Ges., 29*, 246, 1911.

VONKENNEL and WIEDMANN, *Deutsche Medizinische Wochenschrift, 77*, 529, 1944.

VOSA, C.G., *Chromosoma, 30*, 366, 1970.

WAHL, P., PAOLETTI, J. and LePECQ, J.B., *Proc. Nat. Acad. Sci. U.S.A., 65*, 417, 1970.

WEIL, G. and CALVIN, M., *Biopolymers, 1*, 401, 1963.

WELLER, T.H. and COONS, A.H., *Proc. Exper. Biol. Med., 86*, 789, 1954.

WEST, S.S., in: *Physical Techniques in Biological Research, 3, part C: Cells and Tissues.* POLLISTER, A.W. (ed.). New York: Academic Press, 253, 1969.

WITTEKIND, D., *J. Royal Microscop. Soc., 83*, 83, 1964.

YARMONENKO, S.P., *Meditsinskaya Radiologiya* (Moscow), *4*, 52, 1959.

YOUNG, M.R. and SMITH, A.U., *J. Royal Microscop. Soc.*, *82*, 233, 1963.

ZANKER, V., *Z. Physiol. Chem.*, *192*, 255, 1952.

ZANKER, V., *Z. Physiol. Chem.*, *200*, 250, 1952.

ZANKER, V., HELD, M. and RAMMENSEE, H., *Z. Naturforschung*, *146*, 789, 1959.

ZANOTTI, L., *Acta Histochem.*, *17*, 353, 1964.

ZANOTTI, L., PRENNA,G., in: *Second International Congress of Histo-and Cytochemistry*, *Abstracts*, Schibler, Pearse, and Welff (eds.) Berlin: Springer-Verlag, 231, 1964.

ZAVILGELSKY, G.B., BORISOVA, O.F., MINCHENKOVA, L.E. and MINYAT, E.E., *Biochimiya*, *29*, 508, 1964.

ZELENIN, A.V., *Izvestiya Akademii Nauk SSSR, Ser. Biol.* (Moscow), *N6*, 977, 1965.

ZELENIN, A.V., *Nature*, *212*, London, 425, 1966.

ZELENIN, A.V.,*"Fluorescence Cytochemistry of Nucleic Acids."* Moscow: Nauka, 1967.

ZELENIN, A.V., BIRJUSOVA, V.J., VOROTNITSKAJA, N.E. and LIAPUNOVA, F.A., *Doklady Akademii Nauk SSSR* (Moscow), *162*, 925, 1965.

ZELENIN, A.V. and LIAPUNOVA, E.A., in: *Second International Congress of Histo- and Cytochemistry, Abstracts*. SCHIEBLER, PEARSE, and WOLFF (eds.). Berlin: Springer-Verlag, 217-218, 1964.

ZHELESNOV, B.J., *Akusherstvo i Ginekologiya* (Moscow), *1*, *Farmakologija i Toksikologija* (Moscow), No. 6, 751, 1967.

ZHELESNOV, B.J., *Arkhiv Patologii* (Moscow), *26*, 31, 1964. 43, 1956.

ZELESNOV, B.J., *Arkhiv Patologii* (Moscow), *26*, 31, 1964.

NOTES ADDED IN PROOFS

A few extra comments on the main text and its addendum are necessary due to the new delay in the publication
of the book.

The main achievement in fluorescence cytochemistry of
nucleic acids in recent years is connected with the use of
some acridine aminoderivatives primarily quinacrine mustard
and quinacrine dehydrochloride (atebrine) for the investigation and identifying of individual human chromosomes.
This task can be now fulfilled not only on the base of
characteristic curves obtained from reflecting photomeric
measurements but also by visual analysis of the fluores-
ence patterns in photomicrographs. Fluorescence technique
is widely applied for the identification of different
individual chromosomes in normal conditions and for the
investigation of the chromosomes with structural and functional abnormalities. At the same time the cytochemical
nature of the fluorescence chromosome bands still remains
obscure.

For review and literature see: Borganokar and
McKusick, 1971; Caspersson et al., 1971; Commings, 1971;
Ganner and Evans, 1971; Breg, 1972; Pachmann and Rigler,
1972.

During the last two years there also appeared in the
literature a number of new examples of successful use of
Rigler's method for the investigation of DNP properties
in whole cells (Auer et al., 1970; Ringertz et al., 1970;
Kernell et al., 1971).

Some special comments must be made on the use of
fluorescence variants of Feulgen's reaction. New information confirming the applicability of different Schiff-
type reagents for quantitative assay of DNA was recently
published (Ruch, 1970; Sherudilo and Vlasova, 1972). It
seems therefore that this method can be now recommended
for quantitative cytochemistry of DNA beyond any special
doubt.

It should be also mentioned that the data on lysosomal
nature of red cytoplasmic granules in cells vitally treated
with AO has been confirmed in numerous experiments with

vital (supravital) staining of cells and subcellular fraction (Dingle and Barrett, 1967, 1968; Blume et al., 1969; Canonico and Bird, 1969; Fine et al., 1970) and AO is regarded as a reliable nonenzymatic marker for lysosomes (Canonico and Bird, 1969). For review see: Allison and Young (1969) and Zelenin (1971).

REFERENCES

ALLISON, A.C. and YOUNG, M.R., in: *Lysosomes in biology and pathology*, DINGLE, J.T. and FELL, H.B. (eds.). Amsterdam-London: North-Holland, pt. II, 600, 1969.

AUER, G., ZETTERBERG, A. and KILLANDER, D., *Exp. Cell. Res.*, *62*, 32, 1970.

BLUME, R.S., GLADE, P.R. and CHESSIN, L.N., *Blood*, *33*, 87, 1969.

BORGAONKAR, D.S. and McKUSICK, V.A., *Hopkins Med. J.*, *128*, 75, 1971.

BREG, W.R., *Stain Technol.*, *47*, 87, 1972.

CANONICO, P.G. and BIRD, J.W., *J. Cell. Biol.*, *43*, 367, 1969.

CASPERSSON, T., LOMAKKA, G. and ZECH, L., *Hereditas*, *67*, 89, 1971.

COMMINGS, D.D., *Exp. Cell. Res.*, *67*, 441, 1971.

DINGLE, J.T. and BARRETT, A.J., *Biochem. J.*, *105*, 19, 1967.

DINGLE, J.T. and BARRETT, A.J., *Biochem. J.*, *109*, 19, 1968.

FINE, D.L., LAKE, R.S. and LUDWIG, E.H., *J. Virol.*, *5*, 226, 1970.

GANNER, E. and EVANS, H.J., *Chromosoma*, *35*, 326, 1971.

KERNELL, A.M., BOLUND, L. and RINGERTZ, N.R., *Exp. Cell. Res.*, *65*, 1, 1971.

PACHMANN, U. and RIGLER, R., *Exp. Cell Res.*, *72*, 602, 1972.

RINGERTZ, N.R., GLEDHILL, B.L. and DARZYNKIEWICZ, Z., *Exp. Cell Res.*, *62*, 204, 1970.

RUCH, F., in: *Introduction to Quantitative Cytochemistry-II.*

WIED, G. and BAHR, G.F. (eds.), New York and London: Academic Press, 431, 1970.

SHERUDILO, A.J. and VLASOVA, I.A., *Cytologia* (Leningrad), *14*, 527, 1972.

ZELENIN, A.V., *"Interaction of aminoacridines with the cell,"* Moscow, Nauka, 1971.

THE BIOLOGICAL BASIS OF CYTOLOGICAL CANCER DIAGNOSIS

ACRIDINE ORANGE FLUORESCENCE CYTODIAGNOSIS AFTER LUDWIG VON BERTALANFFY

FELIX D. BERTALANFFY

Professor of Anatomy
Faculties of Medicine and Dentistry, University of Manitoba
Winnipeg, Manitoba, Canada

HISTORICAL CONSIDERATIONS

Ultraviolet illumination was first employed by Köhler (1904) for the study of microscopic objects. The earliest special fluorescence microscope for such investigations was designed by Reichert in 1911. During the subsequent forty years, most studies with the fluorescence microscope were confined almost exclusively to botanical material. Examples of such noteworthy studies were those by Strugger (1949), Haitinger (1938), and Bräutigam and Grabner (1949). Among the avid, though quite sporadic, scientists utilizing fluorescence microscopy during that period was the botanist K. Höfler, employing at the University of Vienna the type of fluorescence microscope designed in that city by Reichert for the study of histophysiological processes in plant tissues, in conjunction with various fluorochromes, among them acridine orange (1947, 1949). In 1943, Höfler introduced the biologist Ludwig von Bertalanffy, then likewise active at the University of Vienna, to the fascinating realm of fluorescence microscopy. Although von Bertalanffy realized at that time the great potentiality of fluorescence

---

*The work by the author was supported by research grants from the National Cancer Institute of Canada and the Medical Research Council of Canada.

microscopy also in the study of animal tissues, subsequent
years provided little opportunity for the pursuance of
such investigations. The first such occasion arose in 1949,
after von Bertalanffy had accepted a position at the Medical
Faculty, University of Ottawa. At that time, von Bertalanffy
imported from Vienna a fluorescence microscope, which may
well have been the first such equipment introduced into
Canada. Fluorescence microscopy was applied during that
period in North America only in a few sporadic laboratories
in the United States, and almost exclusively in conjunction
with the fluorescent antibody method, devised by Coons and
associates (1942), then still in its developmental stages.
Using primarily the fluorochrome acridine orange, von
Bertalanffy commenced with a systematic study of a great
series of mammalian tissues, believed at that time to have
been the first major investigation of animal tissues by
fluorescence microscopy. It is of interest to note that,
as it was learned later, similar fluorescence studies, with
the identical fluorochrome acridine orange, were initiated
about the same time independently in Germany by
Schümmelfeder, in England by Armstrong, and in the U.S.S.R.
by Meissel. As this is evident from the following, all
four of these investigations led independently to the important discovery of a distinctive specificity of acridine
orange to nucleic acids.

During the course of von Bertalanffy's studies it soon
became apparent that even within the same cell population
the various cell forms consistently exhibited differential
cytoplasmic fluorescence colors, ranging from greenish to
brown, over reddish brown to orange and red. More intense
reddish or orange fluorescence colors were displayed, for
instance, by the cells composing the lowermost layers of
stratified epithelia, or by the cells of intestinal crypts.
Regenerating liver parenchyma exhibited brightly red fluorescent cells, whereas the cytoplasm of normal liver cells
was merely brown to reddish brown. The most striking picture was yielded by malignant cell populations, for instance,
hepatomas, induced by acetylaminofluorene, and by other
tumors, exhibiting brightly orange to flaming red fluorescent cells. In contrast, other cells, such as many epithelial cells, particularly those in the upper layers of
stratified epithelia, the cells of intestinal villi, and
the cells of many parenchymal organs, such as kidney or
endocrine glands, displayed less intense cytoplasmic fluorescence, ranging from greenish to brown.

In an effort to propose an explanation for the differential fluorescence exhibited by the various cell forms,
a common property of the brightly orange or red fluorescent
cells was ascertained: all of them proliferated actively.
In contrast, mitosis of the greenish or brownish fluorescent
cell types occurred rarely, or not at all. This observation
suggested that the cells with high mitotic activity contained
much larger concentrations of a certain cell chemical, demonstrated quantitatively by acridine orange, than most other
cells that did not proliferate. It had already been known
from several previous investigations that rapidly proliferating cells were characterized by a high content of cytoplasmic ribonucleic acid (RNA). Although the precise significance of RNA had not been elucidated at that time, the
configuration of deoxyribonucleic acid (DNA), which subsequently led to the disclosure of the role of nucleic acids
in protein synthesis, was published by Watson and Crick
(1953) around the same period and it was realized that cells
actively engaged in protein synthesis contained abundant
RNA. The active rate of protein synthesis was, of course,
a requisite in the formation of daughter cells in rapidly
proliferating cell populations.

To test the hypothesis of RNA being conceivably responsible for cytoplasmic fluorescence, and the possibility that
various concentrations brought about the differential fluorescence intensity exhibited by cells, von Bertalanffy and
co-workers treated a series of animal tissues with the enzyme RNase, thereby removing the RNA from the cells. The
cells in such RNase treated tissue sections, after having
been stained with acridine orange, failed to show as little
as even a trace of cytoplasmic fluorescence. The usually
reddish fluorescent nucleolus (composed largely of RNA) was
likewise absent, and its location was betrayed in instances
by a circular unstained area, resembling a vacuole, in the
brightly green fluorescent nucleus. This observation suggested that the basic fluorochrome acridine orange selectively demonstrated the RNA in cells.

The treatment of cells with RNase did not alter the
fluorescence property of their nuclei. Nuclei exhibited
usually green fluorescence, or greenish yellow when they
were small, dense, or hyperchromatic. In RNase treated
tissue sections, the nuclei stood out most strikingly, and
were surrounded by dark halos of non-fluorescent cytoplasm.
This immediately suggested the likely possibility of DNA

being responsible for the greenish nuclear fluorescence,
tested by von Bertalanffy and associates by treatment of
cells and tissues with the enzyme DNase. When such specimens were stained with acridine orange, the nuclei failed
to fluoresce, and consequently remained invisible. In
their place were mere dark oval or spherical spaces, surrounded by normally fluorescent cytoplasm.

This investigation, outlined here merely in a simplified version, signified that acridine orange fluorescence
microscopy was an excellent means of specifically demonstrating nucleic acids in cells and tissues (von Bertalanffy
and Bickis, 1956). Moreover, acridine orange, because of
its metachromatic property, disclosed in a most striking
manner the presence of different concentrations of RNA in
cells. Cells containing RNA only in traces, or none at
all, exhibited greenish or non-fluorescent cytoplasm. When
moderate amounts of RNA were present, the cells were brown
or reddish brown, while those with large amounts of RNA
displayed orange to flaming red cytoplasmic fluorescence.
The reasons for the different RNA concentrations in various
cell types are discussed in the following sections.

Simultaneous independent discoveries of the identical
phenomenon have been made in science on several occasions.
The issue presented is one example of such an event. Within a period of only a few years, the specificity of acridine orange for nucleic acids was independently discovered,
without reciprocation, by the four groups of workers initiat-
ing studies of animal tissues by fluorescence microscopy,
although the technique had been used in botany for some
twenty years previously. The first such report was published in the U.S.S.R. by Meissel (1951), and was followed
by those of von Bertalanffy and Bickis (1956) in Canada,
Armstrong (1956) in England, and Schümmelfeder, Ebschner
and Krogh (1957) in Germany.

Yet it was the original idea of Ludwig von Bertalanffy
to utilize the specificity and metachromatic property of
acridine orange in the development of a novel procedure for
the cytochemical diagnosis of malignancies (von Bertalanffy,
Masin and Masin, 1956). The discussions that follow are
confined to the biological principles underlying the cytodiagnostic acridine orange fluorescence technique (and
cytodiagnosis in general). Numerous previous publications

described the technical details of the procedure (von Bertalanffy, Masin and Masin, 1958; Bertalanffy, 1960, 1961, 1962; von Bertalanffy and Bertalanffy, 1961; Marks and Goodwin, 1962), its practical application and diagnostic reliability as compared to purely morphological techniques of cytological cancer diagnosis (Bertalanffy, 1961; Sani et al., 1964; Ubachs, 1969; Foix et al., 1969; Ayre and LeGuerrier, 1969), as well as the advantages and disadvantages of the fluorescence technique (Bertalanffy, 1962; von Bertalanffy and Bertalanffy, 1962), and its physicochemical principles (Schümmelfeder, 1950, 1956; Schümmelfeder and Stock, 1956). The following account deals chiefly with a number of biological phenomena, serving as the basis of cytodiagnosis in general, and fluorescence cytodiagnosis in particular.

BIOLOGICAL BASIS OF CYTODIAGNOSIS

Renewal of Cell Population

Fluorescence cytodiagnosis is facilitated essentially by similar basic mechanisms of cell biology underlying morphological procedures of cytological cancer diagnosis. To begin with, this principal biological process facilitating cytodiagnosis in general is described, and is followed by a discussion of the implications of this mechanism in cytological cancer diagnosis by acridine orange fluorescence microscopy.

Cytodiagnosis utilizes the free cells present at all times in body secretions and excretions, the product of a continual exfoliation from the epithelia that line the body cavities and cover the body surface. When malignancies arise from such sites, they likewise desquamate cells that mingle with the cellular elements normally present in the secretions and excretions. Samples of such body secretions, for instance from the female genital, respiratory, and digestive tracts, and of excretions (such as urine) as well as of body effusions (from the pleural and peritoneal cavities), are examined cytologically to ascertain the presence or absence of malignant elements among the normal cells.

What is the reason for the continuous presence of the free cells in the various body secretions and excretions?

They are the product of an important histophysiological process, known as *cell renewal*.   Many cell populations, among
them epithelial tissues, hematopoietic and lymphopeoietic
cell communities, and the various representatives of the
reticulo-endothelial system, experience throughout life a
continuous exchange or replacement of their constituent
cells (Bertalanffy and Lau, 1962).   Differentiated cells
become continuously lost from such renewing cell populations,
for instance epithelia, by exfoliating into body cavities,
or hematogenous cellular elements, by entering the circulation.   The extruded cells are replaced by new cells arising simultaneously from mitotic division of usually little
differentiated epithelial cells (such as from basal or
reserve cells), or of the primitive blast or equivalent cell
stages in hemato- and lymphopoietic organs.

The number of cells newly formed in a renewing cell
population is essentially identical to that simultaneously
lost by exfoliation.   Because of this subtle balance between cell formation and cell loss, the size of the cell
population, and the number of its constituent cells remain
unaltered, despite the continuous flow of cells occurring,
at slower or faster rates, through the cell population.
Renewing cell populations are thus in a *cellular steady
state*, maintaining their cell number constant, despite the
continual cell exchange occurring throughout the life of
the individual.   By the interplay between cell formation
by mitosis and cell extrusion, a certain proportion of a
renewing cell population becomes constantly renewed during
a particular period, for instance each day.   Apart from a
few instances where endocrine fluctuations during the
estrous and menstrual cycles affect cell formation and
maturation in certain cell populations (Bertalanffy and
Lau, 1963), the proportion of cells renewed daily in most
other cell communities remains constant.   Inasmuch as a
certain percentage of cells are newly formed and extruded
each day, the cells of a particular renewing cell population become completely replaced within a certain and
rather constant number of days.   Such a period, required
for the renewal of all cells of a cell community, is generally referred to as the *renewal* or *turnover time* of the
cell population.

Conceivably because of their different histophysiological significance, the turnover times of the various

cell populations differ greatly, depending upon whether cell exchange proceeds at fast or slow rates. The velocity of cell renewal is related presumably directly to the histophysiological activity of the cell populations, and at least partly to the environment to which the cells are exposed (Bertalanffy, 1963). The percentages of cells dividing daily for renewal are most readily determined in animal cell populations. From such data, the renewal times of the entire cell populations are calculated. The turnover times of several epithelial cell populations, of significance in cytodiagnosis, are presented in Table 1; merely in the case of the lung, the macrophages (histiocytes) are part of the reticulo-endothelial system.

It is evident from the turnover times presented in Table 1 that the velocity of cell renewal ranges considerably between various cell populations. Renewed most rapidly, within less than two days, are epithelia of the gastrointestinal tract. The rapid renewal mechanisms of these cell populations apparently constitutes a preventive measure, forestalling the exposure of the epithelial cells over longer periods to the powerful enzymatic, largely proteolytic, medium of the gastrointestinal juice; conceivably, the latter might exert a detrimental action on the cells were they exposed to the enzymatic medium longer than determined by their natural life span. The turnover rates of the gastrointestinal epithelia are succeeded by cell populations with moderate durations of renewal time, ranging from about four to nine days; a third category of cell communities becomes renewed at considerably slower rates. In the majority of these cell populations cell renewal may be a measure to forestall possible damage largely brought about by mechanical stress, for instance, caused by contact with firm objects and the resulting friction between them and the epithelial tissues. This seems evident particularly with epidermal tissues, oral and esophageal epithelia, but with others as well. The factor contributing to the normally slow renewal of the respiratory epithelium of trachea and bronchus may be the continuous invasion of fine particulate matter and microorganisms gaining access during inspiration. Some of the tiny particles attain the innermost respiratory portions of the lung, from where they are removed effectively by phagocytic action of the pulmonary macrophages; the latter are in turn extruded largely through the air conducting system, and ultimately with sputum. This

TABLE 1. Turnover Times of Normal Cell Populations in the Adult Rat.

Epithelial portion of	Turnover time in days
Jejunum	1.3
Ileum	1.4
Duodenum	1.6
Pylorus	1.8
Vagina	3.9
Buccal mucosa	4.3
Tongue	4.9
Cervic uteri	5.5
Rectum	6.2
Cornea	6.9
Sebaceous glands	7.8
Lung, macrophages	8.1
Esophagus	8.8
Lip	14.7
Abdominal wall epidermis	15.9
Plantar epidermis	24.4
Bronchus	26.7
Ear epidermis	29.9
Germinal epithelium (♀)	32.8
Mesothelium (pleura, peritoneum)	33.8
Uterine tube	40.6
Trachea	47.6
Ureter	49.0

mechanism of dust clearance from the lung accounts at least partly for the renewal of these macrophages about every eight days (Bertalanffy, 1964). Entire cells become extruded as secretion material from sebaceous glands in the course of holocrine secretions, necessitating their continuous replacement (Bertalanffy, 1957). Finally, epithelial cells leave the ovarian lining of the female germinal epithelium to differentiate into ovogonia; moreover, a slow rate of desquamation of cells from the ovarian epithelium into the abdominal cavity appears conceivable. Exfoliation occurs likewise from the peritoneal epithelium in general, as from the pleural epithelium, whence cells drop into the abdominal and thoracic cavities, respectively. Merely a few examples of most obvious factors that might be responsible for renewal of some cell populations are cited; this is not to imply that other factors, less evident, might not contribute to this process as well.

Chiefly for technical reasons, the majority of data known on turnover times, including those in Table 1, are of necessity available only for animal material. However, technical difficulties have been overcome in the determination of renewal times of some normal human cell populations. Examples of turnover times of four human cell populations are listed in Table 2, together with the number of days required for the renewal of the identical cell populations in the rat.

TABLE 2.   Turnover Time of Normal Human and Rat Cell Populations

Cell population	Turnover time Human	Author(s)	Turnover time Rat	Author(s)
Duodenum	2	F.D. Bertalanffy and Nagy (1961)	1.6	Leblond and Stevens (1948)
Cervix uteri	5.7	Richart (1963)	5.5	Bertalanffy and Lau (1963)
Rectum	6-8	Cole and McKalen (1961)	6.2	Bertalanffy (1960)
Cornea	7	Hanna and Bicknell (1961)	6.9	Bertalanffy and Lau

It is evident from Table 2 that the turnover times were identical in man and rat in all four cell populations. This may suggest that also other human cell populations might be renewed at rates fairly close to those determined for the rat, as presented in Table 1. But even if this were not the case, it can at least be stated with reasonable confidence that all those cell populations observed in rodents to be renewing cell communities presumably represent renewing cell populations throughout the mammalian kingdom. This assumption is supported in human cell populations by the constant presence of exfoliated cells and mitotic figures.

The cell renewal mechanism proceeds in normal cell populations in an exceedingly orderly fashion. In a highly simplified manner it may be stated that typical renewing cell populations are composed essentially of two cell fractions: a proliferative and a differentiating cell fraction (Bertalanffy, 1967). The proliferative fraction is composed of cells that usually have not attained an advanced state of differentiation. They are exemplified by the basal cells of stratified squamous and pseudostratified epithelia, the cells of intestinal crypts, or the primitive cell of myeloid bone marrow and lymphatic tissue. The cells of the proliferating fraction divide continually by mitosis at rates that ultimately determine the renewal velocity of the particular cell population. Multiplication seems to be the principal, and conceivably sole, task of the cells of the proliferative fraction. Some of the daughter cells resulting from division remain in the proliferative fraction and continue division. Other daughter cells differentiate, for instance, while moving upward into the intermediate and superficial cell layers of stratified epithelia, or along the surface of intestinal villi, to eventually form fully differentiated superficial squamous, or secretory and absorptive, cells, respectively. In some types of simple epithelia, basal cells differentiate into columnar ciliated or mucous secretory cells. When differentiating, the cells usually lose the ability for mitotic division; their energy is now aimed solely toward their prescribed tasks of secretion, absorption, or protection. The differentiating cell fraction comprises by far the greater proportion of renewing cell populations, whereas the cells capable of mitosis, composing the proliferative fraction, are confined in instances to a single basal layer, constituting but a small proportion of the entire cell population.

As one aspect of cell renewal, cells become shed continually from the differentiating cell fraction, as from the superficial layer of stratified epithelia, or from the villous tips of the intestinal mucosa. The exfoliated cells are replaced by succeeding generations of cells that differentiated in the meantime, and were supplied by mitosis of the proliferative fraction of the particular cell population. Renewing cell populations are thus characterized by a perpetual flow of their constituent cells, for instance from the basal layers, through the intermediate into the superficial layers, whence the differentiated cells

desquamate. It is thus evident that renewing cell populations are veritably in a continual state of "streaming
equilibrium" or *Fliessgleichgewicht* (von Bertalanffy, 1953).

The cell renewal mechanism detailed previously is responsible for the constant presence of differentiated cellular elements in body secretions and excretions, as they are
encountered and utilized in cytodiagnosis (Bertalanffy,
1963). Apart from epithelial elements, body secretions contain normally various types of leukocytes. These cells
penetrated by diapedesis through capillary walls, and
entered the interstitial tissue spaces. They migrated subsequently through various epithelial linings, such as
through those of the digestive, respiratory, and female
genital tracts, and dropped into the respective body cavities or lumina, mingling with the secretions and cells there
present. This phenomenon constitutes a normal pathway of
extrusion of leukocytes from the body.

CYTODYNAMICS OF MALIGNANT CELL POPULATIONS

Cancer statistics signified that all cell populations
with a high incidence of malignancies (contributing more
than ten percent to the total cancer incidence) represent
normally renewing cell populations. This might imply that
the normal occurrence of mitosis in a cell population aug-
ments considerably the chances for a malignant transformation to occur within the particular cell community. This
assumption is in line with recent observations indicating
that carcinogens conceivably affect a cell primarily during
the DNA synthesis phase, possibly by effectuating some de-
rangement of the chromosomal apparatus. Recent research,
for instance on epidermal carcinogenesis, disclosed that
the primary response of a cell population to application
of a carcinogen is eventually an enhanced mitotic activity.
For example, the mitotic rate of mouse epidermis, belonging to the slowly renewing cell populations after a brief
period of mitotic depression, became increased by a multiple after a few days of benzpyrene application, and continued to augment steadily (Bertalanffy and Chivers, 1970).

This does not imply, however, that malignant cell populations necessarily always proliferate generally at faster
rates than normal renewing cell populations (Bertalanffy,

1967). In fact, the proliferation rates of only a few neoplastic cell populations are able to exceed, or even to approach, those of the normal intestinal epithelium. Similarly, some other normal cell populations proliferate frequently faster than many malignant tumors. This phenomenon is illustrated by comparing in Table 3 the generation times (time required for the division of one hundred percent of the cells in a cell population) of a few malignant animal tumors with the turnover times of several normal rat cell populations.

TABLE 3. Turnover Times of Normal Versus Generation Times of Malignant Cell Populations

Cell population	Turnover or generation time in days
Ehrlich Ascites Tumor	*0.9*
Jejunum	1.3
Ileum	1.4
Duodenum	1.6
Walker Carcinosarcoma	*1.7*
Pylorus	1.8
Rat Fibrosarcoma 1F16F	*2.5*
Mouse Neuroblastoma C1300	*2.7*
Mouse Melanoma B16	*2.8*
Vagina	3.9
Buccal mucosa	4.3
Tongue	4.9
Cervix uteri	5.5
Rectum	6.2
Cornea	6.9
Sebaceous glands	7.8
Lung, macrophages	8.1
C3H Mammary Gland Adenocarcinoma	*8.5*
Esophagus	8.8
Colon	10.0
Methylchol. Rat Fibrosarcoma	*10.6*

Only a few cell populations, among them the Ehrlich ascites tumor, proliferate faster than the epithelial cell populations of the small intestine. The latter cell populations require a mere one and a half days for their complete renewal, including the cells of both intestinal crypts and villi. However, the cells comprising the much larger

differentiating cell fraction of the villous epithelium divide no longer, and mitosis is confined to the smaller proliferative fraction of the crypts. In order to accomplish
the rapid renewal of the entire intestinal cell population,
each crypt cell of the proliferative fraction has to divide once every 9 to 11 hours (Lamerton, 1966). It appears
that the cells of intestinal crypts may proliferate at the
maximal velocity feasible to mammalian cells.

The rates of proliferations of other transplantable
malignant cell populations are somewhat longer than those
of the epithelia of small intestine. This signifies that
some neoplastic cell populations, although highly malignant
and killing the animals in instances within two or three
weeks, proliferate at slower rates than some normal cell
populations for cell renewal. The group of four transplantable tumors is followed in Table 3 by a variety of normal
cell populations proliferating for renewal at moderate ra
rates. Yet, their proliferation rates exceed those of two
more neoplastic tumors, the spontaneous mammary gland adenocarcinoma of the C3H mouse, and a fibrosarcoma induced in
the rat by application of the carcinogen methylcholanthrene.
These observations signify that normal cell populations
frequently proliferate for renewal at more rapid rates
than many malignant tumors (Bertalanffy, 1967).

A somewhat different picture is obtained by comparing the mitotic rates of malignant cell populations and
the rates of their normal tissues of origin, proliferating for renewal. Generally speaking, such a comparison
reveals that malignant tumors proliferate as a rule more
rapidly than the normal cell populations from which they
have arisen. For instance, the majority of mammary gland
adenocarcinomas, induced in rats by administration of the
carcinogen dimethylbenzanthracene, proliferated from three
to six times faster than the normal mammary gland parenchyma
of the virgin rat for cell renewal; the mitotic rates of
anaplastic mammary gland neoplasms was from 10 to 17 times
higher than that of the normal gland (Grahame, 1966). Epidermal squamous cell carcinomas, induced in mice by application of benzpyrene, proliferated from 5 to 8 times faster
than the normal epidermis for cell renewal (Bertalanffy and
Chivers, 1970). Or, *in situ* carcinomas of the human uterine
cervix proliferated twelve times faster than the normal
human cervical epithelium for renewal (Richart, 1963). Observations of this type indicate that although normal cell

populations frequently proliferate for renewal more rapidly
than some malignant tumors in general, neoplasms often proliferate at mitotic rates several times higher than that
of the normal tissue of origin.

Among the prominent differences between normal and
malignant cell populations, two characteristics of malignancy are of major consequence to cytodiagnosis. As pointed
out previously, the great majority of newly formed cells
differentiate in normal renewing cell populations and only
the cells of the smaller proliferative fraction remain
capable of mitotic division. In contrast, apart from occasional more highly differentiated squamous cell carcinomas, cell differentiation is not the rule in malignant
cell populations. As a consequence, tumor cells remain
potentially capable of division, and lose this ability only
when becoming removed from the nutrient medium (blood supply, tissue fluid) in rapidly growing tumors, or are affected by other factors resulting in cell degeneration and
necrosis. The default of malignant cells to differentiate
is responsible for some of the differences between neoplastic cells and the normal cells of the tissue of origin.
For instance, differences in cytomorphology between normal
and malignant cells, as they are utilized in cytodiagnosis,
are largely a reflection of the more primitive state of
the neoplastic cells. Continued division of malignant
cells, presumably afflicted with an altered genetic constitution, yields increasingly atypical mitosis, culminating
in phenomena such as hyperchromasia and anisokaryosis. The
morphological dissimilarities between malignant cells and
the cells of the normal tissue of origin become more pronounced with increasing mitotic activity of the neoplasm.
Thus, frequently the tissue of origin cannot be determined
cytologically of anaplastic malignancies, often proliferating very rapidly and composed of cells that lost all
features characterizing the normal cells from which they
developed. For example, anaplastic tumors arising from rat
liver parenchyma following feeding of 4-dimethylaminoazo-
benzene, with generation times of 3 to 3.5 days, resembled
oat cell carcinomas of the lung more than hepatomas
(Bertalanffy et al., 1970).

Inasmuch as the ability for cell division is maintained
by malignant cells, if unimpaired by necrosis, they continue
actively with protein synthesis in the formation of daughter

cells; consequently, they contain of necessity large amounts
of cytoplasmic RNA. As is explained in the following, it is
this feature in particular that is utilized and of major
consequence in the cytochemical cancer diagnosis by acridine
orange fluorescence microscopy.

When malignant tumors arise from renewing cell populations, they retain a principal characteristic feature of
the latter, that is, they continue to shed cells (Bertalanffy,
1967). Cells thus desquamate continually from both tumors
as from the renewing normal tissues of origin. In effect,
samples of body secretions and excretions from cases afflicted with malignancy contain a mixture of normal and
neoplastic cells. The preservation of this property of
cell exfoliation by malignant tumors, arisen from renewing
cell populations, is fundamental to cytodiagnosis. The procedure would be infeasible had this feature not been preserved by the neoplasms. It follows from this that cytodiagnosis is confined largely to carcinomas of renewing epithelial cell populations, to mesotheliomas, as well as to
leukemic cells occasionally present in some types of secretions and body effusions (Bertalanffy, 1963).

Despite the common property of cell desquamation from
both categories of cell populations, a major divergence
exists in the pattern of cell exfoliation from normal and
malignant cell populations. As pointed out, cell desquamation from normal cell communities occurs in a most orderly
fashion, is precisely balanced by an equivalent quota of
newly formed cells, and contributes to the maintainance of
the cellular steady state equilibrium. In contrast, apart
from a few fairly rare exceptions, a steady state between
cell loss and cell formation is not established in malignant tumors (Bertalanffy, 1967). Although cell loss, both
by exfoliation and necrosis may be considerable in some instances, it is frequently outbalanced by cell formation,
resulting in the expansion or growth of the tumors. Or, as
particularly during more advanced growth phases, the bulk
of tumor may consist of a central necrotic mass of debris,
devoid of mitotic figures. Yet the viable peripheral zone
of the tumor continues to proliferate and expand to invade surrounding tissues, and cells keep on shedding from
its free surface. Such cell loss from tumors, both by
necrosis and exfoliation, proceeds often in a disorderly
or erratic fashion; it may be more extensive from one tumor

than from another of the same type in the identical growth phase. As it is observed in cytodiagnosis, cytosmears from one patient frequently contain a much higher concentration of neoplastic cells than those from another, afflicted with the same type of malignancy. This phenomenon may partly reflect differences in procedures of collecting the specimens; but it is also likely an expression of the erratic mode of cell exfoliation from tumors. Because it is technically most difficult to accurately measure quantitative cell loss (Steel, 1967), it cannot be ascertained whether a correlation still exists in tumors between the rates of cell proliferation and exfoliation, although some such relationship seems likely. But even if a higher mitotic activity would be associated with a more abundant cell exfoliation, a cellular steady state, characteristic of normal renewing cell populations, is rarely attained by neoplasms. Absence of a steady state in most tumors thus constitutes another major difference between normal and malignant cell populations.

CELL PROLIFERATION, DIFFERENTIATION, AND NUCLEIC ACID CONTENT

For reasons that are evident, proliferating cells, whether normal or abnormal, contain as a rule higher concentrations of cytoplasmic RNA than cells that do not divide. A parent cell, eventually yielding by division two equivalent daughter cells, has of necessity to pass through a phase of protein synthesis, presumably as essential as is the duplication of nuclear DNA prior to mitosis. Inasmuch as sufficient RNA is indispensable in this process of protein synthesis, the often quite abundant RNA in the cells constituting the proliferative fraction of a cell population is an appropriate feature. It is further reasonable that cells no longer engaged in the synthesis of appreciable quantities of protein display a greatly reduced RNA content, if any at all. Such a differential RNA content is readily observed in renewing cell populations. The cells of the proliferative cell fractions, situated for instance in the basal layers or crypts, display frequently a fairly high concentration of RNA, particularly in rather rapidly renewing cell populations. In contrast, the amounts of RNA diminish gradually with advancing degrees of differentiation of the cells comprising the differentiating cell

fraction that no longer proliferate (Bertalanffy and Nagy,
1962). Differentiated cells that continue with protein
synthesis, for example in the elaboration of mucoprotein
secretions, usually retain more RNA. The circumstance that
exfoliated secretory cells frequently do not display an appreciably larger RNA content can presumably be explained
by the circumstance that by the time the cells desquamated
they passed the phase in the secretory cycle when they
elaborate secretion material, and are either in the storing
phase or, more likely, have discharged their secretions
recently. For instance, the secretory cells lining the
lower parts of intestinal villi, here mostly elaborating
secretions, appear to have a higher RNA content than those
along the upper villous portions, that contain the material
either stored in the apical cell region, or discharged it
shortly before desquamating from the villous tips. The decreasing content of RNA, with progressive cell differentiation, is evident also in stratified squamous epithelia. A
gradual diminution of RNA content can be demonstrated his-
tochemically from the parabasal through the intermediate to
the superficial cell layers, where demonstrable quantities
of RNA are frequently absent. This phenomenon is observable
by similar means in the intestinal mucosa where the undifferentiated, rapidly proliferating cells in the crypts contain abundant RNA. Despite the presence of mucous secreting cells, the RNA concentration fairly consistently diminishes superficially in the cells lining different levels of
the villi, and attains an only moderate degree by the time
the cells had reached the extrusion zones at the villous
tips.

DEMONSTRATION OF RNA CONTENT IN NORMAL AND MALIGNANT CELLS
BY ACRIDINE ORANGE FLUORESCENCE MICROSCOPY

The fluorochrome acridine orange demonstrates the two
types of nucleic acids by different fluorescence colors.
The nuclei in acridine orange preparations, when viewed
with the fluorescence microscope, appear in brightly green
or sometimes greenish yellow fluorescence. The nuclear
component manifested by the fluorochrome is the DNA chromatin, more precisely the heterochromatin portions of the
chromosomes that remain discernible in interphase nuclei as
granular chromocenters. The nuclei of cells in interphase
therefore often appear speckled with brightly greenish

fluorescent granules of heterochromatin. When DNA is concentrated within a small volume, such as in the small dense
nuclei of lymphocytes or of superficial squamous cells, the
nuclei appear as compact yellowish green fluorescent bodies,
frequently devoid of granular details. Moreover, when nuclei contain multiple amounts of the normal DNA complement,
such as those of polyploid, hyperchromatic malignant cells,
the DNA occurs in large nuclei as unusually coarse greenish
fluorescent granulations. Smaller hyperchromatic nuclei,
where multiple amounts of the normal DNA complement are confined to a small volume, appear frequently as rather homo-
geneously yellowish fluorescent bodies. The chromosomes of
dividing cells exhibit brightly greenish or greenish yellow
fluorescence. The actually green fluorescence of nuclear
DNA may occasionally become masked, or altered, by brightly
red fluorescent cytoplasm, as for instance, in some malignant cells. In such instances, the nuclei may appear to
fluoresce brightly yellow, or even orange, because of a
color combination between the greenish fluorescent DNA and
the superimposed red fluorescent RNA of the cytoplasm. If
such cells are treated with RNase, abolishing cytoplasmic
fluorescence, the true greenish fluorescence of their nuclei is revealed.

    The *cytoplasmic* and nucleolar *RNA* fluoresces in the
reddish range of the spectrum. Because of its metachromatic property, acridine orange appears in various shades
and intensities of brown, reddish brown, through orange to
flaming red hues when bound to different concentrations of
RNA. Cells with a high content of RNA invariably display
bright orange or red fluorescent cytoplasm. In contrast,
the cytoplasm of cells containing moderate or merely small
quantities of RNA fluoresces reddish brown to brown. When
appreciable amounts of RNA are not present in cells, their
cytoplasm either fails to fluoresce, or is merely indicated
by a greenish tinged silhouette, as neutrophil (polymorph)
leukocytes and superficial squamous cells, respectively.

    In practice, the normal cellular components of the dif-
ferentiating fractions of various cell populations contain
mostly moderate to small amounts of RNA and, consequently,
exhibit fluorescence colors ranging from reddish brown to
brownish. Appreciable amounts of RNA are absent in some
fully differentiated cells, such as in superficial squamous
cells, and their cytoplasm remains discernible merely as a

faintly greenish shadow. The decreasing fluorescence intensity with progressive differentiation, concurrent with a
gradual loss of RNA, is observed particularly well in
stratified squamous epithelia. The parabasal cells, arising by differentiation from the proliferating basal cells,
still retain moderate amounts of RNA, reflected by their
reddish-brown cytoplasmic fluorescence. Their further differentiation yields the larger intermediate cells, with reduced quantities of RNA distributed within a larger cell
volume. The cytoplasmic fluorescence of these cells diminishes accordingly to light yellowish brown. The large
fully differentiated superficial cells, having apparently
lost most, if not all RNA, no longer exhibit appreciably
fluorescent cytoplasm; the outline of the latter cells is
discerned by its merely faint greenish tint. A similar
fluorescence gradient is apparent as well in other types
of epithelia, for instance, in intestinal mucosa, where the
epithelium displays decreasing cellular fluorescence from
the crypts toward the villous tips, concurrent with progressive differentiation of the epithelial cells.

In contrast, the normal cellular elements of the proliferating cell fractions are characterized by an usually
high RNA content, required in protein synthesis for the
formation of daughter cells. Accordingly, the proliferating cells (particularly of rapidly renewing cell populations) exhibit, as a rule, brightly orange or red cytoplasmic fluorescence, reflecting the abundant RNA present
in these cells (Bertalanffy and Nagy, 1962). Examples are
the basal cells of stratified squamous female genital tract,
esophageal, and oral epithelia, exhibiting as a rule orange
cytoplasmic fluorescence. The cells of intestinal crypts,
proliferating at exceedingly rapid rates for cell renewal,
often fluoresce brightly red. It is of significance in
cytodiagnosis that these more primitive cell forms of the
proliferating fractions of renewing cell populations normally do not exfoliate. Most of the normal free cells encountered in body secretions and excretions derive from the
differentiating fractions and attain some degree of differentiation. They thus contain less RNA than their more
primitive precursors, and in contrast to the latter exhibit cytoplasmic fluorescence colors ranging from reddish
brown over brightly brown to greenish.

The situation is quite different in regard to cells
arising from malignancies. As was pointed out previously,

malignant cells proliferate frequently at higher rates than the normal cells of the tissue of origin. Consequently, one would expect a larger content of RNA in malignant cells than in the cells composing the proliferative fraction of the normal cell population, for instance in basal cells. Yet of greater significance in cytochemical cancer diagnosis is the circumstance that, unlike the cells of normal cell communities, those of neoplastic populations fail to differentiate, and thereby remain capable of mitotic division. Because the ability of continued proliferation is preserved, and malignant cells frequently multiply more rapidly than the cells of the tissues of origin, their RNA content exceeds often to a very considerable degree that of the normal cellular elements. Consequently, neoplastic cells display bright orange and frequently flamingly red fluorescent cytoplasm, in striking contrast to the merely reddish brown, brown, or greenish fluorescence of the differentiated normal cells, present conjointly in exfoliative specimens.

In the screening of cytological specimens, the striking red-orange fluorescence exhibited by cells with high RNA content is a most beneficial warning signal, readily calling the attention of the examiner to potentially neoplastic cells. It is self-evident that a final diagnosis of cancer cannot be made on the basis of color alone. But the excellent simultaneous presentation of cytomorphology by the fluorescence technique readily permits the morphological evaluation of the cells as well, which in turn should be confirmed by biopsy examination.

The acridine orange fluorescence procedure, developed by Ludwig von Bertalanffy, represents a modern approach to cancer diagnosis, since it utilizes not only aberrant cytomorphological features of cancer cells, as do conventional cytodiagnostic procedures, but it introduces an additional and novel cytochemical criterion based upon the disparity of RNA content of malignant cells, ensuing from their abnormal differentiation pattern. As this is illustrated by contrasting between the cytodynamics of normal renewing and neoplastic cell populations, the cytochemical acridine orange fluorescence technique has a sound histophysiological basis.

SUMMARY

Cytological cancer diagnosis utilizes the free cells
continually present in body secretions and excretions, that
have desquamated from the epithelia lining the various body
cavities and lumina, as well as from malignancies that developed from these cell communities. The exfoliated cells
are the product of a continuous renewal process of the epithelial cell populations lining these body regions. Constant numbers of new cells arise continually by mitotic
division in these epithelial cell populations, and they are
balanced by equivalent quotas of differentiated cells that
simultaneously desquamate. When neoplasms develop from renewing cell populations they continue to shed cells. In
contrast to the normal cell communities of origin, where
cell differentiation is the rule, the cells of most malignancies fall to attain an advanced stage of differentiation,
and all cells remain potentially capable of continued proliferation.

The cells exfoliating from normal renewing cell populations are mostly differentiated cell forms that no longer
proliferate. Consequently, they usually contain merely
moderate to small amounts of cytoplasmic RNA, or none at
all. In contrast, malignant cells, remaining capable of
multiplication, are characterized by their large RNA content. The acridine orange fluorescence technique, developed by Ludwig von Bertalanffy, demonstrates by differential fluorescence colors the various amounts of RNA in
cells. In exfoliative cytodiagnosis, the differentiated
normal cellular elements, with moderate or low RNA content,
display cytoplasmic fluorescence ranging from reddish brown
over brown to green. In contrast, malignant cells, because
of their higher RNA concentrations, display brightly orange
to flamingly red cytoplasmic fluorescence. Von Bertalanffy's
procedure thus introduces to cytodiagnosis a novel cytochemical criterion, based upon the enhanced RNA content of
neoplastic cellular elements.

REFERENCES

ARMSTRONG, J.A., "Histochemical differentiation of nucleic
acids by means of induced fluorescence." *Exper. Cell Res.*
640-643, 1956.

AYRE, J.E., and LeGUERRIER, J.M., "Acridine orange fluorescence microscopy in cervical cancergenesis. Clinical,
diagnostic and Research Applications." *Cancer Cytol.*, *9*,
25-30, 1969.

BERTALANFFY, F.D., "Mitotic activity and renewal rate of
sebaceous gland cells in the rat." *Anat. Rec.*, *129*, 231-
241, 1957.

BERTALANFFY, F.D., "Fluorescence microscopy for the rapid
diagnosis of malignant cells by exfoliative cytology."
Mikrospkopie (Vienna), *15*, 67-72, 1960.

BERTALANFFY, F.D., "Fluorescence microscopy for cytodiagnosis of cancer." *Post-grad. Med.*, *28*, 627-633, 1960.

BERTALANFFY, F.D., "Mitotic rates and renewal times of the
digestive tract epithelia in the rat." *Acta ant.*, 130-148,
1960.

BERTALANFFY, F.D., "Exfoliative Krebsdiagnose mit Akridin-
orange-Fluoreszenzmikroskopie." *Krebsarzt*, *16*, 521-530,
1961.

BERTALANFFY, F.D., "Application of acridine orange Fluorescence microscopy to cytological cancer diagnosis." *Lab.
Dig.*, *25*, Jan. & Feb., 1962.

BERTALANFFY, F.D., "Evaluation of the acridine-orange
fluorescence microscope method for cytodiagnosis of cancer."
Ann. N.Y. Acad. Sci., *93*, 715-750, 1962.

BERTALANFFY, F.D., "Cell renewal as the basis of diagnostic
exfoliative cytology." *Amer. J. Obst. Gyn.*, *85*, 383-396,
1963.

BERTALANFFY, F.D., "Aspects of cell formation and exfoliation related to cytodiagnosis." *Acta Cytol.*, *7*, 362-371,
1963.

BERTALANFFY, F.D., "Respiratory tissue: Structure, histo-
physiology, cytodynamics. Part II. New approaches and interpretations." *Intern. Rev. Cytol.*, *17*, 213-297, 1964.

BERTALANFFY, F.D., "Comparison of mitotic rates in normal renewing and neoplastic cell populations." *Proc. Seventh Canadian Cancer Conference, 1966.* New York, N.Y.: Pergamon Press, 1967.

BERTALANFFY, F.D., "The basis of cell exfoliation and cytochemical cancer diagnosis." *Cancer Cytol., 7,* 13-19, 1967.

BERTALANFFY, F.D., and CHIVERS, B.R., Unpublished data, 1970.

BERTALANFFY, F.D., and LAU, C., "Cell renewal." *Intern. Rev. Cytol., 13,* 357-366, 1962.

BERTALANFFY, F.D., and LAU, C., "Mitotic rate and renewal time of the corneal epithelium in the rat." *Arch. Ophthal., 68,* 546-550, 1962.

BERTALANFFY, F.D., and LAU, C., "Mitotic rates, renewal times, and cytodynamics of the female genital tract epithelia in the rat." *Acta anat., 54,* 39-81, 1963.

BERTALANFFY, F.D., and NAGY, K.P., "mitotic activity and renewal rate of the epithelial cells of human duodenum." *Acta anat., 45,* 362-370, 1961.

BERTALANFFY, F.D., and NAGY, K.P., "Fluorescence microscopy and photomicrography with acridine orange." *Med. Radiogr. Photogr., 38,* 82-91, 1962.

BERTALANFFY, F.D., and PARROT, J.C.W., and OZOHAN, M.L., "Mitotic rates of regenerating liver parenchyma and DAB induced primary hepatoma." *Acta anat., 77,* 216-237, 1970.

BRÄUTIGAM, F., and GRABNER, A., *Beiträge zur Fluoreszenzmikroskopie.* Vienna: Georg Fromme, 1969.

COLE, J.W., and McKALEN, A., "Observations of cell renewal in human rectal mucosa *in vivo* with thymidine-H^3." *Gastroenterology, 41,* 122-125, 1961.

COONS, A.H., CREECH, H.J., JONES, R.N., and BERLINER, E., "The demonstration of pneumococcal antigen in tissues by the use of fluorescent antibody." *J. Immunol., 45,* 159-170, 1942.

FOIX, A., LUCENA, C.M.L., and FRANZANI, W.G., *Atlas de Ginecologia. Microscopia de Fluorescencia*. Buenos Aires, Argentina: Grafico Herman S.R.L., 1969.

GRAHAME, R.E., "Rates of cell division in normal and malignant mammary gland tissue in the rat." M.Sc. Thesis, University of Manitoba, 1966.

HAITINGER, M., *Fluoreszenzmikroskopie. Ihre Anwedung in der Histologie und Chemie, Akadem.* Verlagsges., Leipzig, 1938.

HANNA, C., and BICKNELL, D.S., "Cell turnover in the adult human eye." *Arch. Ophthal. 65*, 695-700, 1961.

HÖFLER, K., "Was lehrt die Fluoreszenzmikroskopie von der Plasmapermeablilität und Stoffspeicherung?" *Mikroskopie 2*, 13-24, 1947.

HÖFLER, K., "Fluoreszenzmikroskopie und Zellphysiologie." *Biologia Generalis, 19*, 90-111, 1949.

KÖHLER, A., "Mikrophotographische Untersuchungen im ultra violetten Licht." *Z. Wiss. Mikroskop., 21*, 274-286, 1904.

LAMERTON, L.F., "Cell proliferation under continuous irradiation." *Rad. Res., 27*, 119-138, 1966.

LEBLOND, C.P., and STEVENS, C.E., "The constant renewal of the intestinal epithelium in the albino rat." *Anat. Rec.*, 357-378, 1948.

MARKS, R., and GOODWIN, A.M., "Comparative evaluation of the acridine orange fluorescence and Papanicolaou methods for cytodiagnosis of cancer." *Brit. J. Cancer, 16*, 390-399, 1962.

MEISSEL, M.N., "Luminescence-microscope analysis of the functional condition of living matter." (Russ.) *Izvest. Akad., Nauk S.S.S.R., Ser. Fiz., 15*, 788-792, 1951, (quoted from *Chem. Abstr., 46*, 6693, 1952).

REICHERT, C., "Das Fluoreszenzmikroskop." *Physik. Z., 12*, 1010-1026, 1911.

RICHART, R.M., "A radioautographic analysis of cellular proliferation in dysplasia and carcinoma *in situ* of the uterine
cervix." *Amer. J. Obst. Gyn., 86,* 925-930, 1963.

SANI, G., CITTI, U., and CARAMAZZA, F., *Fluorescnece Microscopy in the Cytodiagnosis of Cancer.* Springfield, Ill.:
C.C. Thomas, 1964.

SCHÜMMELFEDER, N., "Die Fluorochromieruug des lebenden,
überlebenden und toten Protoplasmas mit dem basischen
Farbstoff Akridinorange und ihre Beziehung zut Stoffwechse-
laktivität der Zelle." *Virchow's Arch. path. Anat. 318,*
119-154, 1950.

SCHÜMMELFEDER, N., "Einfluss der Pufferlösung auf die fär-
berische Bestimmung des Umladungsbereiches von Gewebselementen." *Z. Zellforsch. 44,* 488-494, 1956.

SCHÜMMELFEDER, N., and STOCK, K.F., "Die Bestimmung des Umladungsbereiches (Isoelektrischer Punkt) von Gewebselementen
mit dem Fluorochrom Akridinorange." *Z. Zellforsch., 44,*
327-338, 1956.

SCHÜMELLFEDER, N., EBSCHNER, K.R., and KROGH, E., "Die
Grundlage der differenten Fluorochromierung von Ribo-und
Desoxyribonukleinsäure mit Akridinorange." *Naturwissens-
chaften, 44,* 467-468, 1957.

STEEL, G.G., "Cell loss as a factor in the growth of human
tumors." *Europ. J. Cancer, 3,* 381-387, 1967.

STRUGGER, S., *Fluoreszenzmikroskopie und Mikrobiologie.*
Hanover, Germany: M. & H. Schaper, 1949.

UBACHS, J.M.H., *Acridine Orange Fluorescence Microscopy in
the Cytodiagnosis of Carcinoma of the Uterine Cervix.* Asten,
Holland, Schrok's Drukkerij, N.V., 1969.

von BERTALANFFY, L., *Biophysik des Fliessgleichgewichts.*
Braunschweig, Germany: Verlag Friedr. Vieweg, 1953.

von BERTALANFFY, L., and BERTALANFFY, F.D., "Die Fluores-
zenzmethode in der Zytodiagnostik des gynäkologischen
Karzinoms." *Med. Welt, 35,* 1742-1751, 1961.

von BERTALANFFY, L., and BERTALANFFY, F.D., "Akridinorange-Fluoreszenz-Cytodiagnostik in der Früherkennung des Krebses." *Ärztl. Mitt. 59*, 2393-2397, 1962.

von BERTALANFFY, L., and BICKIS, I., "Identification of cytoplasmic basophilia (ribonucleic acid) by fluorescence microscopy." *J. Histochem. Cytochem.*, *4*, 481-493, 1956.

von BERTALANFFY, L., MASIN, F., and MASIN, M., "Use of acridine-orange fluorescence technique in exfoliative cytology." *Science*, *124*, 1024-1025, 1956.

von BERTALANFFY, L., MASIN, M., and MASIN, F., "A new and rapid method for diagnosis of vaginal and cervical cancer by fluorescence microscopy." *Cancer*, *11*, 873-887, 1958.

WATSON, J.D., and CRICK, F.H., "Genetical implications of the structure of desoxyribonucleic acid." *Nature*, *171*, 737-740, 1953.

ACRIDINE ORANGE FLUORESCENCE MISCROSCOPY IN CERVICAL CANCERGENESIS

CLINICAL, DIAGNOSTIC AND RESEARCH APPLICATIONS

J. ERNEST AYRE

Medical and Scientific Director, National Cancer Cytology Center, New York, New York, and Miami, Florida , U.S.A.

Cytology is capable of detecting the first transformation stage between normal and very early malignant growth with remarkable accuracy. This is particularly true in the uterine cervix. Carcinoma *in situ* has long been recognized as a preinvasive lesion in the human cervix and its relationship on the one hand to normal epithelium and on the other to invasive cancer has been sought. In recent years, there has been wide recognition of a group of cervical precancerous lesions which appear to be further removed temporally from invasive carcinoma than carcinoma *in situ* which have been referred to as precancer, dyskaryosis or dysplasia. These lesions may be subclassified as being minimal, moderate, or marked, and appear to be a definite part of a continuum that progresses in a large percentage of cases to carcinoma *in situ* and invasive carcinoma. There have been relatively few reports of the DNA content of cells from such lesions and these have not conclusively delineated their character or their relationship to cervical neoplasia. Marked cytological changes may be present well in advance of conclusive histological changes and these first cytological deviations from normal to premalignancy are frequently characterized by the cell's DNA-RNA content and their distribution within the cell.

The theory of DNA and RNA production in cells is based upon the fact that there are two kinds of nucleic

acids in the cell: DNA, deoxyribonucleic acid — the essential component in the genes and chromosomes of the nucleus;
and RNA, ribonucleic acid — which is localized chiefly in
the cytoplasm and nucleolus. It is well known that rapidly
growing, regenerating, embryonic and secreting cells, having
high protein synthesis, are rich in cytoplasmic RNA which
is intimately connected with protein synthesis and cell
growth. Malignant cells fall into this same group since
they are rapidly growing cells and they exhibit a charac-
teristically high rate of proliferation. Full understanding of DNA content of single cells can contribute valuable
information to the understanding of the pathogenesis of
cervical neoplasia.

The Bertalanffy method has made a significant contribution to scientific knowledge of human cells in clinical
cytology in both the diagnostic and research areas. Distinctive cytochemical characteristics may be clearly visualized permitting comparison between normal, inflammatory
and premalignant cells in contrast to fully developed
cancer cells.

A close cellular relative to cancer *in situ* was
described by the author in 1947 as the "precancer cell
complex" and in 1953 Papanicolaou described this premalignant cellular phase as "dyskaryosis." Cell studies
have revealed this phase to be a precursor to cancer *in
situ*. One of the most intriguing components of the precancer cell complex is the halo cell, considered by some
to be a virus manifestation [3, 4]. Some researchers
have considered this controversial cell entity an arti-
fact, others a traumatic "torn membrane", and Koss [5] has
named it "koilocytotic atypia."

It was not until von Bertalanffy's acridine orange
technique was explored by Hillemanns and LeGuerrier that
the true nature of this enigmatic cell was demonstrated.
Of inestimable value was their discovery that the trans-
lucent zone surrounding the enlarged, hyperactive, sometimes anaplastic nucleus, rather than being "an empty
space" as described by Dr. Papanicolaou, was actually
filled with RNA, concentrated around the nucleus and fading
out towards the periphery. Equally significant was the
nuclear DNA concentration, still less, but approaching
that observed in cells of carcinoma *in situ*. It must therefore be concluded that this halo cell is a genuine member

of the neoplastic family [6]. Long-term cell behavior
studies, parallel with cytochemical changes, reveal in its
altered morphology the ultimate fate of the halo cell . . .
progression to full blown dysplasia and siappearance of
halo, as lesion merges with carcinoma *in situ*. Truly a
substantial contribution to scientific knowledge of the
genesis of cervical cancer cells!

We have experimented with many staining techniques
in undertaking various research studies of the comparative
DNA-RNA level in cells extending through the various stages
of neoplastic development. While the Papanicolaou staining
technique has proved to be the most widely used cytologic
stain for cell morphology and screening for early carcinoma,
the search continues for a stain which will selectively
identify malignant cells on the basis of a staining reaction.
The acridine orange stain pioneered and widely advocated
for use by Felix D. Bertalanffy has been subjected to considerable testing to ascertain its degree of practicability
in diagnostic screening of cervical cancer.

I would like to report on our research studies of DNA
and RNA findings in developing carcinoma and premalignant
cells of the human cervix using the von Bertalanffy technique with our own modifications. We have concentrated our
acridine orange studies on the comparative DNA-RNA levels
in cells extending through normal, inflammatory, the "halo"
cell stage, cells of dyskaryotic type, carcinoma *in situ*,
and, finally, invasive carcinoma.

RNA, which is localized chiefly in the cytoplasm and
nucleolus, is a requisite for protein synthesis, thus the
RNA content often is an expression of the degree of protein
metabolism of cells (such as rapidly growing regenerating
secreting cells, embryonic cells, etc.). Evidence of the
relative levels of each is of considerable importance in
relation to proliferative activity, both in benign conditions including regeneration as well as in malignancy.
Under precise technical preconditions, our fluorescent
studies have shown complete agreement with the results of
Bertalanffy and have been applied effectively for quantitative estimation of cells utilizing the author's graduation [7] of steps or stages in cervical cancer development from normal through precancerous through carcinoma
in situ. With increasing grades of malignancy, we observe
an increasing AO reaction of both cytoplasm and nucleus.

Most of the normal cells encountered in smears are highly differentiated squamous cells and show a transparent greenish-blue cytoplasm with a light yellow nucleus; the endocervical cells encountered show a brownish-red cytoplasm.

Pathologic conditions, such as inflammation, chronic irritation, and endocervical erosion cause proliferation of some benign cells. Such cells are often present in greatly increased numbers in exfoliated specimens. Because of their faster proliferation they contain more RNA and with the AO technique show some increased cytoplasmic fluorescence.

Our Grade I-B hyperplasia with anaplastic tendencies, show an increased RNA cytoplasmic fluorescence of a more pinkish hue.

The tissue harboring the halo cells revealed, in the basal and parabasal layers, the characteristic increased activity with red cytoplasm and bright yellow nucleus. Pre-halo and deeper halo cells show the same cytoplasmic and nuclear activity. The final perinuclear halo itself is consistent with expectations — RNA positive fluorescence in greatest concentration immediately surrounding the intense nuclear DNA. We interpret the RNA positivity as indicative of active proliferating cells.

The Grade II-B, maximal precancer cell complex, or maximal dysplasia, showed increased RNA cytoplasmic activity as a more orange-red color. Also, of course, the nuclear picture is changing — a deeper yellowish nucleus and the morphological characteristics of this Grade are evident.

In the Grade III-A, carcinoma *in situ*, we found the consistent RNA cytoplasmic picture of flaming red to orange-red with a more compact deeper yellow nucleus. Unusual morphological detail is present in the pictures of carcinoma *in situ* from one of our cases.

Grade III-C, cancer, showed the orange-red cytoplasm intense, and the golden-yellow nucleus. It is interesting to note the persistence of the multiple red nucleoli in the nuclei of the degenerating cancer cell.

Active cells are distinguished from suspicious and malignant elements by their morphology. With routine exfoliative material, only a small proportion of specimens contain active cells. However, their occurrence is a reason why a diagnosis of malignancy cannot be established on the basis of increased cytoplasmic fluorescence alone. In the final evaluation of malignancy, cell morphology has to be a deciding factor. We did, however, find a persistent correlation between the degree of RNA cytoplasmic fluorescence and the Ayre gradation system. Tissue culture of human embryonic cells show a rich homogenous RNA cytoplasmic fluorescence with the DNA of a benign type.

Morphology and cytochemistry of cells together represent the best scientific methods available to predict the biological behavior and fate of neoplastic tumors. The introduction by von Bertalanffy of acridine orange fluorescence microscopy opened up new avenues of discovery in tumor cell development. Morphology alone fell short of defining the biological nature of the premalignant cell which resembled both the normal and the malignant in some respects. But the demonstration of the DNA-RNA manifestations in the premalignant halo cell presented strong evidence that even in this embryonic cellular stage we were dealing with a beginning neoplasm.

Very rarely, in the history of science, has such philosophical talent been brought to bear on practical aspects of science (such as the diagnosis, origin, behavior and cure of cancer) as that of Ludwig von Bertalanffy.

REFERENCES AND FOOTNOTES

1. GAUSE, G.F., *Microbial Models of Cancer Cells*, W.B. Saunders Co., Phila., 1966.

2. AYRE, J.E., "Selective Cytology Smear for Diagnosis of Cancer", *Am. J. Obst. & Gyn.*, *53:4*, 609-617, April, 1947.

3. AYRE, J.E., "Role of the Halo Cell in Cervical Cancer-genesis", *Obst. & Gyn.*, *15:4*, 481-491, April, 1960.

4. DeGIROLAMI, E., "Perinuclear Halo Versus Koilocytotic
    Atypia", *Obst. & Gyn.*, *29:4*, 479–487, April, 1967.

5. KOSS, L., *Diagnostic Cytology*, W.B. Saunders Co.,
    Phila., 1961.

6. AYRE, J.E., *New Horizons in Cancer Through Cytology*,
    N.Y. State J. Medicine, *63:3*, 426–434, February, 1963.

7. AYRE, J.E., *Cancer Cytology of the Uterus*, Grune &
    Stratton, New York, 1951.

BERTALANFFY METHOD IN PATHOLOGY OF UTERINE, ENDOMETRIAL, AND BREAST TISSUES

CARLOS M.L. LUCENA, ANTONIO ROGANTI, ALFREDO R. DARIN,
ROBERTO G. COLES and ROBERTO E. DENIS

Department of Gynecology, Hospital Pirovano, Buenos Aires, Argentina

INTRODUCTION

Our experience with the acridine orange fluorescence method began in 1962, when we became aware of the technique from an article by Dr. Felix Bertalanffy.

It appeared to us of value to investigate the potentialities of that method since it seemed to be simple, rapid and efficient for the early detection of gynecological cancers. Subsequently, we routinely applied this method to all exfoliative materials from patients referred to the Cervical Pathology Service in the Department of Gynecology at the Hospital Pirovano in the city of Buenos Aires, Argentina.

The equipment employed at the beginning was rather modest, composed of a high pressure Philips mercury lamp (HPW 125w.) with the correspondent ballast or coil of reactants. We placed the lamp inside a vertical metallic cylinder lined with an aluminum sheet in order to obtain a high co-efficient of reflection. Between the radiation source and the microscopic mirror we placed a Wood's glass selector to absorb light radiations and ultraviolet shortwaves, permitting passage only of the long ultraviolet waves in the range of 3,650 U.A. A protective yellow

Ray-Ban filter was used in the ocular of the microscopic to neutralize any harmful ultraviolet radiations. The heat generated by this equipment was controlled by an ordinary oscillating fan. Microphotographs with this makeshift equipment required exposure times of 5 to 7 minutes.

We wish to express at this time our appreciation to Dr. Ludwig von Bertalanffy and Dr. Felix D. Bertalanffy who with their advice and collaboration made our work possible. The latter contributed further to demonstrate the accuracy of the acridine orange fluorescence method.

At the outset we conducted a double blind study by employing both the Bertalanffy and the Papanicolaou techniques. The initial results yielded a high percentage of false positive diagnosis with the former method, because of our emphasis on the cytochemical aspect with disregard to the morphological features. However, as our experience increased, and with additional data received from Dr. Bertalanffy, we were able to correct our criteria, relying more also on the morphological characteristics, as this is necessary with the Papanicolaou technique.

Since 1969 we employed a more sophisticated equipment using a Laborlux apparatus with an Osram radiation lamp, HBO 200w. It allowed for a better visualization of the smears and photomicrography.

The smears were classified in accordance with the system by Bertalanffy, Masin and Masin as follows:

Class I

Negative.
Absence of abnormal cells. Morphology and fluorescence normal.

Class II

Negative.
Atypical nonmalignant cells.
1) Cells with normal cytoplasmatic fluorescence and morphology.
2) Cells with normal cytoplasmatic fluorescence, nuclear fluorescence increased, and normal morphology.
3) Cells with normal cytoplasmatic and nuclear fluorescence, but moderate atypical morphology.

Class III

Not conclusive (markedly atypical cells).
1) Cells with markedly increased cytoplasmatic fluorescence, and prominent nucleolus.
2) Markedly atypical cells with increased nuclear fluorescence.

Class IV

Malignancy suspected.
1) Atypical cells with abnormal cytoplasmatic fluorescence.
2) Atypical cells with abnormal nuclear fluorescence (coarse chromatin and prominent nucleoli).

Class V

Malignant.
1) Cells with markedly abnormal cytoplasmatic and/or nuclear fluorescence. Unquestionable malignant morphology.

For practical purposes we grouped the smears as follows:

Negative	Class I and II
Questionable	Class III
Positive	Class IV and V

PRACTICAL APPLICATIONS OF THE ACRIDINE ORANGE METHOD

The acridine orange fluorescence procedure can be applied as a prescreening system, and later on, after more careful observation, as a definitive screening method. The prescreening consists of carefully examining the smears to detect cells with abnormal fluorescence.

In the typical routine smear the major proportion of the material consists of cells with cytoplasmatic fluorescence varying in color from greenish brown to dark reddish brown. The leukocyte nuclei appear green. A bright red or orange cytoplasmatic fluorescence constitutes a "danger signal" requiring a more exhaustive examination by personnel trained in the field of cytology. This second aspect of the procedure, which we call "screening", requires the consideration of the morphological criteria of the suspicious cells as well, to arrive at a final diagnosis.

Complete lysis of malignant cells might cause a lack of the "danger signal" because of the greatly diminished cytoplasm, naked nuclei with atypical morphology but over-looked during the prescreening phase. Yet, smears contain-ing nuclei without cytoplasm are rare and encountered only in exfoliated material from advanced stages of radio ther-apy.

ADVANTAGES OF THE FLUORESCENCE METHOD

1) It is expedient especially in the prescreening phase, saving time and sparing the trained cytologist.

2) The prescreening can be performed by any physician who will refer to the cytologist for final diagnosis only those smears exhibiting abnormal fluorescence.

3) A single dye, used in a simple and practical technique, yielding a clear polychromatic picture.

4) The staining process is much more rapid than with other techniques. A smear can be ready for diagnosis in approximately 10 minutes, even while the patient is still waiting in the office.

5) The smear can be bleached (acridine orange removed) by immersion in 50% ethyl alcohol, and can be restained with any other histological technique.

6) Hemorrhagic smears do not interfere with this technique, because the red cells do not appear with fluorescence microscopy.

7) At the same time, this method introduces a new concept of cell pathology. It emphasized the cytochemical cyto-plasmatic criteria which are an expression of the en-hanced protein metabolism in malignant cells, and induce the morphological changes of the cells.

DISADVANTAGES OF THE METHOD

1) Cell fluorescence disappears rather rapidly. Presently we are testing a frozen technique to preserve fluorescence.

2) The technique requires special equipment, and the acridine orange stained smears cannot be stored for further reference.

3) There is some difficulty in differentiating by fluorescence intensity alone the so-called "active cells" engaged in rapid protein synthesis (basal cells, glandular cells, "inflammatory cells"), from malignant cells.

4) The more minute details of cellular morphology are somewhat less apparent than with purely morphological conventional methods.

OUR EXPERIENCE WITH THE FLUORESCENCE METHOD

This study was conducted at the Department of Cervival Pathology using the following approaches:

1) Staining of vaginal discharge with 1% toluene solution to determine the poassible presence of trichomonas or moniliasis.

2) Smears of exfoliative material from both the exo- and endocervix were prepared, our Service using the method of Bertalanffy, and the Department of Pathological Anatomy using the conventional Papanicolaou technique.

3) Colposcopy was employed after application to the cervix of a 3% solution of acetic acid; following the Schiller's test was performed.

According to the Azocar Espin classification, the colposcopic findings were grouped as follows:

Group I

Cervicitis, erosion, atypical vascularization, normal transitional cells.

Group II

Leukoplakia, "thickened patch", mosaic, papillar base,
polyps, atypical vascularization.

Group III

Combined findings of two or more of the above mentioned
lesions.

Group IV

Exophitosis, granulomatosis, necrosis, markedly atypical
vascularization.

4) If the diagnosis so indicated, we followed up with
   biopsy or conization of the cervix.

   The types of abnormal cells occurring in cytosmears
   originated from the following types of epithelia,
   altered according to the severity of the condition:

HISTOPATHOLOGIC CLASSIFICATION OF EPITHELIAL CELLS OF THE
UTERINE CERVIX (Dr. R. Sanmartino)

1) Slight Dysplasia

   Exocervix
   a) Aglucogenic epithelium
   b) Regenerative epithelium
   c) Simple hypertrophy

   Endocervix
   a) Amucigenous epithelium
   b) Regenerative epithelium
   c) Glandular hypertrophy

2) Moderate Dysplasia

   Exocervix
   a) Hyperplasia of the basal cells
   b) Hyperkeratosis
   c) Parakeratosis

Endocervix
a) Hyperplasia of epithelial cells
b) Metaplasia stratified squamous cells
c) Metaplasia of endosalpingoid cells

3) Marked Dysplasia

   a) Atypical hyperplasia of the basal cells.
   b) Transitional type of epithelium

4) Carcinoma *in situ*

5) Initial invasive carcinoma

6) Microcarcinoma

7) Macrocarcinoma or Invasive Carcinoma

Between January 1963 and July 31, 1970, cytological examinations on 2,320 patients were performed, all of whom had exhibited some evidence of cervical pathology during the routine gynecological examination. The cytodiagnoses of that patient material were as follows:

BERTALANFFY METHOD   PAPANICOLAOU METHOD

Class	Cases No.	%	Class	Cases No.	%
I-II	2038	87.8	I-II	2131	91.9
III	195	8.4	III	122	5.3
IV-V	87	3.8	IV-V	67	2.8
Diagnoses			*Diagnoses*		
False positive	13	0.56	False positive	3	0.12
False negative	4	0.17	False negative	3	0.12

DISTRIBUTION BY AGE

Class	Method	20-29	30-39	40-49	50-59	60-69	70	Total	%
I-II	Bert.	427	638	613	246	84	30	2,038	87.8
	Pap.	428	669	652	262	88	32	2,131	91.9
III	Bert.	16	50	68	41	13	7	195	8.4
	Pap.	12	27	36	26	12	9	122	5.3
IV-V	Bert.	4	19	22	20	13	9	87	3.8
	Pap.	4	14	14	18	10	7	67	2.8

CARCINOMAS (CONFIRMED HISTOLOGICALLY BY BIOPSY): *74* (3.19%)

Distribution of the histodiagnoses of the 74 carcinomas related to the Bertalanffy and Papanicolaou methods.

C A R C I N O M A

	in situ	initial invasive	invasive
BERTALANFFY			
I-II	1	1	2
III	1	1	
IV-V	4	3	61
	6	5	63
PAPANICOLAOU			
I-II	0	1	2
III	2	1	5
IV-V	4	3	56
	6	5	63
2.320%	0.26%	0.22%	2.71%

Overall Distribution of Cytodiagnoses by Both Methods

YEAR	CARCINOMAS	GROUP III	GROUP IV-V	FALSE POSITIVE	FALSE NEGATIVE
BERTALANFFY					
1963-67	42	2	52	12	0
1968	8	0	8	0	0
1969	11	0	10	1	2
1970 (31-7-70)	13	0	11	0	2
	74	2	81	13	4
PAPANICOLAOU					
1963-67	42	4	40	2	0
1968	8	1	7	0	0
1969	11	1	10	1	1
1970 (31-7-70)	13	2	9	0	2
	74	8	66	3	3

CASE HISTORIES OF PATIENTS WITH FALSE POSITIVE DIAGNOSES

1) Case #430 - Age 27. Bertalanffy positive, Papanicolaou positive.
   Colposcopy: Endocervical polyp. Erosion of cervical lip. Group II.
   Pathological Anatomy: Chronic polypoid endocervicitis.

2) Case #436 - Age 35. Bertalanffy positive, Papanicolaou questionable.
   Colposcopy: Erosion of cervical lip. Large areas of cellular transformation. Group I.
   Pathological Anatomy: Chronic endocervicitis with areas of suppuration.

3) Case #652 - Age 31. Bertalanffy positive, Papanicolaou questionable.
   Colposcopy: Erosion of cervical lip. Atypical vascular formation at 6 o'clock. Group II.
   Histopathology: Chronic cervicities. Acanthosis.

4) Case #685 - Age 50. Bertalanffy positive, Papanicolaou questionable.
   Colposcopy: Endocervical polyp. Group II.
   Histopathology: Chronic polypoid endocervicitis.

5) Case #891 - Age 44. Bertalanffy positive, Papanicolaou questionable.
   Colposcopy: Endocervical polyp. Group II.
   Histopathology: Chronic endo- and ectocervicitis.

6) Case #1035 - Age 80. Bertalanffy positive, Papanicolaou questionable.
   Colposcopy: Erosion of cervical lips. Exophitosis on posterior lip. Group IV.
   Histopathology: 1st biopsy: Chronic endo- and ectocervicitis.   2nd biopsy: Acanthoparakeratosis with ulcerated and necrotic areas.

7) Case #809 - Age 44. Bertalanffy positive, Papanicolaou questionable.
   Colposcopy: Erosion of cervical lips. Atypical vascular formation at 3 o'clock.
   Histopathology: Chronic endo- and ectocervicitis with vascularization of epithelium.

8) Case #824 - Age 50. Bertalanffy positive, Papanicolaou questionable.
   Colposcopy: Erosion of posterior lip with erosion and atypical vascular formation. Group III.
   Histopathology: Cystic endocervicitis.

9) Case #1237 - Age 39. Bertalanffy positive, Papanicolaou questionable.
   Colposcopy: Area of cellular transformation on cervical lips. Atypical vascular formation at 5 o'clock. Group II.
   Histopathology: Exocervical acanthosis with areas of moderate dysplasia.

10) Case #1280 - Age 42. Bertalanffy positive, Papanicolaou questionable.
    Colposcopy: Atypical vascularization at 3 o'clock. Group II.
    Histopathology: Chronic external cervicitis with areas of moderate dysplasia.

11) Case #1306 - age 68. Bertalanffy positive, Papanicolaou questionable.
    Colposcopy: Endocervical polyp. Group II.
    Histopathology: Adenomatous polyp.

12) Case #1500 - Age 48. Bertalanffy positive. Papanicolaou questionable.
    Colposcopy: Atypical vascular formation at 2 and 7 o'clock. Group II.
    Histopathology: Cystic endocervicitis.

13) Case #2330 - Age 34. Bertalanffy positive, Papanicolaou questionable.
    Colposcopy: Area of cellular transformation around external os. Atypical vascular formation at 11 o'clock. Group II.
    Histopathology: Chronic ecto- and endocervicitis. Leukoparakeratosis.

CASE HISTORIES OF PATIENTS WITH FALSE NEGATIVE DIAGNOSES

1) Case #2595 - Bertalanffy negative, Papanicolaou negative.
   Colposcopy: Not performed.
   Histopathology: Epidermoid carcinoma and adenocarcinoma
   of endometrium.

2) Case #2604 - Bertalanffy negative, Papanicolaou nega-
   tive.
   Colposcopy: Area of cellular transformation around
   external os. Atypical vascular formation at 12 o'clock.
   Group III.
   Histopathology: Carcinoma *in situ*.

3) Case #2655 - Bertalanffy negative, Papanicolaou
   questionable.
   Colposcopy: Exophitosis. Group IV.
   Histopathology: Infiltrating epidermoid carcinoma.

4) Case #2906 - Bertalanffy negative, Papanicolaou negative.
   Colposcopy: Area of cellular transformation and atypical vascular formation at 1 and 10 o'clock. Group II.
   Histopathology: Epidermoid carcinoma originating from
   endocervical glandular metaplasia, invading the stroma.

We performed colposcopic examinations on 1,180
patients (50.8% of the total), and of this group from 288
patients (24.4%) biopsies were also collected. Carcinomas
were diagnosed in 47 (16.3%) of the cases. For various
reasons the remaining patients had no colposcopy examination.

Between 1963 and 1968, cytological and colposcopical
examinations were performed on 567 patients. 200 biopsies
(35.2%) were collected of which in 25 cases (12.5%) evidence of malignancy were apparent.

From 1969 to July 31, 1970, a total of 613 patients
were examined. Biopsies were collected from 88 (14.3%) of
them, with 22 (25%) manifesting evidence of malignancy.

The observations of the studies compparing between
the cytological diagnoses and colposcopy are as follows:

| | Colposcopy | | | | Total |
BERTALANFFY	I	II	III	IV	
Negative	603	400	43	3	1,049
Questionable	17	51	15	3	86
Positive	1	9	6	29	45
					1,180

| | I | II | III | IV | |
PAPANICOLAOU					
Negative	605	399	46	3	1,053
Questionable	15	54	12	6	87
Positive	1	7	6	26	40
					1,180

The following table correlates histopathological diagnoses of the 288 biopsies with the corresponding colposcopic observations:

| | Colposcopy | | | | Total |
	I	II	III	IV	
Dysplasia (slight to moderate)	30	168	35	3	236
Marked dysplasia	0	1	3	0	4
Carcinoma *in situ*	0	3	3	0	6
Initial invasive carc.	0	2	1	2	5
Invasive carc.	0	1	10	25	36
					287

One remaining case was affected with tuberculosis of the uterine cervix.

The principles aim of the present study was the early detection of gynecological cancers. The following table presents the diagnoses achieved with cytodiagnosis and colposcopy of those cases where the subsequent histopathological examination revealed severe dysplasia, carcinoma *in situ*, or carcinoma with initial invasion of the connective tissue stroma.

| Biopsy No. | Cytodiagnosis | | Colposcopy |
	Bert.	Pap.	Group
Marked dysplasia			
1427	II	II	III Basal mosaic
3468	III	III	II Leukoplasia in cervical lips
10937	III	III	III Atypical vascularization, cervical erosion
15943	III	III	III Basal leukoplastic mosaic, atypical vascularization

Biopsy No.	Cytodiagnosis		Colposcopy
	Bert.	Pap.	Group

Carcinoma in situ

3186	IV	IV	III Leukoplasia, atypical vascularization
3915	III	III	II Area of cellular transformation, atypical vascularization
6937	IV	IV	III Leukoplasia, atypical vascularization
7743	V	V	II Area of cellular transformation, leukoplasia
15571	IV	IV	II Area of cellular transformation with atypical vascularization
15849	II	III	III Basal atypical vascularization

Initial invasive carcinoma

7386	IV	IV	III Basal atypical vascularization, cervical erosion
7581	III	III	II Area of cellular transformation with atypical vascularization
16059	IV	IV	IV Exophitis, atypical vascularization, basal cervical erosion

Biopsy No.	Cytodiagnosis		Colposcopy
	Bert.	Pap.	Group
16340	IV	IV	IV Exophitis, large area of leukoplasia around external os, basal at 6 and 12 o'clock
17138	II	II	II Area of cellular transformation with atypical vascularization

OBSERVATIONS WITH MATERIAL FROM BREAST TISSUE

In 150 cases of surgical removal of breast tumors, smears of the tissue excised were prepared to be studied by the method of Bertalanffy. Moreover, some material of the suspected tumor was prepared and stained according to the technique of Bertalanffy and Nagy. The diagnoses were as follows:

FROZEN SECTION BIOPSY		BERTALANFFY METHOD		SUBSEQUENT BIOPSY
Positive:	53	Positive:	51	Positive: 57
		Questionable:	3	
Negative:	65	Negative:	96	Negative: 93
	118		150	150

Frozen Section Biopsy: 1 false negative

Bertalanffy Method: 6 false negative
1 false positive

In 3 suspected cases hisopathology revelaed one to be a carcinoma and 2 dysplasia of breast tissue.

Summary of false negative diagnoses:

1) Case #188 - Age 56. Frozen section biopsy: Trabecular carcinoma; subsequent biopsy: same.

2) Case #293 - Age 57. Frozen section biopsy: Trabecular carcinoma; subsequent biopsy: same.

3) Case #296 - Age 62. Frozen section biopsy: Medullary carcinoma; subsequent biopsy: papillary adenocarcinoma secondary to sclerocystic mastopathy.

4) Case #327 - Age 43. Frozen section biopsy: not performed; subsequent biopsy: trabecular carcinoma.

5) Case #332 - Age 59. Frozen section biopsy: Intraductal carcinoma; subsequent biopsy: noninfiltrating intraductal carcinoma.

6) Case #286 - Age 44. Frozen section biopsy: Medullary carcinoma; subsequent biopsy: same.

Summary of false positive diagnoses:

Case #116: Post-surgical fistula following a radical mastectomy. Post-operative x-ray therapy administered.

Fistulectomy: Frozen section biopsy: not performed; subsequent biopsy: giant cell infiltration and inflammatory granuloma. Absence of neoplastic processes.

OBSERVATIONS WITH MATERIAL FROM ENDOMETRIUM

Exfoliated endometrial material was collected from 100 patients. The smears were fixed in alcohol and stained according to the technique of Bertalanffy and Nagy. The diagnoses were as follows:

Negative	Questionable	Positive	False Positive	False Negative
72	10	18	4	1

Malignancy confirmed histologically: 17 cases.

Of the 10 questionable cases, histopathological examination revealed two cases of adenocarcinoma.

Summary of false positive diagnoses:

Histopathological examination indicated 2 glandular-cystic hyperplasias, 1 endometrial proliferative phase, and 1 endometrial regression phase.

Summary of false negative diagnoses:

H. Cl. #8092 - Age 61. Biopsy:.Adenocarcinoma of endometrium.

DISTRIBUTION OF ENDOMETRIAL CASES BY AGE

Age	Negative	Questionable	Positive	False positive	False negative
30-39	1	0	0	0	0
40-49	31	2	2	2	0
50-59	27	3	5	2	0
60-69	7	2	7	0	1
70-79	6	3	4	0	0
	72	10	18	4	1

BIBLIOGRAPHY.

1. ARMSTRONG, J.A.,"Histochemical differentiation of nucleic acids by means of induced fluorescence." *Esp. Cell. Re.*, 11:640, 1956.

2. BENAIM, Victor Pinto and CABALLERO, Humberto,"Citologia ginecologica de fluorescencia. Metodo de Bertalanffy (1956)." *Acta cient. venez.*, *13*(2), 65-74, 1962.

3. BERTALANFFY, Felix D.,"Cytodiagnosis of cancer by acridine orange fluorescence microscopy." *Triangle*, *5*(3), 152-156, 1961.

4. BERTALANFFY, Felix D.,"Evaluation of the acridine orange fluorescence microscope method for cytodiagnosis of cancer." *Ann. N.Y. Acad. Sci.*, *93* (Art. 16), 715-750, 1962.

4a.   BERTALANFFY, Felix D. and NAGY, Katrina P.,"Fluor-
      escence microscopy and photo-micrography with acri-
      dine orange."*Med. Radiogr. Photogr., 38*, 82-91, 1962.

4b.   BERTALANFFY, Felix D. and NAGY, Katrina P.,"Acridina
      anaranjada en la microscopia y totomicrografia fluor-
      escentes."*Radiografia y fotografia clinicas, 29*, 2-11,
      1963.

5.   von BERTALANFFY, Ludwig,"The consultant."*Acta cytol.,
      8*(5), 377-380, 1964.

6.   von BERTALANFFY, Ludwig, Fluorescence microscopy of
      irradiated cells, *Acta cytol., 3*(3), 367, 1959.

7.   von BERTALANFFY, Ludwig, MASIN, F. and MASIN, M."Use
      of acridine orange fluorescence technique in exfoli-
      ative cytology."*Science,124* (3230), 1024-1025, 1956.

8.   FRIEDMAN, H.P.,"The use of ultraviolet light and
      fluorescent dyes in detection of uterine cancer
      vaginal smear."*Am. J. Obst. and Gyn.,* 59:852, 1950.

9.   LUCENA, Carlos M. et al.,"Citodiagnostico por micro-
      scopia de fluorescencia en la patologia del endo-
      metrio."Primer Congreso Argentino-Paraguayo de Can-
      cerologia, 1969.

10.   LUCENA, Carlos M. et al.,"Evaluacion de Metodos de
      diagnostico in Patologia Cervical."V Reunion Anual
      de la Sociedad Argentina de Patologia Cervical, 1969.

11.   LUCENA, Carlos M. et al.,"Citodiagnostico por micro-
      scopia de fluorescencia en patologia mamaria."Primer
      Congreso Argentino-Paraguayo de Cancerologia, 1969.

12.   ROGANTI, A., LUCENA, Carlos M. and COLES, R.,"Fluoro-
      microscopia en el cito diagnostico ginecologico.",
      Rev. Soc. Obst. y Gin. de Buenos Aires, 582:29, 1963.

A FLUORESCENCE MICROSCOPY METHOD OF CYTOLOGIC STUDY OF RECTAL SMEARS AS A SCREENING TECHNIQUE FOR CARCINOMA OF THE LARGE BOWEL

T.C. ARMINSKI
Fisher Building, 23077 Greenfield Rd., Southfield, Mich. 48075, U.S.A.

In a survey of approximately 500 specimens of carcinoma of the colon and rectum resected at The Grace Hospital, Detroit, Michigan, during a recent five-year period, 85 per cent of the lesions were over 4 cm in diameter and 87 per cent extended deep into or through the bowel wall. Thus, with our present method of case finding which is based on the patient's evaluation of their symptoms, malignant lesions of the large bowel at the time of treatment are usually in an advanced stage; that is, they are not small, they extend deep into or through the bowel wall, and they often show lymph or blood stream invasion. Some have contended that the signs and symptoms of colonic carcinoma make themselves apparent early in the course of the disease. Obviously, this is not so. Not only do the signs and symptoms manifest themselves late in the disease, but often there are delays by patients in seeking the cause of their symptoms. In addition, there are, at times, delays by physicians in carrying out those procedures which may readily establish the diagnosis.

The techniques, extent, and adjuvants of surgery of carcinoma of the large bowel have been so perfected that further improvement in the cure rate cannot be expected without earlier diagnosis. The refinements in the techniques and the development of certain adjuvants are

are most significant when dealing with lesions corresponding to those of Groups A and B of Duke's classification.
These same techniques and adjuvants become inconsequential
when applied to more advanced lesions corresponding to
those of Group C of Duke's classification. It is quite
apparent that if we continue to depend on the patient to
come in for examination because of symptoms, little improvement in the cure rate of carcinoma of the large bowel is
possible. Our ultimate goal should be to find those individuals who are asymptomatic, but harbor lesions; or to
identify those without lesions who are potential devel-
opers of carcinoma.

Generally quoted are the statistics that the incidence of carcinoma of the large bowel is 34 and the mortality 25 per 100,000 adults, and that it ranks first in
incidence among malignancies of an individual organ. To
diagnose this large number of lesions, the clinician has
at his disposal various procedures. First, the value of
the digital examination cannot be over-emphasized. It is
easily carried out and should be a part of every physical
examination. Anoscopic, proctoscopic and sigmoidoscopic
examinations, done as a part of a routine physical examination, often detect asymptomatic tumors. Fiberoptic
colonoscopic examinations go a step beyond the sigmoido-
scope. The barium enema examinations with their various
modifications are able to identify small defects surprisingly early. Cytologic studies of colonic washings,
plastic mold enemas and isotopic studies are other methods
useful in uncovering early tumors, but all of these techniques, as useful as they are, do not fulfill the requirements of a good, rapid screening method.

Richart, studying pre-cancerous changes manifested by
cells of smears of the cervix, observed that long before
the development of carcinoma, there were cells showing
evidences of dysplasia. In his investigations, a follow-
up of six years of 500 women with cervical cellular dysplasia showed a progression to carcinoma *in situ* in about
25 per cent. It was his impression that dysplasia occurring in the early years is definitely a precursor to invasive cancer. Nieburgs, in his study of women with cellular dysplasia, found that about one-third progressed to
carcinoma *in situ*, and another one-third progressed
through carcinoma *in situ* to invasive carcinoma. Bell and
co-workers, studying cell growth using tritiated thymidine,

found that in adenomas, cell proliferation occurred on
the surface of the mucosa as well as in the deeper portions
or at the base of the glands. They also reported finding
these same abnormalities in the adjacent mucosa despite
the fact that the mucosa was of normal histologic appearance. In a study of 100 specimens of resected carcinoma
of the large bowel, we found mucosal changes in the form
of adenomas, hyperplasias, and mucosal excrescences in
about 75 per cent. With these observations as a basis, we
designed a study to determine the possibility of identifying abnormal cells in scrapings of the rectal mucosa
associated with large bowel malignancy utilizing some form
of rapid cytologic screening method.

Various investigators have studied the feasibility
of identifying carcinoma of the large bowel by cytologic
studies (Table 1). The majority were done by utilizing a
technique by which the cells were obtained by colonic
lavage or washings. Some used smears of the mucosa or the
lesion itself. One utilized the silicone foam enemas
from which the exfoliated cells were washed and studied.
While the reported results are quite good, cytologic
studies of the large bowel have never become popular or
widely used. Raskin considers exfoliative cytology a useful technique in the diagnosis of malignant lesions of
the large bowel, but feels that apathy on the part of the
clinician and cytologist preclude its wide use.

An adequate and acceptable screening procedure must
fulfill certain basic requirements. It must be simple,
requiring a minimum of effort by the examiner, and no
effort or morbidity by the patient. The technique of
preserving, staining and examining specimens must be
simple, with a minimum of cost. Finally, the accuracy
index must be fairly high. Since carcinoma of the large
bowel occurs in about one per 2200 adults, any exhaustive
or complicated procedure of case finding is entirely
prohibitive in time and expense. A method whereby one
might reduce by 90 to 95 per cent the number of individuals
to be studied more completely would certainly be useful.
Thus, if one could, by some simple, rapid technique,
reduce the number from 2000 to 100 or 50 to be studied
more extensively, it would be advantageous.

PRESENT STUDY

One thousand patients from our practice have been
utilized in this study. The patients were seen for various large bowel and anorectal complaints generally present in a proctologic practice. The study was carried out
strictly on a double-blind basis. The specimens were
taken and smears made and later numbered at random by the
technician. The technician kept a record of the slide
number and corresponding patient. One of us (TCA) examined every slide in a similar manner with no knowledge as
to the source of the specimen. The cytologic examination
consisted of scanning across the slide four times, which
required no longer than 30 seconds. The slide number was
recorded and the cytologic interpretation was designated
as either normal or atypical. One technique of staining
was used on one day and another the next day, so that both
slides of any given patient were never examined on the
same day.

Various methods of cytologic study of rectal smears
are available, particularly the Papanicolaou, Leishman,
and acridine-orange methods. Prior to selecting any particular method, extensive studies were done for several
years utilizing the various staining techniques as well
as the various acridine orange modifications of the
original technique by Bertalanffy. After extensive trials
using the various modifications of the acridine-orange
method, it was decided to use the method as described by
Bertalanffy and a method which we employed using a weak
acridine-orange solution without the use of buffers. The
acridine-orange technique seems more suitable to use with
rectal smears than the Papanicolaou method. It is quicker
and the scanning can be done more rapidly since most of
the non-mucosal structures do not stain orange and can be
easily overlooked.

At the original examination, two slides were made
of scrapings of the rectal mucosa. These were made with
the handle-end of a wooden Ayre cervical biopsy stick
through an anoscope. Preparation of the patient consisted
simply of an enema prior to the examination. The material
on the slides was air-dried and then fixed in a 50 per
cent alcohol-ether mixture for about two hours. After
fixing the slides were stored until staining and scanning.

TABLE 1. Results of Cytologic Studies of the Large Bowel

Authors	Technique	Number of cases	Number benign	Per cent accuracy	Number malignant	Per cent accuracy
Wisseman, et al., 1949	Smear at sigmoidoscopy	110	87	95.0	28	57.0
Blank and Steinberg, 1951	Smears of lesion	66	21	100	29	64.0
	smears below lesion	21	2	100	19	5.4
Bader and Papanicolaou, 1952	Rectal washings through sigmoidoscope	200	161	98.0	14	73.7
Rubin, et al. 1953	Colonic lavage	55	22	100	33	81.0
Galambos and Klayman, 1955	Colonic lavage Method 1	58	32	100	9	22.0
	Method 2				17	82.0

TABLE 1. continued

Raskin, et al., 1958	Colonic lavage	122	97	100	25	84.0
Burn and Sellwood, 1962	Colonic lavage	50	27	96.9	19	82.5
Knoernschild and Cameron, 1963	Mucosal swab					
	visualized carcinoma	132			104	78.0
	non-visualized ca.	96			5	5.0
	normal	14,731	14,719	99.94		
Spjut, et al., 1963	Cells from silicone foam enema	40	21	90.5	19	80.0
Vacca, et al., 1968	Colonic lavage	140	120	96.6	20	80.0

Specimens were obtained until 1000 patients with adequate smears were studied. Those not having two adequate
slides were deleted. Smears were primarily inadequate
because of the lack of cellular material, the presence of
large amounts of blood, fecal matter, lubricating jelly,
or mucus on the slide which appeared to interfere with
proper fixation.

The acridine-orange staining method gives good cell
detail, but there is no actually definitive separation of
normal from abnormal cells. Normal mucosal cells generally are dark orange to brown, but young, rapidly proliferating cells may fluoresce brilliant orange. Atypical
or abnormal cells may not always fluoresce bright orange.
The decision as to whether a cell is normal or abnormal
was not based on its staining intensity, but rather on
its configuration. This is in accord with the opinions
expressed by Stevenson and von Hamm, von Bertalanffy,
and Grubb. We went one step further, making it our policy
not to judge isolated cells, but to evaluate the smear
on the appearance of clumps of cells. Normal mucosal
cells are generally arranged in a uniform-appearing architecture, with some forming normal-appearing glands. The
nucleus is small with an abundance of cytoplasm. The
nuclei are uniform in size from cell to cell in the clump.
Atypical cells are usually clumped together in a hap-
hazard manner. The clumps are usually smaller than those
of normal cells. The nuclei are enlarged, and they vary
in size. The amount of cytoplasm is definitely reduced,
and the nucleolus is enlarged and quite distinct.

After a smear was scanned, it was designated as
either normal or abnormal. If both smears of any given
patient were designated as abnormal, we arbitrarily called
these patients positive. In the series, there were 22
patients with subsequently clinically proven carcinoma
of the colon or rectum. Seventy-five per cent of the 22
patients with adeno carcinoma were found to show atypical
cells on both smears, each scanned on a different day.
In this group reported as positive, two had carcinoma of
the cecum and the remainder had carcinoma of the left
colon or rectum. Three patients with clinically proven
carcinoma had only one positive slide. Of these, all
lesions were in the left colon. Two patients with carcinoma
of the cecum had both slides reported as negative (Table 2).

TABLE 2. Cytologic Findings in Rectal Smears of 22 Patients
with Subsequently Proven Cacinoma of the Colon and Rectum

Both Slides Positive	17	77.3 per cent
One Slide Positive	3	13.6 per cent
Both Slides Negative	2	9.1 per cent

Fifty-five patients (5.7%) were reported to have
atypical cells on both slides, but clinically, by sig-
moidoscopy and barium enema examination, showed no
carcinoma. Ninety patients were reported as having
atypical cells only on the first slide stained by
Bertalanffy's method, and 109 had atypical cells only
on the second slide stained by our method. Seven hundred and twenty-four (74.0%) of the patients without
clinical carcinoma had both smears reported negative
(Table 3).

TABLE 3. Cytologic Findings in Rectal Smears of 978
Patients with no Evidence of Carcinoma of Colon and
Rectum

Both Slides Negative	724	74.0 per cent
One Slide Negative	199	20.3 per cent
Both Slides Positive	55	5.7 per cent

Since the smears were not permanent, it was impossible
to review or restudy the material. In order to do this,
during the second half of this study, all positive findings
were photographed. The 450 micro-photographs thus obtained
were properly labeled and placed in projection trays in
no particular sequence for further review and restudy.
Among this group of 450 micro-photographs, there were 62
that were taken of smears from 18 patients with proven
carcinoma of the large bowel. After a careful review of
these photographs when they were mixed in with all of the
other slides, 48 or 80 per cent were classified as definitely abnormal. Fifteen carcinoma patients had two or
more micro-photographs taken of the rectal cells. In 14 of
these, the majority of photographs were interpreted as
being positive. Three carcinoma patients, each with only
one micro-photograph, were interpreted as negative. It
would appear that the false negatives are related to the
inadequate amount of material present for study.

In the group with no carcinoma, there were 388 micro-
photographs of cells considered to be atypical on scanning.
On careful, unlabeled, review of these photographs, 185
or about one-half were classified as definitely atypical.
Thus, it would indicate that after careful restudy, using
probably more rigid criteria and a more detailed evaluation, about one-half of the false positives may be eliminated.
As previously mentioned, 55 cancer-free patients
(5.7%) showed atypical cells in both smears. One third of
these were found to have polyps. Four had polyps over
1 cm. in diameter, but the majority had polyps under
5 mm. in size. This group of patients will be followed
closely to see if any subsequently develop carcinoma.

Fig.1(upper left). Case 128. Normal rectal mucosal cells
    stained with acridine orange and examined under ultra-
    violet light.
Fig.2(upper right). Case 175. Normal rectal mucosal cells.
Fig.3(center left). Case 98. Normal rectal mucosal cells
    fluorescing bright orange and filled with mucus.
Fig.4(center right). Case 362. Normal rectal mucosal cells
    undergoing degeneration with nuclear vacuolization.
Fig.5(lower left). Case 302. Normal highly fluorescent rectal
    mucosal cells in a patient with no evidence of carcinoma.
Fig.6(lower right). Case 346. Atypical highly orange
    fluorescent rectal mucosal cells in a patient with no
    evidence of carcinoma.

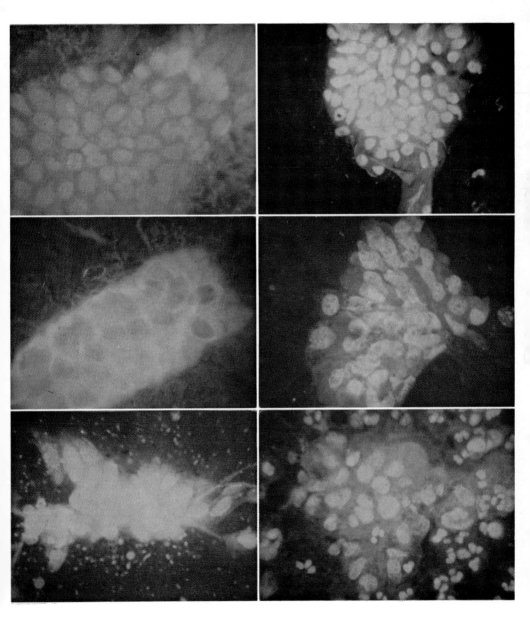

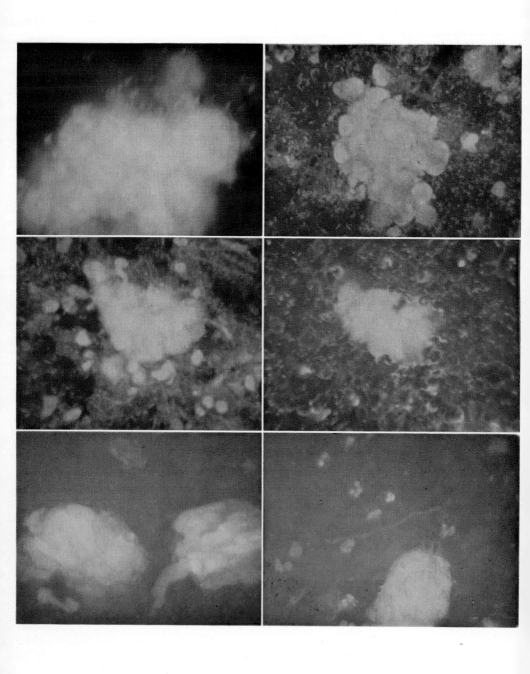

Fig.7 (upper left). Case 14. Atypical orange fluorescent
        rectal mucosal cells in a patient with carcinoma of the
        distal sigmoid.
Fig.8 (upper right). Case 597. Atypical rectal mucosal cells
        from a patient with carcinoma of the rectum.
Fig.9 (center left). Case 31. Atypical highly fluorescent
        rectal mucosal cells from a patient with carcinoma
        of the rectosigmoid.
Fig.10 (center right). Case 813. Atypical rectal mucosal cells
        from a patient with a malignant polyp of the rectum.
Fig.11(lower left). Case 438. Atypical orange fluorescent
        rectal mucosal cells from a patient with previously-
        resected carcinoma of the rectum.
Fig.12(lower right). Case 743. Atypical fluorescent rectal
        mucosal cells from a patient with a benign polyp of the
        proximal sigmoid.

DISCUSSION

Cytologic studies of cervical smears seem to indicate cellular changes present long before the clinical appearance of invasive carcinoma. This smear may be true in other sites. In our study, it is difficult to determine whether the atypical cells we have identified represented true carcinoma cells or atypical dysplastic changes. Further investigative studies will have to be carried out to determine this. The 55 individuals with two positive slides as well as those with one positive slide will be followed carefully to see if there is any increased tendency to form carcinoma of the large bowel. Studies of this particular nature should be carried on with particular cooperation between the cytologist and the clinician.

BIBLIOGRAPHY

ARMINSKI, T.C. and McLEAN, D.W., "Evaluation of Screening Methods for Carcinoma of the Large Bowel: Based on a Cytologic Study of Rectal Smears Using Fluorescence Microscopy". *Dis. Colon and Rectum*, 12, 399-405, 1969.

BADER, G.M. and PAPANICOLAOU, G.N., "The Application of Cytology in Diagnosis of Cancer of the Rectum, Sigmoid and Descending Colon". *Cancer*, 5, 307-314, 1952.

BELL, B., DESCHNER, E., ALMY, T.P. and LIPKIN, M., "Patterns of Cell Proliferation in Gastro-intestinal Disease". *Dis. Colon and Rectum*, 10, 107-111, 1967.

BERTALANFFY, F.D., "Cytodiagnosis of Cancer by Acridine Orange Fluorescence Microscopy". *Triangle*, 5, 152-156, 1961.

BERTALANFFY, F.D. and NAGY, K.P., "Fluorescence Microscopy and Photomicrography with Acridine Orange". *Med. Radiogr. Photogr.*, 82ff., 1962.

von BERTALANFFY, L., "Fluorescence Cytodiagnosis: A Way Toward Expansion of Early Cancer Detection". *Alberta Med. Bull.*, 27, 94-98, 1962.

BLANK, W.A. and STEINBERG, A.H., "Cytologic Diagnosis of Malignancies of the Lower Bowel and Rectum". *Am. J. Surg.*, *81*, 127-131, 1951.

BURN, J.I. and SELLWOOD, R.A., "The Results of Exfoliative Cytology Studies in 50 Patients with Symptoms of Large Bowel Disorder". *GUT*, *3*, 32-37, 1962.

DART, L.H., Jr., and TURNER, T.R., "Fluorescence Microscopy in Exfoliative Cytology: Report of Acridine Orange Examination of 5491 Cases with Comparison by the Papanicolaou Technique". *Lab. Invest.*, *8*, 1513-1522, 1959.

GALAMBOS, J.T. and KLAYMAN, M.I., "The Clinical Value of Colonic Exfoliative Cytology in the Diagnosis of Cancer Beyond the Reach of the Proctoscope". *Surg., Gynec. and Obstet.*, *101*, 673-679, 1955.

GRUBB, C., "Acridine Orange Fluorescence Microscopy in Endometrial Cytology: Endometrial Aspirations". *Acta. Cytol.*, *10*, 74-79, 1966.

KNOERNSCHILD, H.E. and CAMERON, A.B., "Mucosal Smear Cytology in the Detection of Colonic Carcinoma". *Acta. Cytol.*, *7*, 233-235, 1963.

NIEBURGS, H.E., "Significance of Cervical Dysplasia". *Med. Tribune*, *8*, 3, 1967.

RICHART, R.M., "Significance of Cervical Dysplasia". *Med. Tribune*, *8*, 3, 1967.

RIVA, H.L. and TURNER, T.R., "Fluorescence Microscopy in Exfoliative Cytology: A ten-second Acridine Orange Staining Technique for Cytologic Cancer Screening". *Obstet. Gynec.*, *20*, 451-457, 1962.

RASKIN H.F., KIRSNER, J.B., PALMER, W.L., PLETCKA, S. and YAREMA, W.A., "Gastrointestinal Cancer: Definitive Diagnosis by Exfoliative Cytology". *Arch. Surg.*, *76*, 507-516, 1958.

RUBIN, C.E., MASSEY, B.W., KIRSNER, J.B., PALMER, W.L. and STONECYPHER, D.D., "The Clinical Value of Gastrointestinal Cytologic Diagnosis". *Gastroenterology*, *25*, 119-138, 1953.

SPJUT, H.J., MARGULIS, A.R. and COOK, G.B., "The Silicone-
foam Enema: A Source for Exfoliative Cytological Specimens".
Acta. Cytol., 7, 79-84, 1963.

STEVENSON, J.L. and von HAMM, E., "The Application of
Immunofluorescence Techniques to the Cytodiagnosis of
Cancer". *Acta. Cytol., 10*, 15-20, 1966.

VACCA, V.F., PINTO, A., SPIRO, H.M. and DELUCA, V.A. Jr.,
"Colonic Exfoliative Cytology by an Improved Technique".
Am. J. Digest Dis., 13, 727-734, 1968.

WISSEMAN, C.L., Jr., LEMON, H.M. and LAWRENCE, K.B.,
"Cytologic Diagnosis of Cancer of the Descending Colon and
Rectum". *Surg., Gynec. and Obstet., 89*, 24-30 ,1949.

SECTION IV

GENERAL SYSTEM THEORY IN THE BEHAVIORAL

SCIENCES: TOWARD A NEW IMAGE OF MAN

INTRODUCTION

GENERAL SYSTEM THEORY IN PSYCHOLOGY, PSYCHIATRY, BEHAVIORAL, AND SOCIAL SCIENCE: TOWARD A NEW IMAGE OF MAN

This last section is dedicated to the behavioral sciences. It comprises contributions in psychology, psychiatry, anthropology, sociology, management science, and theoretical history. The concept of "system" having become central in the behavioral-social sciences, the "diversity" in the individual contributions and in the wide fields represented is brought closer to "unity" by common guiding ideas.

The section opens with an essay by Professor W. Metzger, the recognized dean of German psychology and one of the original founders of gestalt psychology. This is not a coincidence; the close parallelism of gestalt psychology of Metzger's imprint and organismic biology has long been recognized. A Textbook like Metzger's gestaltist *Psychologie* (1941) "could be translated, so to speak, theorem by theorem, into organismic language " [1].

Appropriately, Metzger's essay is entitled "Do Schools of Psychology Still Exist?" and so sets the key for the examination of psychology and the behavioral sciences in general. This essay is a comprehensive and deeply-reaching critique of the fundamental principles of conventional psychology as well as a consideration of alternatives open to a new psychology. What Metzger is doing is analyzing primarily the tenets of behavioristic psychology, of neo-behaviorism and related trends in the present academic establishment. Arthur Koestler, well known essayist, novelist, dramatist, and avowed student of psychology, has brilliantly stated that the so-called "dead horses" of behaviorism are still very much alive and enjoy robust,

burgeoning health in the overwhelming majority of psychology departments [2]. A large segment of modern
psychology, here and abroad, has been put to work in the
psychological engineering of modern societies of differing
basic ideologies. An image of man has been created by, or
evolved from, behavioristic psychology which regards man as
a machine, an animal, a drive-automaton, or as an expendable
unit. Metzger ends his essay on an optimistic note, stating
that the future will belong to non-behavioristic psychology,
something akin to organismic psychology, and his reasons,
rational and logical though they may be, appear to me somewhat unrealistic.

I have been a student of psychology for more than forty
years. I have studied psychology and its derivatives in
classrooms, in laboratories, and in hospitals. I have applied psychology in classroom teaching of typical and
atypical children, in industry, and in my medical career as
a psychiatric specialist. The major trends of the past
four decades, unfortunately, have not been toward the human-
ization of psychology, but rather away from it. The best
known psychologist of the civilized world, the one with the
greatest volume of book sales, is B.F. Skinner, Professor
of Psychology Emeritus at Harvard. Skinnerian rats and
pigeons are infinitely better known than were Thorndike's
cats of an earlier generation. Laws of learning and principles of operant conditioning, be it positive or negative
reinforcement, all add up to nothing new, but have added
the force of modern technology through teaching machines,
computers, and other devices toward an inexorably dehumanizing trend.

The basic psychology a person believes in, that is a
person of some sophistication and training, is more important than many will admit. Psychology was once taught
in conjunction with philosophy, or was actually referred to
as metaphysics and, as such, human values and purpose were
part of its domain. Behaviorism, indeed all derivatives of
stimulus-response psychology, did away with that "error",
believing that the consideration of values, goals, feelings,
and sentiments was outside the scope of scientific psychology. The psychology taught us by the early leaders of
psychoanalysis brought us conceptual models of a dynamic
sort. Many, however, were derived from diseased, decompen-
sated, non-functional patients. Universal generalizations

were derived from too few cases and there were too many
premature conclusions drawn from sexually extrapolated
material. General System Theory has never rejected psycho-
analytical models, merely reminded us that there are other
general and living systems within which we work and play
and create, systems which cannot be understood through the
writings of even the most recently acknowledged leaders of
psychoanalysis.

How important is psychology anyway? Why not ignore its
subject matter? Isn't it a waste of time? Psychology is
broadly defined as the study of mental processes, but it
must include studies of personality function, motivation,
behavior in a generic way, and medical psychology, as it is
referred to in some English speaking coutries, or psychiatry
in this country. "Psychosomatic medicine" is a popular and
useful term because it brings into one word psychic and
somatic, two adjectives perpetuating a dualism of earlier
times, but which still lives, at least now, in one word.
Educational psychology, or pedagogy, deals largely with
how to influence the learning process, how to program
youngsters culturally or educationally. Sales psychology
is one of the most important driving forces behind the
American economy. "Your automobile is your second biggest
monetary investment ". For many auto buyers who cannot buy
a home it is the biggest. Industrial psychology, animal
psychology, social psychology, child psychology, and human
psychology are other subdivision. Psychology is everywhere,
whether one believes in it or not. Sometimes it is a mental
scheme, individualized up to a point so that it does not
intrude noticeably into conscious awareness. One man's
psychology may be nothing but his life style, his attitudes,
his view of himself in relationship to the world about him,
reflecting and projecting outward his own inner images.
One man may be laying bricks while the man beside him is
helping to build a museum or a cathedral. Who works with
more satisfaction?

We are living in an era of super-specialization of the
sciences in which fragmentation and fractionation appear
inevitable, especially in the study of man. One's own
psychology is, ultimately, his own world view, how it all
fits together for him. It has been true, in this country
at least, that the study of psychology has not been highly
respected, excepting as indicated above as a means of

achieving certain extraneous goals, usually materialistic
or overly specific. Holistic, gestalt, or organismic psy-
cology which considers first the learner in a learning
situation made up of many factors of ever-changing character, has never been popular in America for several reasons.
It is more difficult to understand than the stimulus-response model, based on the myth of straight line causality.
Organismic psychology is considered by some to be a foreign
import and therefore, suspect. When von Bertalanffy's
Robots, Men and Minds was reviewed in the New York Times
Book Review section three years ago and, later, in *Contemporary Psychology* both reviewers listed a number of observations some of which bear repeating. It was considered
regrettable by the reviewers that a non-psychologist, von
Bertalanffy, was chosen to give Heinz Werner lectures at
Clark University. They stated that Werner had been a
gentle critic of American psychology whereas von Bertalanffy
damned the establishment and had none of the "committment
to the field ". Correct, von Bertalanffy's committment is
to man and his unique nature, the totality of his problems,
not to a fractionated or fragmented version of man. To
study man psychologically without some knowledge of humanistic
psysiology in both health and disease is a gross inadequacy
and this is precisely the failure of many so-called human
psychologists. It is also true that von Bertalanffy men-
tions some unpalatable facts, i.e., in some states up to
twenty times more is spent per annum on the custodial care
of one chronically and irreversably ill human than on the
education of a healthy youngster.

By marked contrast to behavioristic psychology, the
contributors to section IV are deeply concerned with studying man, the human condition, and man-made institutions.
There is a trend towards a "humanistic" psychology, that
is one emphasizing, exploring, and expressing what is
specifically "human" in man's behavior, while psychoanalysis, behaviorism, and the comparative study of behavior
(ethology) alike were essentially zoomorphic and reduction-
ist. That is, in the current emphasis of the animal and
even bestial in man, they tended to overlook and suppress
the *differentia specifica* between human and subhuman behavior. The late A. Maslow was a thorough humanist in his
theoretical framework. His last essays expressed a holistic
view not unlike that of F. Matson, author of the brilliant
study *The Broken Image* [3]. Von bertalanffy's formulation

arose from the biologist's question as to what distinguishes
human behavior. His answer, epitomized by the key concepts
of "active personality system" and "symbolic activities,"
was essentially formulated at an early stage of his career
[4]. The latter conception brought him near to E. Cassirer's monumental work [5], although he arrived at it
independently. The identical conclusion reached by Cassirer
starting from neo-Kantianism and by von Bertalanffy in-
quiring into the "ethological" question of the species-
specifics of human behavior certainly enhances the correctness of the newer "image of man" implied in von Bertalanffy's
concepts.

One of the questions arising is the classical problem
of body and mind. The answer proposed by Professor
Rothschuh, a leading organismic physiologist [6], is
closely parallel to that of von Bertalanffy. Dr. S. Arieti,
renowned schizophrenia researcher and editor of *The American
Handbook of Psychiatry*, follows up the considerations of his
recent book, *The Intrapsychic Self* [7]. Although trained
in the psychoanalytic tradition, Arieti goes far beyond it
by emphasizing cognitive processes, normalcy, and creativity.

From normal psychology it is only a step to abnormal
psychology, that is the clinical field of *psychiatry*. As
already mentioned, it is in this field that von Bertalanffy's
ideas have already exerted a particularly strong influence.
This fact has found an outward expression in von
Bertalanffy's election in 1967 as an Honorary Fellow of the
American Psychiatric Association; a signal honor to a
biologist, in view of the fact that the APA at the time
numbered only sixteen Honorary Fellows among its 18,000
members and that von Bertalanffy's election took place
simultaneously with that of Anna Freud. Among the leaders
of American psychiatry, Dr. Karl Menninger, at a previous
occasion, stated, "I consider Dr. von Bertalanffy to be one
of my most influential teachers, one who changed many of my
opinions in various respects " [8]. These opinions are
restated accordingly in his now famous book, *The Vital
Balance*. The same recognition is reflected in the psychiatric contributions to the present volume.

Dr. N. Rizzo shows systems theory "in action" in the
psychiatric field. He reviews his experience with General
System Theory and its application to community mental

health programs, especially in court clinics. Prince
Auersperg, late Director of Psychiatric University Clinic
in Conception, Chile, and von Bertalanffy's friend of some
thirty years, brings together the conceptions of von
Bertalanffy with the Gestaltkreislehre of Viktor von
Weizsäcker and the considerations of existentialism in
interesting fashion. Von Weizsäcker, little known in the
United States, has been very influential in Germany.

We next come to the social sciences. As any modern
investigator will agree, "system", ever since Talcott
Parsons' work, has become a central notion in sociological
theory. There are, however, wide differences in its definition. General System Theory in von Bertalanffy's sense
has exerted a strong influence in sociology and related
fields, such as geography [9]. As expressed by a variety
of authors, "The intellectual fundament of functional
theory in sociology is the concept of a 'system' ". Von
Bertalanffy sees the system concept "as a scientific common
denominator and expands it in terms of General System
Theory ". Just as Sorokin ranges between cultures, von
Bertalanffy ranges across disciplines. Physics, biology,
mathematics, ecology, psychology, economics, and sociology
are all within his grasp and ken. In all of this von
Bertalanffy "enriches the discussion by widening its
boundaries, specifying its ground rules, and providing
relevant criteria for evaluation ", [10].

The sociological section appropriately includes a
contribution by Professor K.E. Boulding, well-known protagonist of systems theory and (with von Bertalanffy,
Rapoport, and Gerard) co-founder of the Society for General
Systems Research. The methodological problems of "research
strategies" is further pursued by Dr. R. Jones with Professor L. Gross, head of the Sociology Department and
colleague of von Bertalanffy's at Buffalo. There follow
comparisons of von Bertalanffy's views with contemporary
currents in sociology. Professor P. Sorokin's death resulted in the loss of a personal contribution he had intended [11], but Dr. K. Peter, of Simon Fraser University,
ably outlines the comparison of Sorokin's sociology and
von Bertalanffy's system approach to the study of group
phenomena*. Dr. F.E.Katz, of State University of New York
at Buffalo and Tel Aviv University, introduces

---

*See Volume I, Section I.

introduces the interesting question of indeterminacy in hierarchical systems, a seldom-envisaged problem which von Bertalanffy answered to the effect that "the degree of freedom seems to increase as we move to higher levels" of hierarchical organization. This is shown, for example, in structures from low-molecular compounds with strict structural formulas to statistically determined polymers to "mesoforms". i.e., molecular arrangements ordered only in one or two dimensions of space such as fibrillar structures [12].

Problems of more practical, as well as of more immediate relevance in the field of economics, are discussed by Maloney. Existential psychology is discussed by an acknowledged leader, V. Frankl. D. Campbell's essay on language learning is both challenging and stimulating. Modern organization theory, as has been justly stated, "leads almost inevitably into a discussion of General System Theory", [13]. These relations are elaborated by the leading German representative of the field, the distinguished Professor E. Grochla of the University of Cologne.

Here, eventually, we come to the point where sociology in the conventional sense fuses into history of the past and in the making. It is in this sense that Professor J.D. Singer ingeniously analyzes international conflict in terms of feedback and vicious circles as we, unfortunately, see them at work in contemporary politics. As von Bertalanffy, for nearly fifty years, was interested in the cyclic theory of history [14], it is fortunate that we are able to present a posthumous work of Professor F. Keiter, a leading German cultural anthropologist tragically killed in an airplane accident. Keiter, unaware of von Bertalanffy's interest in problems of history, based his theories on the biological views of von Bertalanffy, because he recognized their bearing on historical questions. Keiter, also, outlined the life cycle of cultures. In a somewhat similar vein, Dr. F.C. Happold, author of well-known books on mysticism [15], considers our period as a "leap epoch" of history thus accounting for the many troubles with which we are confronted.

The editors hope that the Festschrift presents a panorama of broadest scope. Beginning with highly abstract considerations of General System Theory and then traversing

biophysical and biological research the Festschrift leads
to the inception of a new image and science of man. It
terminates with a theory of history and a study of the
urgent problems of our own epoch. Conceived as an homage
to one single individual, it has become, we hope, considerably more. There is in these pages an expression of a new
world view which emerges now in various shades and disguises,
a view which may penetrate and change the intellectual
climate of our times. Hopefully it may be potent enough
to dispel the various narrow and fragmented scientific
hypotheses from which we suffer no less than from the pol-
luting agents in our physical environment. If so, the
present work has served its purpose.

Nicholas D. Rizzo

REFERENCES

1.   von BERTALANFFY, L., *Problems of Life*, 194, New York:
      Harper Torchbooks, 1961.

2.   KOESTLER, A., *The Ghost in the Machine*, 349, New York,
      Macmillan, London, Hutchinson, 1967.

3.   MATSON, F.W., *The Broken Image*, New York: Braziller,
      1964.

4.   e.g., von BERTALANFFY, L., "Das Weltbild der Biologie"
      In: *Weltbild und Menschenbild*, MOSER, S. (ed.)
      Salzburg: Tyrolia, 1948.

5.   CASSIRER, E., *The Philosophy of Symbolic Forms*, 3 vols.
      New Haven: Yale University Press, 1953-57.

6.   ROTHSCHUH, K.E., *Theorie des Organismus*. 2nd ed.
      Munchen, Berlin: Urban und Schwarzenberg, 1963.

7.   ARIETI, S., *The Intrapsychic Self*, New York, London:
      Basic Books, 1967.

8.   In: *General Systems Theory and Psychiatry*, GRAY, W,
      DUHL, F.D. and RIZZO, N.D., (eds.), 447. Boston: Little,
      Brown, 1969.

9. e.g., HARVEY, D., *Explanation in Geography*. London:
    Arnold; New York: St. Martin's Press, 1969.

10. DEMERATH, N.J., III, and PETERSON, R.A., *System, Change
    and Conflict*. "A Reader in Contemporary Sociological
    Theory and the Debate over Functionalism. New York:
    Free Press, 1967, 96, 141, and elsewhere.

11. But cf. SOROKIN, P.A., *Sociological Theories of Today*,
    133-145. New York: Harper & Row, 1966.

12. von BERTALANFFY, L., *Problems of Life, An Evaluation
    of Modern Biological Thought*, 172 ff.; New York:
    Wiley & Sons; London: Watts & Co., 1952, cf. also WEISS,
    P., In: *Beyond Reductionism*. KOESTLER, A., and
    SMYTHIES, J.R., (eds)., New York: Macmillan; London:
    Hutchinson, 1969.

13. SCOTT, W.G., "Organization Theory: An Overview and an
    Appraisal." In: *Organizations: Structure and Behavior*.
    LITTERER, J.A., (ed.), New York: Wiley, 1963.

14. von BERTALANFFY, L., "Einfuhrung in Spengler's Werk",
    Literatur Blatt, Kölnische Zeitung, May, 1924.

15. HAPPOLD, F.C., *Mysticism, A Study and an Anthology*.
    Penguin Books, 1963.

DO SCHOOLS OF PSYCHOLOGY STILL EXIST?

WOLFGANG METZGER

Universitat Munster, Rosenstrasse 9, Munster,
Federal Republic of Germany

FORMULATION OF THE QUESTION

If today we were to ask a psychologist, "what is left of the great disputes which determined the image of psychology in the Twenties?" the answer would be overshadowed by a kind of a tacit agreement: "Those disputes belong to history. Psychological schools do not exist any more. Those particular conceptions which used to be the cause of fights as bitter as those over the articles of faith became part of our general psychological knowledge. We have found that their validity is not a general one, but rather limited to certain partial areas and problems. They are, in a sense, banished to that place in the general image of psychology where they belong".

It is an odd concept of science, which is pronounced here: a specific clear-cut image of the human being and of human mental life is renounced. Psychology becomes a collection of correlations between all possible psychological facts including all physiological, physical, geographical, sociological, etc., facts which might be found in their vicinity; sometimes, it becomes a collection of mathematical formulas which define those interrelations somewhat more exactly. However, those who would hope to find in contemporary psychology something that would lead to understanding of one's self and of others would fail to find it. In reality, the situation is even worse. In his very knowledgeable essay (*Nebraska Symposium on*

Motivation, 1965), J. McV. Hunt draws attention to the very peculiar contradiction between the basic conceptions of modern psychology and those of successful progressive educational practice.

Hunt considers the present pedagogical-psychological way of thinking a schizophrenic one as far as suggestions for educational practice are concerned. With those suggestions derived from the basic concepts of modern psychology, a pedagogue may be only amused or offended. Modern psychology can offer nothing more than rewards for the desired behaviour and punishments for the undesired one by means of which certain habits are supposed to be built up and others eliminated. On the other hand, modern pedagogics maintains that these are the most dubious means of education. That means, then, that our nice concept of the unity of psychology is a thoroughly false one. Two sciences on the same subject, Hunt continues, contradictory in their basic assumptions and inferences cannot be both true at the same time. Sooner or later, one of them will have to give up. And Hunt supposes that it will be psychology rather than pedagogics.

His assumption is supported by two experiments (among others) published almost at the same time: Schenk-Danzinger's experiment with a human child and Harlow's experiment with the child of the rhesus monkey. According to them it appears, first, that the question of whether those beings will accept or not the social behavior desired in their group is decided at a stage of their development, where they *cannot* have any experience with pleasant or unpleasant consequences of their behaviour in the group - which, according to the S-R-model of the classical learning theory, is the necessary condition for the appropriation of suitable patterns of social behaviour - because they are still hanging on the breast of their mothers. Second, there has not been, as yet, a successful attempt to return an uncared-for to the path of virtue, i.e., back to the desired social behaviour, by punishing his undesired behaviour and rewarding the desired one. To this end, quite different measures are needed, as we may read - to name only the sources on hand - in the classical studies of Aichhorn, and also in the works of Alfons Simon and H. Zulliger.

However, is it really so bad with psychology? Is the S-R scheme, including the modifications introduced by passive and active conditioning, really all that psychology has to offer for the solution of educational problems? This question is parallel with that of the unity of psychology, i.e., with whether there are really no more differing conceptions and schools in psychology. Should the answer be affirmative, it would be necessary – to cope with the knowledge and needs of the pedagogues – to invent immediately a new psychology which would correspond better to the reality of man.

Moreover, an affirmative answer would mean that psychology is no longer a young, vital, progressive science, as such sciences are characterized by continuous emerging of new problems bringing about the most contradictory assumptions or hypotheses. And it is an age-old experience that one of the most significant driving powers of progress is the effort to find among these contradictory assumptions the correct one. The notion "assumption" or hypothesis" should not be understood here in the diluted sense of statistical lingo where it means only one of several possible outcomes of a situation, which – if it does not come true – is "rejected." This notion means something more to us: a not yet or not yet sufficiently proved assumption concerning a more or less broad scope of functional relations, in about the sense in which the notion "model" is understood today, but without the presently much advocated meaning that only a mathematical formulation makes a full-fledged model out of a hazy idea. (See also Droesler). Thus, we understand the notion "hypothesis" in the old sense, as a statement, which could be promoted to the status of a theory by sufficient experimental proof.

Of course, there will always be hypotheses of very different ranges. And only in those cases where the hypotheses had a sufficient range, a sufficiently broad area of validity, a basic significance, was it customary to speak about a "school," especially when it advocated several different, logically independent but "matching" hypotheses at the same time.

Thus, the question appears to be as follows: are

there still some differences in the opinions concerning
the basic questions in psychology?

THE PRINCIPLES OF CONTEMPORARY PSYCHOLOGY

Let us take, as our first example, orthodox behaviourism, as has been represented, for example, by
Skinner, because it is widely considered *the*
psychology of the present time (also by Hunt). Analysis
shows that it is built up of about a dozen principles
conceived by the prominent representatives of the school
as axioms or articles of faith. However, they *might* be
nothing more than unproved hypotheses.

(1) *The Principle of Objectivity*

Only data which can be observed and recorded from
outside may be used in psychology if it is supposed to be
scientific psychology. Psychology can cope with its
ambition to be an empirical science only as a science of
behaviour.

This is not a hypothesis concerning the facts of
psychology; rather, it is a methodic rule, or, more
clearly, a *prohibition* to evaluate certain data because of
their lack of reliability.

(2) *The Principle of Passivity or of Primary Reactivity*

The psycho-physical organism starts to function
only because of external influence. Thus, the objective
of the science of behaviour is to assess the relations
between the influences *from* outside (stimuli or situations,
"S") and the reactions *towards* the outside world
(responses, "R"), i.e., the "S-R relation." The reactions
R bring about a mostly new situation respectively a new
kind of influence S_2; thus, the elementary relation as
a whole may be symbolized as $S_1 - R - S_2$.

(3) *The Principle of Genetic Identity of Psychophysical Systems*

The hereditary or innate psychic apparatus is the *same* for·all men, if not for all vertebrates. Therefore, for experimental research of human behaviour, doves or rats may be used.

(4) *The Principle of Minimum Genetic Outfit (of Tabula Rasa)*

Without taking into account some elementary reflexes, there are no hereditary relations between the influences S and the reactions R. All differences in the reactions R are the result of previous differences in surroundings S (i.e., S from birth till the respective moment): *milieu theory* or environmentalism. What a person knows, he has learned during his individual existence. The capability of learning is the basic property of the psychic. Theoretical psychology is basically a theory of learning.

Principles (3) and (4) form together the doctrine called *empiricism* since the 18th Century.

(5) *The Principles of Elementarism and Connectionism*

Learning is a process of formation of connections between elementary facts, of enforcement of such connections or of weakening or extinction of connections already existing.

(6) *The Principle of Contiguity (Principle of Contact)*

The decisive condition for any connection is time-space vicinity, if possible, repeated many times.

(7) *The Principle of Contingency respectively of Arbitrariness*

There is no principle of connection formation but for that of contingency; that means that chance or an arbitrary decision of the experimentor is the only decisive factor. The factual pertinency ("matching",

"mutual demandedness") of the facts to be connected
plays no role.

Thus, no distinction is made between the attainment
of a (desired) goal on one side (e.g., of a correct
solution of a problem by following, without error, some
suitable proceedings) and getting a pleasant reward
(a piece of candy) as a result of observing an arbitrary
(prescribed by the experimentor) behaviour on the other
side.

The principles (5), (6) and (7) form together the
so-called "associationism". From the beginning they
have also been the principal rules of empiricism (principles (3) and (4). The new associationism differs —
because of principles (1) and (2) — from the old one in
that it deals with connections of situations S with
reactions R (passive conditioning), rather than with
connections between contents of consciousness ("ideas").

(8) *The Machine Principle*

There are an older and a new version of the assumptions concerning the relations between situations and
reactions; incidentally, they do not exclude each other.

a)   The older one is the *automaton model*. It is
divided — according to the assumptions about the energy
sources — into two subtypes;

a_1 — The conduction or Telephone network type: the
       stimulus S penetrates as an impulse through a recep-
       tor cell into the nervous system and there it pro-
       ceeds — *because of the central network of connec-
       tions* — to the effector organ where it leaves the
       organism as the reaction R.

a_2 — The Trigger type: the stimulus S acts — like a pres-
       sure on a push-button or a dime dropped in the slot —
       as a trigger which releases a ready-to-work but, until
       the moment of stimulation, blocked mechanisn; then,
       the mechanism starts to work with its own energy.

b) According to the newer concept of the homeostatic or
tension-reduction model (borrowed from Cannon), the

stimulus S disturbs the equilibrium state of an organ
system, and the reaction R restores it again.

The needs are just these disturbances of equilibrium
or increases of tension, and the gratification of a need
is just this reduction of tension. Von Bertalanffy calls
all three variants together "the robot model of man". As
was shown by W. Köhler, the notion of homeostatic processes
with their necessary feed-backs already exceeds the limitations of the classical machine principle, since the
process *may affect itself* at least at one single spot,
though by means of special conductive connections.

According to the tension reduction model the psycho-
physical system seeks under all circumstances a quiet
state; this model may therefore be understood as an expression of the *principle of quietism*: i.e., all activity is
the result of disturbances and "sweet leisure" is the
normal state of man.

(9) *The Principles of Chance and Effect*

In order to understand the formation of new connections
and the extinction of existing ones, as in passive ("classical" Pavlovian) conditioning, no new principle is needed,
as conditioning is but another name for association introduced for the special case in which one of the elements
to be connected is an activity of the subject.

If new types of performance are needed as in trial
and error learning respectively operant or instrumental
conditioning, these can — as a consequence of principle
(7) — only be found *by chance* and recognized as suitable
and retained *by their effect*.

(10) *The Principle of Activity of Personality Structure*

The S-R connections reinforced by success-failure learning are also called habits. Personality or character is
the sum of habits. Any of these habits may be induced or
eliminated individually without changing anything in all
other habits (vegetable bed model). From these ideas of
formation and elimination of habits results immediately the
old, traditional, but, by modern pedagogics, rejected

practice of "candy and whip". As the desirability or
undesirability is determined by the educating society, the
result of such an education is the maximum obtainable degree
of adaptation (adjustment) or conformity, in other words,
opportunism.

(11) *The Principle of Reductionism*

There are no autochthonous psychic or mental dynamics.
All dynamics, e.g., that of learning, of thinking, of explor-
ing, serves the purpose of decreasing organismic tensions.
He who is not hungry does not think.

(12) *Principle of Primary Social Atomism* (as a Consequence
of Reductionism in Social Psychology)

There are no primary social needs and desires. They
are only secondarily formed by conditioning, i.e., by the
realization that certain persons are exceptionally suitable
tools or means for the gratification of certain organismic
needs and/or for the reduction of certain organismic tensions.
In this respect, there is unanimity between behaviourism
and psychoanalysis.

AXIOMS OR HYPOTHESES?

A question arises here: are the above principles
axioms, i.e., necessary presumptions of any psychology, or
are they hypotheses, which — in the present state of the
science — would have to permit the existence of other hypotheses and eventually — perhaps even now — give way to
them; in other words, are there still opposite schools in
psychology? Thus, our question is: are the above principles necessary: And, in addition, are they sufficient?

(1) *On the Principle of Objectivity*

The principle of subjectivity cannot be considered an
alternative to the objectivity principle. It characterizes
a historical phase of psychology which continued until the
introduction of behaviourism. As the objectivity principle
is a prohibition, the alternative would be a psychology
without this prohibition. This alternative is realized in
phenomenological psychology, in "Gestalt theory" and in a

number of other approaches of present psychology, and, as we shall see, it is successful.

Incidentally, behaviourism itself — even at its extremes — disregarded its own prohibition from the moment it started to speak about the "concealed", "internal", "preceding" "behaviour", meaning processes which cannot be registered by physiological means, but which are rather unequivocally identical with the acts and contents of subjective psychology. The confession of having given up a principle which played an outstanding role in the establishment declaration of behaviourism is, of course, embarrassing. However, it is even more embarrassing that this abandonment of a basic principle not only was not confessed but rather veiled by semantic manipulations, by adding to the names of these subjective facts the suffix "behaviour".

Thus, a psychology without the principle of objectivity is not only possible but rather inevitable. That is why we have a new variant of behaviourism calling itself "subjective behaviourism" (G.A. Miller, E. Galanter, K.H. Pribram, 1960). The adjective, of course, inevitably annuls the only clear denotation of the word "Behaviourism" as a *non*-subjective psychology.

(2) *On the Principle of Primary Reactivity*

The alternative is not a concept of a psycho-physical organism characterized by exclusively spontaneous activity but is an organism capable as well of spontaneous activity as of reaction, and in which the reactive behaviour patterns are in many cases only superposed on the primary spontaneous ones.

As it was proven by Coghill, the first movements of the amblystomic larva are spontaneous because they occur at a stage of development when the receptor nerves do not yet have connections with the motor centers. The same was shown by von Holst, e.g., that the thyrthmic locomotor fin movements of the fish are not triggered and maintained by external stimuli and that these stimuli only modify them. Behaviour in play and in exploration goes also beyond the limits of the S-R scheme, as the opportunity for it is *looked for* even by animals and as it immediately starts anew after each conclusion, i.e., after each reduction of tension.

In this case as well, the unavoidable necessity to accept these facts is veiled by behaviourists by a notorious renaming manoeuvre: in the place of the objectively observable — that means originally unequivocally external triggering situation S (with respect to the organism) — simply a non-observable intra-organismic environment of the *motor centers* is introduced; and it appears as if the meaning of the term reaction had not been changed.

Anyway, a psychology rejecting the principle of primary reactivity is not only possible, but rather required by the facts.

(3) *On the Principle of Genetic Identity*

The principle of genetic identity of psycho-physical systems is identical with the denial of inborn traits. Here also, the alternative would not be a psychology which would try to reduce all differences in the behaviour of different individuals to differences of predispositions but rather a psychology that would avoid dogmatic presuppositions with regard to the contribution of genetic and environmental factors to individual differences.

As to the validity of this principle for all vertebrates this was clearly refuted by an abundance of results of recent comparative behavioural research, obtained under pure conditions, e.g., in the Kasper-Hauser experiment.

As to the differences in human psycho-physical genetic outfit, no basic doubts exist any more. The existing controversy pertains only to the *relative effects* of innate apparatus and environment.

In spite of all this, behaviourism is still stuck with the principle of genetic identity. This is a result of an attitude that is even less scientific than the method of renaming, namely simply ignoring all facts not corresponding to one's principles. (See K. Lorenz, 1961)

Altogether, it appears that a psychology without the principle of genetic identity is not only possible, but — in the face of the existing facts — necessary.

(4) *On the Principle of Genetic Minimum Outfit*

In the discussion of this principle it is necessary to take into account the fact that the principle of objectivity was already rejected by behaviourism itself (see above). The most significant arguments against the minimum outfit principle are derived from the subjective sphere.

In contrast to the *tabula rasa* approach, all sensual data enter:

a) *an already existing* and *unchangeable* system of dimensions — not more and not less than three space- and one time-dimension. Moreover, this is in a framework of a system of elementary qualities *already existing*. Interestingly, this system may in a given subject differ from others in a clearly definable way according to his basic apparatus (Daltonism).

b) The bulk of the sensual data is divided and grouped spontaneously in accordance with a *given* system of categories.

c) This grouping is distributed all over the three given space dimensions according to the minimum and optimum principles (pregnancy tendencies) which are inherent to the system and not modifiable by individual experience, thus only partially according to experience, but partially defying experience. (See among others, E. Mach, W. Metzger, G. Kanisza).

The facts a), b) and c) are not consequences of experiences, but rather *conditions* which make it possible to acquire any experience; they are "pre-empirical".

The principle of reaction patterns inherent to the system is not to be confused with the principle of nativism. Nativism maintains only — in contrast to empiricism — that adjustment to reality is in certain aspects reached phylogenetically rather than ontogenetically. It does not mention system-specific reaction patterns at all.

Moreover, there are in the case of animals, many and, in the case of men, at least several structures originating from the above laws, without any previous experience respectively success and error learning with biologically

specific releasing functions. These cannot be understood
without admitting some analogue of the much abused "idea
innata". (The English expression IRM — innate releasing
mechanism, as well as the German AAM — angeborener aus-
lösender Mechanismus, adequately reflect these facts only
in their first two words, but the word "mechanism" is misleading and should be replaced by the word "cue", in German
"Merkmal".

All this means that the principle of genetic minimum
apparatus is not consistent with the facts. Thus, a psychology without this principle is not only possible but rather
necessary.

(5) *On the Principles of Elementarism and Connectionism*

Under the assumption that the principle of objectivity
is rejected, it becomes necessary to discuss the above two
principles with a view to the three following problems:
1) The problem of autonomous motions (motorics)
2) The problem of the surrounding world (situations)
3) The problem of the relation between the situation and
motorics, which is the basis of behaviour.

The alternative to the statement that all larger complexes in the psychological sphere result from the connection
of elementary facts is not the statement that, in the
psychic life, "everything is interconnected" at the beginning and that, only in time, by means of maturation and
learning processes, this universal interconnection is gradually split up (William James, Hans Cornelius, Felix Krueger,
Heinz Werner).

The alternative is rather an assumption that the development and learning processes:
a) split up and resolve existing larger complexes;
b) combine existing small complexes, which, in extreme cases,
    may have the character of elements, into larger com-
    plexes; and
c) that existing structures may change into others
    by simultaneous resolving and recombining.

In such a psychology, too, the question arises as to
whether one of these processes is primary and, if this is
the case, which one. Here only the following is certain:

1) In the motor sphere, the primary process of development is the process a), the differentiation of the originally total, i.e., all available muscles employing pattern of motions (Coghill).

2) Similarily, in establishing the structure of the surrounding world, the primary one is not the problem of combining "units" but rather that of establishing *boundaries*, that means, again, the problem of differentiation, a).

3) On the other hand — at least in the case of man — the secondary connection between the situations and activities in the sense of behaviourism seems to be the more frequent or perhaps the main means of change even when, as the possibility of extinction of existing connections proves, not the only one.

(6) *On the Principle of Contiguity or Contact*

Contact or time-space vicinity is an important but neither a sufficient nor necessary condition for the formation of connections.

It is not sufficient. The perception field is a continuum without gaps. Thus, the problem arising here may be verbalized in the following way: how is it possible that two processes A, B, taking place in an immediate contact with each other, form a unity whereas two processes B, C, taking place in an immediate contact with each other as well, differentiate from each other. Apparently, other principles must be involved.

The same as has been said about the primary field differentiation may be repeated in the case of association experiments. Under completely identical time-space conditions, very different numbers of repetitions are needed in order to establish a connection independent of the materials which are to be connected. In addition, the durability of such connections is very different. Even in this case it is not possible to speak of an exclusive effectiveness of the space-time factor.

On the other hand, the space-time vicinity is not necessary. In problem-solving processes, the facts which are "required" in order to fill in a specific gap are often brought from a considerable distance. This does not always happen through an active search but frequently it results immediately from the dynamics of the process.

(7) *On the Principle of Contingency or of Arbitrariness*

What is missing in the principle of time-space vicinity for the explanation of the primary field differentiation is provided for by the principle of *non*-arbitrariness of the connections. The connections and differentiations occur unequivocally according to optimum and minimum conditions. (Metzger, 1966).

On the other hand, the animal and human nervous systems, beyond the primary field differentiation, have a very remarkable capacity to form and preserve completely arbitrary (accidental or deliberately chosen) connections, for instance, that of a person and a name or of a name and a telephone number, apparently on the grounds of a mere "togetherness".

Ceteris paribus, however, between the meaningless and meaningful connections, there exists a remarkable difference in the ease of their establishment, and in the stability of their preservation. Here, the expression "meaningful" has two denotations:

a)   one of the facts may be an image of the other one as e.g., series of numbers and series of digits on a dial, or it has similar or corresponding "general properties";

b)   one of the facts is "missing" in the other one — it is "required" by the other one. By its introduction, a "complete" whole of a uniform lawful structure is formed. (Wertheimer, 1945)

The furthering effects of consistency hold according to everyday experience for the S-R relation as well. This, naturally, is to be assessed by further systematic research.

As it appears in a more precise analysis, the multiplicity of the behavioural patterns produced during the first phase of the trial and error process is in no way, as maintained, arbitrary with regard to the sought goal. Rather, from the infinite multitude of possible behavioural patterns, a choice is made in the sense of an —

at least seeming — goal relevance, i.e., in the sense of preferring those actions which promise, because of their character, the possibility of attaining the goal.

All in all, a psychology in which the principles of contiguity and contingence would be banished to a more modest place which is proper for them is possible as well as required by the facts.

(8) *On the Question of the Machine Character of the Relations between Situations and Reactions*

As shown above, behaviourism has three different models of this relation — two strictly mechanistic, and one with dynamic properties. The mechanistic models are:
a) the conduction and switching model (telephone network type) and
b) the release mechanism model (trigger type).
The quasi-dynamic one is the homeostatic model.

According to the first two models, the organism is an aggregate of mechanisms, according to the third one, an aggregate of subsystems with feedback connections remaining in a state of rest unless their equilibrium is disturbed. The aggregate structure is characteristic of all three models. Further, all three models maintain that a psycho-physical organism, if not stimulated, is in a quiet state which is changed by stimulation into activity only *for a limited time*. In the first and second case, this reflects the fact that the psychic subsystems are considered mechanisms ready for eventual use; in the third case, that the equilibrium state of the subsystems is understood as a static equilibrium.

However, there is a fourth possibility, the most probable one (taking into account the fact that the psycho-physical processes take place in a living organism). It has two complementary assumptions:
a) Not only within the subsystems of the psycho-physical system there exists a dynamic relation between their between their elements. Such a relation also exists between the different subsystems themselves and between the total psycho-physical system and the rest of the organism as well. Thus, there exists a highly complicated system of highly sensitive equilibria with a hierarchy of smaller and larger areas.

b) As to these equilibria, they are not static. Rather, in each point of the system, there constantly exists a characteristic static diseqilibrium which preserves certain active processes. In physics these processes are called stationary or quasi-stationary processes. Ludwig von Bertalanffy introduced the simple expression "steady states".

That means, however, that the organismic subsystems are constantly active. Thus, the "stimulus" S *does not cause the activity* of the organism; as a change in the conditions surrounding the organismic system, it only modifies an already existing activity. This was already supposed by E. Hering (in his Chromology). Wolfgang Koehler, proceeding from an idea of Max Wertheimer (1912), proved in the years 1920-22 that this supposition is in accordance with the current ideas of physics and used it in his theory of perception. Ludwig von Bertalanffy, proceeding from biological facts and ideas, showed the basic significance of the steady state. E. von Holst, in his theory of position reflexes, strictly proved the fact of continuous activity of the nervous system *modified* only by external conditions.

Static equilibria and steady states have one characteristic in common. Both tend towards structurally defined, time-independent, final states, determined solely by the parameters of the system, and thus independent of the initial conditions. These final states are established or re-established (in case of disturbances) in different ways according to the initial conditions. Thus, the entire process achieves a character of *finality* without defying natural laws.

Moreover, systems preserving a steady state have some properties which are missing in the systems tending towards a static equilibrium only. The processes which enable a system in a steady state to stay in it take materials from the surroundings of the system, and, with them, "negative entropy". There is another fact which is connected with this which was shown by W. Koehler and Ludwig von Bertalanffy in independent works. They have a capability of transition into states of higher complexity and regularity, into states of higher order, and, that means of lower entropy. Thus, they behave *seemingly* in defiance of the second law of thermodynamics.

This holds true not only for the development of more and more highly organized beings in the course of phylogenesis and for the development of a mature organism from the fertilized ovum (morphogenesis), but also for the productive psychic processes. Apparently, they do not take their energy from the external surroundings, like the whole organism, but rather from the psychic surrounding field, from the psychic neighboring systems, so that, in the limit case of a (sound) obsession by a (scientific, artistic, technological, organization) problem, these neighboring systems may become deprived of energy and the respective man, as it were, "consumes himself" (W. Koehler). In other words, during these processes, the dynamics of the gratification of elementary needs may become more or less and, at least for a certain time, the less significant one.

This dynamic approach to the relation between the situation and reaction allows clarification not only of the facts which were already explained in another way by behaviourism, but also of two basic psychological facts which were not explained by behaviourism: finality and productivity.

The fact that this not so simple idea was founded on the basis of both objective (von Bertalanffy, von Holst) and subjective data (Koehler, Wertheimer) indicates that the denial of scientific usefulness of subjective data (the first principle of behaviourism) was apparently based on insufficient facts. By the way, both "subjective data" (Sign-gestalt) and finality is admitted in the "purporsive behaviourism" (Tolman, 1932).

(9) *On the Theory of Learning by Success*

According to the behaviouristic theory of learning, it may be ascertained only on the basis of a *success arrived at already* whether some behaviour approaches the goal or not (if there are no previously acquired mechanisms or behaviour patterns).

But, there are certain problem situations, natural or deliberately introduced, which are so accidental or so unclear that there is no other possibility in coping with them but for the classical active conditioning. However, here the question arises as to whether the conditioning may serve as a model *for all possible problem-solving processes*. If this should be correct, then the basic principle would be as follows: There is no *primary finality* in the behaviour of living beings. This thesis cannot be valid, as was demonstrated in the preceding paragraph. Wolfgang Koehler in his intelligence tests of anthropoids was successful in 1917 in proving the primarily goal-centered behaviour in *new* situations without any ready behavioural patterns available. As to the primary finality of the productive mental processes of man, see, first of all, Max Wertheimer, 1945.

The constantly reappearing assertion that the insightful solving of problems occurs "in reality" through trial and error, and that it is only transferred from exterior to interior (to imagination, or, in the behaviouristic nomenclature, on the "hidden level") has never been proven as yet, and, preserving the principle of objectivity, cannot be proven at all.

Replacing overt trials by the assumption of "internal" attempts, "preceding" the external behaviour, misses the essential. First, if a person decides to go to the right around a big round table to reach his goal and not to the left, he does not need to try both possibilities in his imagination in order to find out that it takes a couple of steps less if he goes to the right. Rather, he can *observe* in his *surrounding world* that the way to the right is shorter. Second, even intelligent problem solving is often not possible without (external) attempts. However (and this is the decisive point), whereas according to learning theory, one of the attempted activities *must have already succeeded* in order to be recognized, accepted and memorized as useful, in reality, for an intelligent, primarily goal-centered activity it is characteristic that it displays *a priori* a choice of attempts limited with a view to the goal itself. But, moreover, in a typical case of an external attempt, as it can possibly occur even in the course of intelligent problem solving, long before success or failure are arrived at, it is possible to recognize whether it serves the desired use or not. Blind trials of any activities in the sense of the behaviouristic theory of learning are thus possible and sometimes unavoidable. But in no way are blind trials the only or even the only preferred way of problem solving.

(10) *On the Principle of Additivity in the Development of Personality*

W. Koehler and L. von Bertalanffy proved half a century ago that, besides the vegetable bed model of personality as presented by the behaviouristic theory of learning, another model is possible, i.e., the model of a very complex open system with a hierarchy of interrelated subsystems, in full accordance with known natural laws. In the light of our present knowledge of the processes in living organisms, this model is even more probable. It is an important characteristic of such a system that it shows reactions which cannot be understood on the basis of a local disturbance (failure of a certain apparatus) but rather on the basis of a disturbance of the general system equilibrium, and which are therefore to be handled accordingly. The psychoanalytic concept of neuroses, with all that it has in common with S-R psychology, is, in this respect, clearly in accord with the system theory from the very beginning.

In the framework of the new theories and models, it was possible to establish approaches to the process of education which surpass the dubious reward-punishment model. To this, we shall return later.

(11) *On the Principle of Reductionism*

It is a common observation that a living being sometimes stresses its psychic abilities just to get some food under unfavourable conditions, i.e., just to gratify an elementary (organismic) tension. However, the assertion that *all* psychic activity serves only to gratify elementary tensions and, in the psychoanalytic version, to subjectively gratify the achievement of local pleasant feelings contradicts the facts observed not only in the case of great thinkers, scientists, inventors and organizers, but even in the case of an animal exploring new surroundings or a playing child. The tension of an unsolved problem and the restless activity which it induces in a scientist or in an artist, as well as in an interested student and in a rat transferred to unknown surroundings, on the grounds of immediate observations is to be considered as just as elementary as the tension of hunger or of the sex drive. Moreover, this may be conceived theoretically as well on the basis of the facts given in paragraph (8).

The question as to whether the tension resulting in a mental effort is an autochrhonous one or whether it is induced by elementary needs, or whether both occur simultaneously, is thus not a question of principle but rather a factual one and it can be answered only for this or that actual case. In paragraph (8), it was shown that the energy for elementary needs may be consumed by mental interests. What happens here sometimes is in a way similar to the Freudian "sublimation". However, the dynamic relation differs. Whereas in Freud's concept the block of normal gratification of the accumulated drive energy results in a mental activity, in the model of the open system the opposite appears. An intensive mental activity attracts the energy available in the neighboring systems like fire attracts the air with which it grows and preserves itself.

(12) *On the Principle of Primary Social Atomism*

Primary social atomism is, as has been shown already, a subspecies of reductionism. Behaviourism and psychoanalysis agree here again. In the latter, it is expressed even more clearly in the description of the "Erogenous zones" which are supposed to be the main gratification areas in early infancy, in labelling the other man as an "object" of the drive, i.e., as the tool of the primary body-centered gratification, and in that it considers the organism as the main source of gratification so that other people are not indispensable even as tools.

Again, the question arises: is there an alternative? This question can be divided in the following six sub-questions:
1) Are there some primary and, at the same time, vital social needs?
2) Have other people and beings who form groups together with the Ego really the psychological character of tools serving the Ego, or are they possibly, for a normal human being, of the same psychological relevance and of the same significance as the Ego, and, under some conditions, possibly even of greater importance?
3) Are the social structures in whose framework the individual exists and lives realities of the same relevance as his own Ego?
(4) Is the way in which the individual participates in his group relevant to his manner of general behaviour, first of all for his capability of *normal* behaviour?

5) Does there possibly exist a basic relation between the social needs or tendencies of the individual group members and those of the group as a whole?

6) Do these structures have system properties? For instance, have they autochthonous tendencies towards transition into extreme or optimum states and towards stabilization in these states?

There is no doubt about the answer. The sensitivity of small children towards separation from the second year of their life, discovered by Rene Spitz, tells all that is necessary as to question 1). Concerning the second question, from the abundance of facts pertaining to it, let us mention only the phenomenon of conformity pressure. Questions 3) and 4) were answered affirmatively long ago in the individual psychology of Alfred Adler, and recently in certain forms of neo-psychoanalysis. See also Schulte (1924). It should be stressed here that the proneness to a socially desirable behaviour, which, as was shown at the beginning, cannot be practically influenced by rewards and punishments, is based essentially on the consciousness of one's pertinence to a group as a member, accepted without reserve and enjoying full rights. Only those educational efforts which take account of this fact can be successful. Clearly affirmative for question 5) are the facts found by Lewin and Lippitt (1938-39), and from here it is possible to find illustrative and provable insights even for question 6).

There is no doubt any longer that it is possible in this way to derive immediate suggestions of modern education for which classical behaviourism had no explanation.

AN ANSWER

Now, we are able to answer the question of whether there are still different schools in contemporary psychology, and the answer is a clear "Yes".

There are essentially two such schools. One of them is American behaviourism and the Russian doctrine on the highest nervous activity which have much in common. The other is Wertheimer's and Koehler's Gestalt theory and von Bertalanffy's theory of open systems which is largely in accordance with Gestalt theory, and, in the sphere

of psychotherapeutic schools, Adler's Individual Psychology.
(Orthodox psychoanalysis is somewhere in the middle. It
clearly conceives the total personality as a dynamic system.
In other respects, however, it corresponds largely with
behaviourism). The antagonism of these two approaches could
hardly be more profound and comprehensive. Thus, we may
state in full confidence that the tensions between anta-
gonistic and feuding schools, which are the *spiritus agens*
of all the progress of science, still exist at their fullest
in contemporary psychology. In the number of its advo-
cates and followers, the second school is hardly more than
a lost handful, and one can hardly avoid the conformity
pressure of the world-ruling first school. Nevertheless,
everything goes for the second school, and, as in the
search for truth the principle of democratic majority *does
not hold*, there is no doubt that the future will belong
to it.

BIBLIOGRAPHY

ADLER, A., *Praxis und Theorie der Individualpsychologie*.
München: Bergmann, 1927.

AICHHORN, A., *Verwahrloste Jugend*. Vienna: Intern. Psychoanal. Verlag, 1931.

ASCH, S.E., "A Problem in the Theory of Associations",
Psychol. Beitr., *6*, 553-563, 1961.

ASCH, S.E., "Effects of Group Pressure upon the Modification
and Distortion of Judgment". *Documents of Gestalt Psychology*, HENLE, Mary (ed.), Berkeley: U. of California Press,
1961.

von BERTALANFFY, L., "Der Organismus als physikalisches
System". *Naturwiss.*, *28*, 521-531, 1940.

von BERTALANFFY, L., *Biophysik des Fliessgleichgewichts*.
Braunschweig: Vieweg, 1953.

CANNON, W.B., *The Wisdom of the Body*. New York: Norton,
1932.

COGHILL, G.E., "The Development of Movement in the Hind Leg
of Amblystoma". *Proc. Soc. Exp. Biol. Med.*, *27*, 1929.

COGHILL, G.E., "Integration and Motivation of Behavior as Problems of Growth". *J. Genet. Psychol.*, *18*, 1936.

CORELL, W. *Lernpsychologie*. Donauwörth, 1963.

CORNELIUS, H., *Psychologie als Erfahrungswissenschaft*. Leipzig: Teubner, 1897.

CRUTCHFIELD, R.S., "Conformity and Character". *Amer. Psychologist*, *10*, 191-198, 1955.

DRÖSLER, I., "Modell versus Schema in der Wahrnehmungspsychologie". *Kongr. Ber. 24* (Göttingen 1965), 65-68.

FREUD, S., "Zeitgemässes über Krieg und Tod". *Ges. Werke, X*. Frankfurt: Fischer, 324-355, 1963.

FREUD, S., "Das Ich und das Es". *Ges. Werke, XIII*. Frankfurt: Fischer, 236-290, 1963.

HARLOW, H.F., "The Nature of Love". *Amer. Psychologist*, *12*, 673-685, 1958.

HECKHAUSEN, H., "Entwurf einer Psychologie des Spielens". *Psychol. Forsch.*, *27*, 225-243, 1964.

HERING, E., *Grundzüge der Lehre vom Lichtsinn*. Berlin: Springer, 1920.

von HOLST, E., "Vom Wesen der Ordnung im Zentralnervensystem". *Naturwiss.*, *25*, 1937.

von HOLST, E., "Entwurf eines Systems der lokomotorischen Periodenbildung bei Fischen. Ein kritischer Beitrag zum Gestaltproblem". *Z. Vergl. Physiol.*, *26*, 481, 1939.

HORNEY, J. McV., "Intrinsic Motivation and its Role in Psychological Development". *Nebraska Symposium Motivation 1965*, 189-282.

JAMES, W., *Principles of Psychology*. New York: Holt, 1890.

KANIZSA, G., "Der empirische Faktor in der Wahrnehmung". *Vortrag gehalten anläszlich der 1. Zusammenkunft der Psychologen aus den Donauländern*. Sept. 14-19, 1967. Bratislava, CSSR.

KÖHLER, W., *Intelligenzprüfungen an Anthropoiden*. Abh. Preuss. Akad. Wiss., 1917.

KÖHLER, W., *Die physischen Gestalten in Ruhe und im stationären Zustand*. Erlangen: Weltkreisverlag, 1920.

KÖHLER, W., "Gestaltprobleme und Anfänge einer Gestalttheorie". *Jber. ges. Physiol., 3/1*, 512-539, 1925.

KÖHLER, W., "Zum Problem der Regulation". *Roux' Arch. Entwicklungsmech., 112*, 315-332, 1927. •

KÖHLER, W., "Direction of Processes in Living Systems". *Scient. Monthly, 80*, 29-32, 1955.

KÖHLER, W., "The Obsessions of Normal People". Paper read at the inauguration of the Graduate School of Arts and Sciences at Brandeis University, 1958.

KÖHLER, W. and von RESTORFF, H., "Zur Theorie der Reproduktion". *Psychol. Forsch., 21*, 56-112, 1935..

KRUEGER, F., "Über Entwicklungspsychologie". *Arb. Entwicklungs psychol., 1*, 1915.

LEWIN, K. and LIPPITT, R., "An Experimental Approach to the Study of Autocracy and Democracy". *Sociometry, 1*, 292-300, 1938.

LEWIN, K., LIPPITT, R. and WHITE, R.K. "Patterns of Aggressive Behavior in Experimentally Created 'Social Climates'". *J. Soc. Psychol., 10*, 271-299, 1939.

LORENZ, K., "Phylogenetische Anpassung und adaptive Modifikation des Verhaltens". *Z. Tierpsychol., 18*, 139-187, 1961.

MACH, E., *Die Analyse der Empfindungen*. Jena: Fischer, 1918.

METZGER, W., *Psychologie*. Darmstadt: Steinkopff, 1963.

METZGER, W., "Figuralwahrnehmung" in *Wahrnehmung und Bewusstsein. Hdb. d. Psychol.*, METZGER, W. and ERKE, H. (eds.), Göttingen: Hogrefe, *1/1*, 693-744, 1966.

MILGRAM, S., "Rationality and Conformity". *Sci. Amer.*, *205*, 45-51, 1961.

MILLER, G.A., GALANTER, E., and PRIBRAM, K.H., *Plans and the Structure of Behavior*. New York: Holt, 1960.

SCHENK-DANZIGER, LOTTE. "Die psychischen Grundbedürfnisse des Kindes". *Westerm. Paed. Beitr.*, *1*, 16-18, 1953.

SCHULTE, H., "Versuch einer Theorie der paranoischen Eigenbeziehung und Wahnbildung". *Psychol. Forsch.*, *5*, 1-23, 1924.

SIMON, A., *Verstehen und Helfen*. München: Oldenbourg, 1951.

SKINNER, B.F., *The Behavior of Animals: An Experimental Analysis*. New York: Appleton-Century-Crofts, 1938.

SPITZ, R.A., *Die Entstehung der ersten Objektbeziehungen*. Stuttgart: Klett, 1960.

TOLMAN, E.C., *Purposive Behavior in Animals and Men*. New York: Appleton-Century-Crofts, 1932.

WERNER, H., *Einführung in die Entwicklungspsychologie*. München: Barth, 1959.

WERTHEIMER, M., "Experimentelle Studien uber das Sehen von Bewegung". *Z. Psychol.*, *61*, 161-265, 1912.

WERTHEIMER, M., "Untersuchungen zur Lehre von der Gestalt II". *Psychol. Forsch.*, *4*, 301-350, 1923.

WERTHEIMER, M., *Productive Thinking*. New York and London: Harper Brothers, 1945. German version: *Produktives Denken*. Frankfurt: Kramer, 1957.

ZULLIGER, H., *Helfen statt Strafen auch bei jugendlichen Dieben*. Stuttgart: Klett, 1956.

ZULLIGER, H., *Jugendliche und Halbstarke. Ihre Psychologie und ihre Führung*. Zürich: Classen, 1958.

CAUSALITY, AWARENESS, AND PSYCHOLOGICAL EVENTS

SILVANO ARIETI

103 E. 75th St., New York, N.Y. 10021, U.S.A.

Causality has been a great philosophical concern since Plato. It is not within the scope of this article to review the philosophical implications of this problem. I merely want to indicate some additional difficulties and some hypotheses which come up for consideration when we examine the issue from the particular point of view of psychological and psychopathological events.

As a philosophical background from which to depart I shall recall that traditionally the notion of causality has assumed three forms. The first sees in causality a rational connection. The effect can be deduced from its cause, which is its reason. The second form sees causation as an empirical or temporal connection. The effect is not rationally deducible from the cause, but can be predicted. In a third or teleologic form the notion of causality is blended with finalism: the end result is the cause of any type of organization. The future determines the present. This third notion was expanded chiefly by Aristotle, but both Plato and Aristotle attribute the origin of it to Anaxagoras.

---

* This article contains some excerpts from the book of the author, *The Intrapsychic Self: Feeling, Cognition and Creativity in Health and Mental Illness.* New York: Basic Books, 1967.

With some exceptions, science has repudiated this
third notion of causality, which, nevertheless, continues
to play an important role in biological and psychological
conceptions. The phenomenon of adaptation, recognizable
in living organisms, makes it difficult for some authors
to remove teleology or finalism from science. All
organisms undergo phylogenetically and ontogenetically
some changes which seem to have been preconceived for the
purpose of enhancing the survival of the individual or of
the species. In some cultural milieu these changes were
interpreted, and still are, as evidence of a purpose which
transcends the survival of subhuman species, but is
related to man's benefit. In the early 19th Century, the
validity of Aristotelian teleology seemed evident to the
prominent biologist Cuvier who "could think of no better
reason for the existence of fishes - which he considered
poor things, even to the watery, unromantic nature of
their *amours* - than that they provide food for man"
(quoted from Simpson, 1963).

The existence of living organisms was viewed as fulfilling God's aim of providing food for man. A teleological point of view thus became blended with a theological
point of view. One of the clearest expressions of this
way of thinking is that expressed on November 18, 1957 by
Pope Pius XII. Addressing an audience composed of several
hundred workers from a Roman slaughterhouse, the Pope
said, "He would err who considered it reprehensible to
kill animals that man needs for food. Your work, beloved
sons, therefore, is just and under certain conditions even
praiseworthy. Everything has, in fact, been created by
God: Men, animals, plants, things; and as a consequence
everything must be used in his service." Pius XII added
that of all created things only man loves God and can
praise and love Him. It is for this reason that "by
divine disposition minerals serve the plants and plants
serve the animals and the animals serve man: so that all
may, through man, serve God. But man, in order to use
animals must often, alas, make them suffer and must often
kill them. There is therefore nothing intrinsically
reprehensible in this" (from the *New York Times*, November
19, 1957).

Actually science has been able to explain deterministically the process of life and evolution. Darwin could demonstrate how variations (later more appropriately called mutations) and natural selection bring about this apparent finalism. In the next section we shall discuss how some apparently finalistic systems, which I call prepsychological, do not require teleological causality. In some psychological systems teleology can be maintained, but can be reconciled with determinism, of which it is considered only a derivation or subvariety.

The relation between determinism and psychological causality, awareness, motivation, volition, spontaneity, and unconscious motivation will be discussed in subsequent sections.

PREPSYCHOLOGICAL SYSTEMS

The non-biological world is susceptible of being interpreted almost in all its known parts with the first, or, if we prefer, second form of causality. The universe can be seen as constituted of endless chains of causes and effects. These are series of events which follow one another in some kind of order. For instance, if the humidity of the air reaches a certain point of saturation, clouds and eventually rain are formed. If the temperature drops below a certain degree, rain changes into snow; if the temperature rises again the snow changes into water, etc. Each element of the series brings about a subsequent one. The chain of causes and effects can extend indefinitely. We do not know the beginning of any series, nor the end. What we can hope to do is to observe or study segments of these endless chains. With the increase of our scientific knowledge we constantly enlarge the length of these segments, but that is as much as we can aspire to. The chains we have referred to are typical of what is generally called deterministic causality. They have the following characteristics:

1. They are endless.

2. With some questionable exceptions, events regulated by this type of causality seem also to be regulated by the second principle of thermodynamics, or entropy;

that is, bodies tend to become less organized through
the passage of time. A progressive disorganization
leads to simpler structures.

3. The chains follow the unidirectional arrow of time.
In a series A ⟶ B ⟶ C ⟶ D ..., B follows A, C
follows B, etc., indefinitely. A is also preceded by
an endless series of antecedents. For the sake of
simplification we have taken into consideration here
only a simple chain series, but connected systems of
causal relationships are the rule.

We shall examine now instead what happens in a
biological or organic set-up. We shall consider a very
primitive organism which we shall designate as V (from
vivus, alive). Many researchers are currently studying
how V came to be transformed from a colloidal system into
an organism, but I shall not take into consideration this
problem. V is subject to all the rules and vicissitudes
to which all the entities of the world are subjected, and
is involved with segments of deterministic chains of
causes and effects. But V has a special characteristic.
Among a very large number of different possibilities it
may come into contact with a special substance which we
shall call C (from *cibus*, food). C produces a special
effect on V, so that V will continue to be as it is,
without degrading, and will continue to react in the same
way, if and when it has a second encounter with another
quantity of C. To give an example, C is like the oxygen
which we are breathing in this moment, and which enables
us to breathe again a moment later. The V-C sequence is a
very improbable occurrence, but in a cosmic order ot time,
among billions of combinations, eventually such an accur-
rence takes place. Now the relation between V and C can
be viewed in the following way:

that is, as parts of a circular system. C acts on V, but
V will act again on the C which will become available. V
will act on C by incorporating it. C will act on V, by
permitting V's prolongation in time, so that it will be
able to react again to C. The chemical essence of C

permite V to prolong its entity as V. The survival of V
enables V again to react to C in the same way. If instead
of C only other substances within a certain period of time
will come into contact with V, V will decompose or degrade
so that it will never again react to C. V will undergo
chemical changes which will constitute segments of
longitudinal deterministic chains of causes and effects
and not necessarily of circular systems.

Now, any form of life can be seen as an enormously
complicated reproduction of the cycle we have described.
The life of all known organisms does not consist of two
stages only, but of cycles which include perhaps trillions
of successive steps which have to occur in a given
sequence. Each stage follows the previous one in a
deterministic way. Only when the living cycle unfolds in
a particular order does it repeat itself; that is, it
survives*. If the stages cease to be in a special
sequence the cycle is interrupted and each of its elements
will have a position only in longitudinal deterministic
series. The cycle will be recognized as consisting of
many feedback or servo-mechanisms, as described in
cybernetics (Wiener, 1948) and with the systemic
characteristics described by von Bertalanffy (1956).

Cycle situations do not occur, of course, only in
living organisms. Cybernetics and the new science of
computers have amply illustrated the cyclical course of
many phenomena. They are also found in the universe at
large: for instance, a solar system is a self-regulating
cyclical mechanism. Not only biology and physiology but
also sociology and organization theory have illustrated
many cyclical mechanisms. After a while we no longer know
what was the cause and what the effect, what was "the
purpose" and what was the achieved "aim." For instance, a
factory produces several tools. These tools are used to
build other factories. A cycle thus originates. Are the
tools necessary to build factories or are factories

---

* For the sake of simplicity, we omit considering
here that extremely important part of the cycle which is
concerned with reproduction and permits the continuation
of generations of V's. Reproduction is a subcycle within
a cycle.

necessary to build tools? Another example: a feeling of
religiosity makes a small community build a church. The
church perpetuates the feeling of religiosity, which otherwise would weaken or be discharged into other outlets.

From these examples it appears that when a cyclic
system occurs in a previously longitudinal series of
events: 1) a purpose seems to emerge, 2) we lose track of
which of the events comes first (problem of the chicken
and the egg). In the biological examples, the purpose
seems to be the preservation of the vital cycle. Actually
each step of the cycle occurs in a deterministic way.
Only we, who are outsiders in relation to the cycle, see a
purpose. We see a purpose because we can see the whole
cycle. Another hypothetical observer, whose life span is
shorter than that of the cycle, would see only a
deterministic sequence, not a purpose.

Purposefulness, finalism, or teleologic causality, *in
relation to this level of organization, is only an
outsider's attitude toward a cyclic variation of
deterministic causality*. The self-preserving cycle can be
interpreted deterministically.

Deterministic causality may be represented in the
following way:

. ————————→ . ————————→ . ————————→ . . . ., ad infinitum.

Each event (represented by a dot) leads to a subsequent
event.

Cyclic or pseudo-teleologic causality can be
represented in the following way:

The cycles are part of a deterministic chain. The coincidence of a very improbable set of circumstances
permits the cycle to exist and to repeat itself. When
these circumstances are altered the cycle will break. A
cyclic system, be it that of the life of a virus or of a
solar system, is an interlude in a deterministic
succession.

By genetically retaining some mutations, living organisms develop the capacity for *adaptation*; that is, of having available alternative segments of the vital cycle, which will make the survival of the whole cycle more probable when unusual circumstances threaten its continuity. For instance, reactions of immunity toward invading germs are examples of adaptational alternatives. These adaptive mechanisms are the result of the long range moulding of the organism by selective evolution, through the interplay of mutations and environmental factors (Dubos, 1966). At times improved function, and not necessarily survival, seems the immediate goal.

Adaptation can be studied phylogenetically, through the study of the changes which favor the survival of the species, and, ontogenetically, through the study of the changes which favor the survival of the individual.

It should be clear, however, that adaptation can be seen deterministically as the result of the interplay between environmental factors and mutations more favorable than others to survival. More probable survival is not a purpose; it is an effect of some environmental conditions and mutations, which in our human evaluation, seem desirable. Adaptation is thus a cyclical variation of deterministic causality, which is possible when the cycle permits a limited range of alternate courses. It is thus unfortunate that some psychological and psychoanalytic schools (for instance, the school of Rado[*]) have assumed the name of adaptational schools to indicate their tenet that adaptation is the basic mechanism of the psyche.

Although it is true that many psychological phenomena can be seen in an adaptational frame of reference, the psyche, as we shall see later, follows more specific mechanisms. Adaptation is a term which should be reserved to biology at large, including both vegetable and animal forms, and not to the psyche.

---

[*] See RADO, S., *Psychoanalysis of Behavior*. New York: Grune and Stratton, 1956.

AWARENESS AND MOTIVATION

When awareness emerges as a result of complicated and improbable successions of mutations, a revolutionary event has occurred in the universe. No longer does the vital cycle depend exclusively on physico-chemical factors or on simple adaptational mechanisms, but on the awareness of what is pleasant (and to be searched for) and of what is unpleasant (and to be avoided) (Arieti, 1960). Awareness will direct the response of the organism: at first, withdrawal or approach, later, with much more complicated responses.

A thirsty animal, for instance, is not just thirsty; by the state of thirst, it is moved toward searching for water. The subhuman animal is not aware in a cognitive sense of the danger of dehydration; but is driven to remove the unpleasant sensation of thirst. If the animal could not experience thirst it could die of dehydration. It is obvious that species provided with this type of sensation have much more probability of survival. Natural selection has thus favored the evolution of awareness.

Unpleasant sensations trigger off responses which lead to the removal of the unpleasant feeling. Pleasant sensations trigger off responses which lead to the search for ways to prolong or renew the pleasant feeling. At times there are mixed forms of sensations.

We may recognize in the life of animal forms a rule, although a rule with many exceptions: what is pleasant enhances survival and what is unpleasant decreases the chance of survival. Pleasantness and increased probability of survival thus become associated and their association is transmitted from generation to generation. Although this association is imperfect and susceptible of many unfavorable exceptions in relation to individual cases, it is a statistically favorable one from the point of the preservation of the species.

Awareness or subjectivity, thus, brings about in the universe that revolutionary phenomenon which, according to various points of view, is called purposiveness, teleologic causality, or motivation. The organism is now equipped with a subjectively experienced purpose and therefore can no longer be equated to a machine or to a

cybernetic system. Purpose does not exist only for an
outsider who contemplates a self-perpetuating cycle, but
for the subject itself which constitutes the cycle. We
can no longer speak here of pseudopurposiveness or pseudo-
teleologic causality but of real purposiveness, real
motivation. Of course, at this level purposiveness is of
the most primitive type: search for (or the need to seek)
pleasure and the removal of (or the necessity to avoid)
non-pleasure.

The universe seems to be regulated no longer only by
deterministic (or efficient) causality, but also by
teleologic (or finalistic) causality. An aim, that is,
something involving something else not yet present (for
instance, satisfaction of hunger), is directing present
animal behavior. It seems as if, contrary to what happens
in the rest of the world where only the past determines
the present, now the future too participates in directing
the present.

In my opinion, purposiveness, or motivation, as it is
more frequently called in psychological studies, is not in
contradiction with determinism, but is a variety of it.
To consider again our example of the thirsty animal, the
animal is thirsty *now*; its *present* state of thirst
determines its forthcoming movements and behavior. The
animal is pushed *a tergo*. However, the *a tergo* feeling of
being pushed becomes connected with a future event and
therefore can be considered purposeful. Purposefulness is
thus a special type of adaptation which is connected with
awareness: more specifically with a feeling that has
something to do with the present and future state of the
organism.

Let us remember, however, that this purposeful
adaptation cannot be considered just a reaction to the
environment, similar to that of some man-built machines.
Between the environment and the reaction there is an inner
experience, a subjective phenomenon. It is this subjective phenomena which constitutes the essential element
of psychological life and, among others, of the phenomenon
of purposiveness.

The present author's position is thus the opposite of
that maintained by the behavioristic school. Skinner

(1954), for instance, states that, "By arguing that the
individual organism simply reacts to its environment,
rather than to some inner experience of that environment,
the bifurcation of nature into physical and psychic can
be avoided." The bifurcation to which Skinner refers is
something which, to many thinkers, both in the field of
science and philosophy, is hard to accept. We may hope
that one day man will be able to make the craved synthesis
between the two branches of the bifurcation. But, by
simply following Skinner's suggestion of denying the
existence of one of the two branches, not only do we
arbitrarily refuse to face the issue, but we also refuse
to come to grips with the essential characteristic of what
we want to study. It is indeed the emergence of subjectivity that brings forth into the universe a new
category of events, namely the psychological.

Some authors have seen in purposiveness the most
important aspect of life, even more important than
awareness (E.S. Russell, 1945; du Noüy, 1947; Sinnot,
1955). Russell speaks of directiveness which he calls an
irreducible activity, that is, an activity which cannot be
understood in terms of its physico-chemical properties or
of mechanical deterministic causality.

It seems to me that awareness is a prerequisite for
purposefulness, which should not be confused with the
various forms of cyclical causality, including adaptation.
The emergence of awareness, with consequent experience of
pain and pleasure, and behavior directed toward avoidance
of pain and search of pleasure, are parts of long
deterministic chains of causes and effects. But, when the
animal experiences pain and pleasure and puts into effect
some movements aimed at the avoidance of pain or search
for pleasure, its behavior becomes motivated. That is, in
the long deterministic chain of causes and effects there
is a series of events which become associated with a
purpose. The purpose is experiential: that is, is not
yet evaluated by cognitive processes but is felt as a
subjective tendency.

With the evolution of animal species, the motivation
is no longer that of avoiding physical pain and searching
or maintaining physical pleasure. The expansion of the
cognitive, and especially the symbolic, functions of man,

permits us to visualize more complicated aims. With the
evolution of society, the avoidance of physical pain and
the search for physical pleasure, and of increasing the
probability of survival, are no longer the only goals.
The concepts of personal significance, of self-identity,
of one's role in life, of self-esteem, acquire prominence
and could not exist without complex cognitive constructs.
These concepts, however, are connected with high emotions,
which replace the primitive sensations of pain and
pleasure. These high emotions constitute the motivational
aspects of these concepts (Arieti, 1960, 1967).

As a matter of fact, as I have already done elsewhere
(Arieti, 1965a, 1965b, 1967), I would like to stress that
in psychiatry, psychology, and psychoanalysis, the
emphasis so far has unduly been on the motivational
importance of bodily needs, instinctual behavior, and
primitive emotions, which can exist without a cognitive
counterpart or with a very limited one. In the second
half of the Twentieth Century, fewer men than ever before
starve for food or sex, and yet psychological malaise and
mental illness have increased, not decreased. It seems to
this author that many of the important emotional factors
which motivate or disturb men are among those which need
to be sustained or actually engendered by complicated
symbolic processes. According to the Freudian school
these concept-feelings are only displacements, detours, or
rationalizations which disguise instinctual drives or more
primitive constructs. Although it is so in several cases,
it is a reductionistic point of view to think that it is
so universally or in most instances.

According to this writer, another dimension has to be
considered with the emergence in the universe of the
feelings of pain and pleasure: the eventual possibility
at a human level of ethical experience. According to the
writer, inherent ethics is the aim, often only indirectly
actualizable, of removing pain from others and from the
self, and if possible of making pleasure available to
others and to the self. Pain and pleasure start as crude
sensations, but, with the development of the cognitive
functions, they consist of very complicated symbolic and
emotional constructs.

Summarizing, we could say that motivation (or
psychological causality, or purposefulness) starts with

the appearance of sensuous pleasure and pain, but later
transcends its origin by means of symbolic and complicated
emotional processes. Motivation becomes thus a fundamental psychological force. There is no need to believe
that a psychological force must consist of a physical
energy, libido, or cathexis. It is a readiness to
activity which is determined by feelings and cognitive
evaluations, and is maintained by the excitability of some
parts of the nervous system. Physiologists have
repeatedly stated that it is not necessary to postulate
the existence of psychic energy to explain the occurrence
of motivation or of other physiological mechanisms
(Lashley, in Lashley and Colby, 1957). Not all animal
functions are motivated. Most of them are the results of
physico-biochemical mechanisms which operate in the framework of selective evolution and are transmitted
genetically. In other words, these non-motivated
functions may still be interpreted as belonging to
adaptational or even pre-adaptational systems.

WILL AND SPONTANEITY

    The subjective experiences which promote or impel us
to search for pleasure and avoid pain can be
conceptualized as drives or as wishes. The word drive is
more properly applied when the organismic state, subjectively felt as an experience, leads to behavior which
will remove the pain or attain the pleasure. The word
wish is more properly applied when the search for pleasure
or avoidance of pain are anticipated by means of images or
more complicated cognitive constructs.

    Drives and wishes constitute the backbone of what is
called motivation and a large part of psychological
causality. However, psychological causality may appear in
even more complicated forms. Human action is not
determined only by drives and wishes but also by the will.
If Freudian psychoanalysis differed from behaviorism by
giving importance to inner life, it joined ranks with
behaviorism in eliminating the role of volition from the
study of the human psyche. On account of these, in this
respect converging theoretical orientations, the psyche
has come to be interpreted by many as a reacting entity, a
robot, something pushed or pulled by external forces (see

von Bertalanffy, 1962, 1964). Other psychological schools
which are particularly concerned with motivation, either
ignore volition or deny that such a thing as volition
exists, or confuse volition with motivation.

Incidentally, some philosophical schools made a
similar confusion when they equated will with what in
Latin was called *appetitio*. According to this viewpoint
to will means to *wish*, or to choose the wished alternative.
Actually, Freud stressed the point that to follow the wish
is to live according to the pleasure principle and not
according to the reality principle. The child learns that
some wishes should not be actualized. If he actualizes
them, some unpleasant effect will be brought about by some
environmental forces, existing either in his family or in
society at large. The child develops the ability to
choose between actualizing or inhibiting the forbidden
wish. Throughout his life the individual will find himself confronted with many contrasting wishes. He must
choose among them. We may see man as pushed and pulled by
different goals, or as the actualizer of personal choices,
among multiple possible goals. At times the individual
chooses a course of action not in accordance with the
strongest of his wishes but in contrast to it. An act of
will may consist of resisting a wish – or the strongest
wish. This occurs, for instance, when following the
ethical principle, man decides to follow a course of
action which will not remove his pain or attain his
pleasure, but that of others. Critics of this point of
view believe that willing to resist the wish is also
determined by a wish, namely the wish to resist the wish.
We must partially accept this point of view and state that
to act ethically, and not for the exclusive benefit of
oneself, is also motivated action.

We could say that it is a volitional function to
choose the motivation, even the weakest, when the cognitive processes have permitted the visualization of the
different choices and their effects. The possibility of
choosing among the motivations permits the entrance of a
universe of values. No value exists for man as long as he
cannot choose (von Bertalanffy, 1964a). When volition
appears, evolution, as simply biological, has run its
course. The law of the jungle (or of the pleasure
principle), by which Darwin partially explained selective

evolution, is now in competition with values which permit
even the weak, the defective, the unfit, in general, to
survive and to be respected in their human dignity. At
the level of evolution where choice enters, the possibility arises of a revolution greater than the Copernican,
that is, capable of superseding the principles of biological evolution, adaptation, and even pleasure-oriented
motivation.

Choice permits the attributing of the quality "value"
even to needs, experiences, or things, which existed
before the possibility of choice emerged. For instance,
primitive pleasure acquires a hedonistic value, once man
has the prerogative of accepting or rejecting such
pleasure.

A mistake, commonly made in the study of volition, is
that of assuming extremist positions. We have already
mentioned one, namely, denying will altogether and
accepting only the existence of motivation as the
psychological determinant of action. Not only psychoanalysts of the orthodox Freudian school, but also many of
neo-Freudian orientation believe that every act is
motivated, not freely chosen. Not the will, then, but the
motivation, conscious or unconscious, or the strongest of
the possible motivations, would determine the choice. If
motivation removes the possibility of free choice then the
only act of free will would be the one which is not
motivated. But an act which is not motivated at all is
not performed *voluntarily* by any human being; it is automatic or reflex. Some psychoanalysts believe that everything follows conscious or, most of the time, unconscious
determinism and that we fool ourselves into believing that
we choose. For instance, acting against wish A is an
effect of wish B. But even wish B, which on the surface
looks like a willful determination, rests on another unconscious wish C.

Some philosophers and legislators, who are concerned
with individual legal responsibility, assume a completely
opposite point of view and would like to establish that a
completely free choice exists. The will would be like a
sphincter. It would be up to the individual to contract
or relax the sphincter, when certain potential actions
exert pressure to pass through. Partial choice and

partial volition would thus be inherent contradictions. They appear as contradictions, however, only if we forget the tortuous courses the psyche has to go through before reaching certain positions. We may, for instance, remember that what seemed logical and final truths at times have originated from primitive paleological, and, according to usual standards, illogical forms of thinking (Arieti, 1962, 1965b, 1967). Although we may still be under the influence of a general universal determinism, our range of choices or relative freedom is always increasing. This increase is obvious when we compare different levels of development in the phylogenetic and ontogenetic scales. It is also a common experience that our possibilities of behavior expand in the state of mental health, and vice versa, tend to become more rigid, or reduced to fixed, more automatic and less voluntary patterns, in the state of mental illness. Moreover, human creativity increased the range of possible forms of experience and of behavior for all men. Creativity is not restricted to practical and immediate goals but increases the realm of our ideals and ethical concepts.

It is beyond the purpose of this article to discuss the various hypotheses about the neurological and psychological mechanisms of will. I have, to some extent, studied this problem in other writings (Arieti, 1955, 1961, 1967).

We must mention, however, that if we connect free will with freedom from necessity or from causality, we then approach the difficult problems of chance, indeterminacy, non-causality, spontaneity, and even creation *ex nihilo*, which is a theological concept. Indeterminacy and chance have to be disconnected from the phenomenon of will. It is common evidence that a willed act is not a chance or random act, but a result of a personal determination, which points toward the same or the opposite direction of conscious or unconscious motivation. Moreover, it is well known that many events, allegedly explained by chance, are caused by factors which exist but cannot be determined. In situations other than those determined by will, what we call chance is actually the impossibility to find the causes. For instance, if we play Bingo and we have all the available numbers in a bag, we say that, for example, it is due to chance that we pick

up the number 32 instead of 47 or another one. Actually
each number is printed on a round chip. The man who
picked up the number could not see the fine movements of
his fingers, but the position where the hand and fingers
stopped determined which chip was picked up. If the hand
had made a movement that had stopped, let us say, an
eighth of an inch upward or downward, backward or forward,
another number would have been picked up. Thus, the
number which is picked up is determined by the original
position of the numbers, the force of gravity, and the
movements of our hand. Inasmuch as we do not know the
position of the number and we cannot determine the exact
amplitude of the movements of the hand, we believe that
chance "determines" the number which is picked up. The
type and amplitude of the movements of the hand are due to
physiological variables, which we cannot measure.

To be more exact, we could say that in the long
deterministic chain of causes and effects, we have
segments where for practical purposes we can assume that
indeterminacy reigns. These are the segments in which the
occurrence of events is dependent on a very large number
of indeterminable and uncontrollable factors in space and
time. Mathematical operations can then give us only the
statistical characteristics of probability. The author of
this article is not competent to discuss Heisenberg's
principle in relation to subatomic mechanics. From
biology, however, we may take as an example an act of
fecundation. We cannot predict which one of the available
sperms will impregnate the available egg. If we know that
one fourth of the sperms carry a particular dominant or
recessive gene, we can, in accordance with Mendelian laws,
calculate the probability of the occurrence of a certain
trait. However, which sperm will reach the available egg
is not determined by chance, but by the location of the
sperms, of the egg, and by many untraceable local
conditions.

Similarly, what we call spontaneous behavior may not
be spontaneous at all, but the result of innumerable
factors which not only cannot be measured, but cannot even
be recorded. This consideration probably can be made also
for those movements described in animal forms which do not
seem to be reactions to external forces but an inherent
faculty of the living organism. Von Holst (1936, 1937)

has described the so-called autorhythmic movements which
are not elicited by external stimuli. From these
spontaneous movements of the organism, eventually reflexes
or fixed patterns of responses emerge in evolution. However, we cannot call these autorhythmic movements
volitional. Their so-called spontaneity may be related to
a variety of factors, inherent in the organism, which
cannot be determined at the stage of our knowledge. For
practical purposes we may call this motor activity
spontaneous - a spontaneity that perhaps is related to
what later on will emerge as volition. Von Bertalanffy
(1962) refers to these autorhythmic movements in relation
to his conception of the organism as a spontaneously
active system.

According to the present writer, spontaneity means a
certain range of organismic possibilities offered by the
intrinsic qualities of the organism. These possibilities,
however, at a given level of evolution do not tend to
remain spontaneous, but to follow the law of effect. When
a spontaneous activity becomes connected with an environmental situation and the effect is good from the
point of view of survival or of improved function, it
tends to remain fixated and eventually to become an automatic or even innate function.

When mutations occur, new gamuts of spontaneity
unfold, from some of which good results will develop. And
so on in the phylogenetic scale. Spontaneity, as we have
defined it, plays a very important role in evolution.

Spontaneous variabilities are probably ultimately
based on the fact that the complicated molecular groupings
which constitute living entities have inherently a margin
of instability. The bonds between the atoms form
arrangements which are likely to have a number of
alternatives. Unascertainable reasons, occuring in space
and time, may favor one rather than another possible form.

As we have already mentioned, von Bertalanffy refuses
to see the organism as a robot, manipulated by external
forces, and gives great importance to this spontaneous
internal activity. The present writer agrees with von
Bertalanffy and believes that this internal activity is
ultimately based on this structural instability.

However, we must remember that spontaneity is not enough to characterize the organism. Because of the mentioned feed-back mechanisms which mediate the good effect and the survival of the fittest, spontaneity is followed by *growth*, that is, by evolution. This growth becomes fixated or arrested, until new spontaneity or mutation occurs. Thus, seemingly disorderly spontaneity comes under the ordering effect of natural selection. The result is growth in structuralization.

The greatest range of spontaneity is offered by the symbolic apparatus of man. New combinations are continuously formed, and those which lead to good or reputedly good effects, remain more or less fixated in the culture and transmitted through learning from generation to generation. Creative man must again combine his spontaneous urges with other factors in order to bring about new symbolic forms. Spontaneity often presents itself as reappearance of archaic or obsolete forms (Arieti, 1966, 1967). To some degree, that is, when the good effects are good only for the individual and not accepted by society, growth remains a private personal affair.

It seems to this writer that even if we conceive symbolic growth as the result of factors which have been determined, we should consider it as the most meaningful aspect of human life, perhaps the meaning of human existence. Whether we believe in God or not, whether we believe that life has a teleological foundation or not, there is nothing wrong in giving to this tendency of symbolic life to grow the meaning which we ourselves give to our life and the goal that we want to pursue.

The ethical aim to eliminate pain from others and ourselves is originally in conflict with the natural environment, as evolution is mainly based on the survival of the fittest, and therefore requires pain and premature death of the less fit. However, when symbolic growth can be transmitted from the creative person to others, even the unfit may survive and may be freed from pain. We have then reached that stage at which the new Copernican revolution takes place; the collective symbolic patrimony becomes accessible to all human beings and may be used to compensate for the inborn inequalities of men. Men shall

tend thus to attain symbolic and spiritual equality*. Of
course, means should be devised to prevent the approximation of equality from becoming inimical to further
growth.

If we return to the point made earlier in this
section, we must conclude that choice is related to the
spontaneity we have spoken about, to the possibility of
symbolic alternatives and of various levels of motivation,
and to the presence of inhibiting mechanisms. The
phenomenon which starts as spontaneity must go through all
these processes in order to become volition†.

If we say that the psychological phenomenon of choice
is "dependent on" the factors that we have mentioned,
don't we deny with these very words the concept of
freedom? Not necessarily, if we follow an example from a
more advanced science, physics. According to Galileo's
principle, each body will continue in its uniform motion
until it is deviated by an outside force. As far as we
can ascertain, this principle is true. The whole field of
mechanics is based on it; and yet there is no body in the
universe that is not subjected to outside forces, for
instance, to the force of gravity. Undeviated motion thus
does not exist in reality; it is only a concept, but a
concept on whose truth any motion is susceptible of some
understanding. We hope that we are not following a
fallacious analogy when we advance the idea that undeter-
mined or free will may exist in the same way as undeviated
motion exists. The concept of free will may be retained
as an ideal that accompanies man in his journey of
symbolic and ethical growth. In following this ideal we
renew the endless effort to transcend our deterministic
origin and to add a historical dimension to the physico-
chemical universe.

---

* A minority of theorists believe that growth and
self-actualization come before any other value.

† It is worth noting that the word "spontaneity"
derives from the Latin *sponte*, which has both meanings:
one indicating spontaneity; the other one's will, choice,
determination and initiative. Thus, etymologically too,
spontaneity and volition are related.

UNCONSCIOUS MOTIVATION

We have seen that man tends toward symbolic growth, which is potentially infinite, and toward freer and freer choice, which permits ethical realization. There are, however, other aspects of the problem which indicate that an opposite tendency is also present in man. More than any other great thinker, Freud (1893, 1901, 1938) has illustrated how limited is the freedom of our actions. Many actions of ours, which we believe are put into effect by our conscious determination, are instead caused by forces unknown to us. Many wishes, of which we have no awareness, determine part of our behavior. Let us remember, however, that Freud has indicated that this behavior, which does not depend on our will, is nevertheless motivated. The major concept of psychoanalysis is probably that of "unconscious motivation." Our behavior is determined by wishes, but we remove these wishes from consciousness when they are primitive or replicas of infantile strivings and we are ashamed of them. These secret wishes and drives are objected to by society or by the more mature part of ourselves.

Although we do not conceive any more today of the unconscious as a special division of the psyche, we do generally accept the existence of unconscious motivation in normal and especially in pathological conditions. This motivation, however, operates similarly to conscious psychological teleological causality. For instance, a man has a hysterical amnesia and forgets his home address. Psychoanalytic investigation discovers that the patient had the unconscious wish to forget his address, because he did not want to go back to a home where he was subject to much unhappiness. Textbooks of psychoanalysis are replete with similar examples. The author of this article has described the phenomenon of progressive teleologic regression in schizophrenia (Arieti, 1955).

Must we consider these unconscious motivations as forms of adaptive mechanisms, similar to those, pre-psychological in nature, that we find in subhuman animals and also in vegetables? Undoubtedly many pathological phenomena described in general medicine must be interpreted in this way, as first illustrated by Claude Bernard. For instance, in infective diseases fever may occur as an adaptative reaction to the invasion of foreign proteins. Only organisms that are able to build up adequate defenses against foreign proteins can survive and transmit genetically such possibility.

However, what occurs in psychopathology is more difficult to explain. The symptom seems to have been purposely selected to fit the general psychological picture. For instance, the patient mentioned, suffering from amnesia, underwent what, from the point of view of his immediate desire, was a pleasant escape from his troubles. It is also important to remember that Freud and the whole psychoanalytic school have demonstrated that unconscious motivation plays a large role not just in pathological conditions, but also in normal life.

The writer is inclined to believe that although natural selection has favored the evolution of awareness, at a human level too much awareness became harmful, especially in cases of psychological conflict. Repression, or loss of previously existing awareness, became an adaptational mechanism. However, we must remember that conscious purposiveness, or teleological causation, must exist in the human being before it can be lost. The human mind could not have developed to the extent it did without the faculty of consciousness. Consciousness must still be regarded as the most important characteristic of the psyche, necessary for relatively rapid growth.

The unconscious motivational mechanisms can be considered purposeful and teleological, as long as they retain characteristics or goals which for their occurrence needed a previous state of consciousness. However, they become more adaptational in a general sense and less teleological, the more ingrained they become with other mechanisms of the psyche which never attained consciousness.

Loss of consciousness occurs in man and in subhuman animals through other psychological processes, such as automatization, subliminal perception and distractibility. These processes, which we cannot take into consideration in this article, in their physiological mechanisms are probably related to the phenomenon of repression.

ORIGIN OF THE CONCEPT OF CAUSALITY

We have examined the phenomenon of causality in relation to determinism, adaptation, motivation, volition, spontaneity, and unconscious motivation. Inasmuch as the main interest of the author of this article is in the psychiatric and psychological sciences, it is understandable that he wants to tackle also the problem of how the concept of causality has been acquired by man. Piaget (1930) has studied the problem ontogenetically. The present author's approach is somewhat different. Space limitations will permit only a summary of views he has expressed in greater detail elsewhere (Arieti, 1967).

Although deterministic causality precedes any other form of causality, it has been one of the last to be understood by man. It is followed historically only by unconscious motivation, brought to full light by Freud. To be explicit, will and wish (that is, teleological causality) have been understood earlier than determinism in phylogenesis and ontogenesis as causative mechanisms. Ancient people often resorted to a teleological type of explanation. If it is not human will, it is divine will which has caused an event to occur. Apollo, god of the Sun, is tired and goes to sleep - that's why night occurs. You are sick because your enemy wants you to become sick. Mythology is to a large extent an attempt to interpret nature in accordance with teleological, not physical, causality. Trees, rivers, lakes, seas are anthropomorphized. Epidemics, droughts are the result of the anger of personal gods and have no scientific basis.

The study of early interpersonal relations may explain how teleological causality develops in childhood. Before the surrounding human beings assume symbolic importance, the life of the child is almost governed by reflexes, conditioned and unconditioned, and by autonomous mechanisms. Simple associations are taken for granted. Hunger, for instance, is followed by the appearance of mother's breast. Events seem to occur just by temporal or spatial contiguity, in a sort of natural sequence.

Somewhat later, but still before the child has acquired the ability to speak, he can already sense some kind of vague intentionality in the surrounding adults.

For instance, he understands in a primitive way that it is
up to mother to feed him, to keep him on her lap, to
fondle him. He could even, through imagery, expect these
things to happen and anticipate them. However, this vague
intentionality cannot yet be abstracted or conceived as a
causal factor or as an act of will, until the child can by
means of words represent people and actions, and detach
them from the total situation in which he finds himself.
When the young child acquires a rudimentary language he
learns to interpret everything in a teleological way -
everything depends on the will or actions of others. The
child makes a generalization and comes to conceive everything in nature as consequence of a will. The "because"
with which he explains events means only "for the purpose
of," that is, for the purpose of fulfilling a wish or a
willed determination. It will be very difficult for the
child to relinquish later such beliefs, unless he is
helped to do so. School and life in general in a
civilized world will help him to proceed to another order
of causality. The transition will be rapid because the
child is offered, ready-made, new concepts and systems of
symbolism with which it will be relatively easy to grasp
new concepts of causality.

When the child reaches a more advanced level of
cognition, the phenomena which, by a generalization of the
early interpersonal experiences, had been anthropomorphized, are depersonalized again. Wish and will are
disconnected from causality. "Because" now may mean not
only "for the purpose of" but also "on account of." For
instance, the water became ice because (on account of the
fact that) the temperature was below 32 degrees.

It is surprising how seldom, even in such high
cultures as those of the Hebrews, Greeks, and Romans,
deterministic causality was recognized. Undoubtedly the
individual person was able to see causal deterministic
connections, but the culture as a whole was not permeated
by such a concept. Just as in some stages of child
development the two causalities overlap, first with a
preponderance of teleological causality and finally of
deterministic, so in some periods of history we find a
preponderance of teleologic thinking gradually changing
into a preponderance of deterministic thinking. It is
only at the time of the Renaissance, after Bacon, Kepler

and, especially, after Galileo, that deterministic causality became dominant.

Deterministic causality, which seems so evident as to have been classified by Kant as one of the *a priori* categories, was only recently recognized as a concept. People undoubtedly lived as if they knew of its existence, but did not have a clear and distinct idea of it. Even in such expressions of high-level thinking as Aristotle's philosophy deterministic causality played a dubious role.

How was the transformation from teleological to deterministic causality possible phylogenetically? Probably as a result of a prolonged and gradual process which evolved through thousands of years, man became aware that inanimate objects have a group of distinct characteristics to which the notions of volition and consequently of responsibility are hardly applicable. Objects are recognized as being moved, not as movers. The last things in the physical world which in man's conception lose will and responsibility are moving things, like rivers, brooks, seas, winds, lakes, storms, etc. At levels of primitive cognition, things retain, at least partially, teleological qualities. They are things-of-action, as Heinz Werner (1957) called them, and disturbers of the organism. Eventually the object is transformed into an *it*. Such process of "itification" may become exaggerated, for instance in some neurotics who go to the extent of dehumanizing persons (Arieti, 1957). It is well known that also many scientists eliminate completely the concept of free will and consequently of responsibility from human beings.

If A is recognized as an *it*, it will be eventually understood that it is not A's *intention* to bring about B. This understanding will remove teleological causality, but might bring about in rare instances a return to a form of understanding which is based on naive precausal association. This form of interpretation is typical of a very low level of cognition (Arieti, 1967). A return to naive associationism has also been contemplated by some philosophers as a desirable possibility. Hume and Kant, for example, have tried to determine with philosophical arguments whether we are justified in seeing in causality more than precausal association.

It is beyond the purpose of this paper to prove or disprove the validity of the concept of deterministic causality. However, we can state that if we study the vicissitude of deterministic causality as a psychological mechanism, we find that when teleologic concepts are removed from the A-B association there is no going back to a psychological understanding based on naive associationism. What takes place between A and B will be interpreted as a special relation: B is associated to A because it is grounded in the nature of A to bring about B. We could perhaps say that deterministic causality is at first conceived as teleological causality, minus the concepts of volition and responsibility.

REFERENCES

ARIETI, S., "Special Logic of Schizophrenic and Other Types of Autistic Thought," *Psychiatry, 9,* 325, 1948.

ARIETI. S., *Interpretation of Schizophrenia.* New York: Brunner, 1955.

ARIETI, S., "The Two Aspects of Schizophrenia," *Psych. Quart., 31,* 403, 1957.

ARIETI, S., "The Experiences of Inner Status." KAPLAN, B. and WAPNER, L., (eds.), *Perspectives in Psychological Theory.* New York: Int. Univ. Press, 1960.

ARIETI, S., "Volition and Value: A Study Based on Catatonic Schizophrenia," *Comprehensive Psych., 2,* 74, 1961.

ARIETI, S., "The Microgeny of Thought and Perception," *Arch. Gen. Psychiatry, 6,* 454, 1962.

ARIETI, S., "Conceptual and Cognitive Psychiatry," *Am. J. Psychiatry, 122,* 361-366, 1965.

ARIETI, S., "Contributions to Cognition from Psychoanalytic Theory." MASSERMAN, G., (ed.), *Science and Psychoanalysis.* New York: Grune and Stratton, *8,* 1965.

ARIETI, S., "Creativity and Its Cultivation: Relation to
Psychopathology and Mental Health." ARIETI, S., (ed.),
American Handbook of Psychiatry. New York: Basic Books,
1967.

ARIETI, S., *The Intrapsychic Self: Feeling, Cognition and
Creativity in Health and Mental Illnes*. New York:
Basic Books, 1967

DUBOS, R., *Man Adapting*. New Haven: Yale Univ. Press,
1966.

du NOÜY, Lecomte P., *Human Destiny*. New York: Longmans,
Green and Co., 1947.

FREUD, S., "On the Psychical Mechanism of Hysterical
Phenomena," (1893), *Collected Papers, 1*(24). London:
Hogarth Press, 1946.

FREUD, S., *The Interpretation of Dreams* (1901). New York:
Basic Books, 1960.

FREUD, S., "Psychopathology of Everyday Life." BRILL,
A.A., (ed.), *The Basic Writings of Sigmund Freud*. New York:
Modern Library, 1938.

LASHLEY, K.S. and K.M. COLBY, "An Exchange of View on
Psychic Energy and Psychoanalysis," *Behav. Sc., 2*, 230-
240, 1957.

New York Times (Nov. 19, 1957). News reported by Arnaldo
CORTESI. Vol. 107, p. 16, col. 5.

PIAGET, J., *The Child's Conception of Physical Causality*.
New York: Harcourt, Brace, and World, 1930.

RADO, S., *Psychoanalysis of Behavior*. New York: Grune
and Stratton, 1956.

RUSSELL, E.S., *The Directiveness of Organic Activities*.
Cambridge: Cambridge Univ. Press, 1945.

SIMPSON, G.G., "Biology and The Nature of Science,"
Science, 139, 81-88, 1963.

SINNOT, E.W., *The Biology of the Spirit*. New York: Viking Press, 1955.

SKINNER, F., "Critique of Psychoanalytic Concepts and Theories," *The Scientific Monthly*, *79*, 300-305, 1954.

von BERTALANFFY, L., "General System Theory." von BERTALANFFY, L. and RAPOPORT, A., (eds.), *General Systems 1*, 1956.

von BERTALANFFY, L., *Problems of Life. An Evaluation of Modern Biological and Scientific Thought (1952)*. New York: Harper Torchbook, 1960.

von BERTALANFFY, L., "General System Theory - A Critical Review," *General Systems, 7*, 1962.

von BERTALANFFY, L., "The World of Science and The World of Value," *The Teachers College Record, 65*, 496-507, 1964.

von BERTALANFFY, L., "The Mind-Body Problem: A New View," *Psychosom. Med., 24*, 29, 1964.

von BERTALANFFY, L., "General System Theory and Psychiatry." ARIETI, S., (ed.), *American Handbook of Psychiatry, 3,*705-721. New York: Basic Books,1966.

von HOLST, E., "Vom Dualismus der Motorischen und der Automatisch-Rhythmischen Funktion in Ruckenmark und vom Wesen des Automatischen Rhythmus Pflug," *Arch. ges. Physiol., 237,*356, 1936.

von HOLST, E., "Vom Wesen der Ordnung in Zentralnervensystem," *Naturwissenschaften, 25,* 625-631, 641-647. 1937.

WERNER, H., *Comparative Psychology of Mental Development*. New York: Int. Univ. Press, 1957.

WIENER, N., *Cybernetics*. New York: John Wiley and Sons, 1948.

THE MIND-BODY PROBLEM

THE PRESTABILIZED HARMONY OF SOUL AND BODY ACCORDING TO GOTTFRIED WILHELM LEIBNIZ (1646-1716) AND THE BINOMIAL PSYCHOPHYSICAL PARALLELISM OF BODY AND SOUL

K.E. ROTHSCHUH

*Institut für Geschichte der Medizin
der Universität Münster, 44 Münster,
Waldeyerstr. 27, Germany*

THE SOLUTION OF THE BODY-SOUL PROBLEM ACCORDING TO DESCARTES AND LEIBNIZ

For many years Ludwig von Bertalanffy has continued to work on the universal and fundamental problems of living matter (1932, 1942) and has indicated their importance for our world view. In 1951 he was successful with his "General Systems Theory" in doing more justice to the peculiarities of living matter, seen from the universal solution formulations of the Natural Sciences, than was possible until then with the purely physical-chemical solution experiments. Similar questions in theoretical biology and medicine have actively concerned the writer of this article for a long time. He arrived at this problem from a different, more medical viewpoint, with a "double observation" of natural phenomena: (1) according to *causes* (biotechnical mechanism) and (2) according to their *significance* in the context of the total organism (binomial significance). This was explained *in extenso* in his "Theory of Organism" (1964). This method of solution, consistently thought out, leads to a conception of body-soul relations, which not only

stands the test as a summary of innumerable experiences
but also continues to stimulate new thoughts. This theory
- called binomial psychophysical parallelism - is a sort
of reversal of Leibniz's doctrine of the prestabilized
harmony of body and soul. It was presented in the
Leibniz-Memorial year.

As late as Descartes, the conception was still
dominant in philosophy and medicine, that the activity of
organism in all its realms not only served the soul but
also that the body alone owed its "suitability" to the
soul. Jean Fernel (1542), for example, defines the soul
as producing material outputs and making use of the organs
as "instruments" of single functions. This capacity of
the soul, the physical incentive powers or *facultates
animales*, join in the *facultates animae animales* (sensi-
bility, motion, comprehension, morale), the *facultates
animae vitales* (heart beat, respiration) and the
facultates animae naturales (reproduction, nutrition,
"growth"). Incentive power and direction of activity are
then primarily not a question of the material of the body
but of capacity of the soul (cf K.E. Rothschuh, 1964).

R. Descartes was the first to make a radical break
with this Western tradition. In his juxtaposition of *res
extensa*, of the expanded body world, the animal and human
organism was stamped as the *res extensa* of the body world
belonging to the *machina corporis*, to an automaton, which
works in all functions and processes according to the
mechanical laws of motion of matter. Descartes explained
his different outlines of a physiology of man (l'homme),
for example, heart beat, muscle movement and nervous
functioning (which were not finished during his life-time
but were published after his death (cf K.E. Rothschuh,
1966)), according to the principles of mechanism and
thermodynamics. In its incorporeal state the soul has no
power of manipulation to intervene as a force in this
mechanical motion, for the total sum of all movements in
the world is constant. The world owes its supply of
motive forces to the creator, who introduced them to the
world with their unalterable laws. However, Descartes
allows the soul to exert a control function on the body
processes in *one* place - it formatively influences the
flow of nerve spirit from the pineal gland, influencing

its position and sphere of function in such a way that, for example, it sets in motion the muscle groups corresponding to the will, whether it be stimulated by sense impressions or by conceptions. He explains the emotions with their corporeal appearances (grief, joy, fear) in "des Passions de l'âme" not in the sense of Aristotle, who localizes them in the heart, but in the sense that the nerves of the heart change according to the type of situation, with the heart activity, and at the same time the quantity and the essence of spirit rising from the heart to the brain changing and imparting to the soul the emotion from the pineal gland.

Gottfried Wilhelm Leibniz whose death, 250 years ago will be remembered on the 14th November of this year, argues against this interpretation. Leibniz rightly stresses the inconsequence of the Cartesian law of motion, for the sum of all powers of motion in the world is not only constant but, still more, a body without active power also retains its *direction* of movement; for it too is a matter of materially agitated particles. The incorporeal soul can therefore not at all influence the direction of the movement of the corporeal spirit particles in the brain. According to this theory of Leibniz a possibility of action is impossible on the grounds of physiological processes, and conversely, corporeal processes cannot reach the soul. However, from the beginning there exists through the creator of this world an arranged (prestabilized) harmony between the processes of the corporeal world and the processes in the realm of the soul. For the world of the corporeal the laws of effective causes and material connection are valid, and for the world of the psychic the linkages of conceptions of "perceptions" are valid. Caused by an inherent striving (*conatus*), significant consequences arise from conception, which either occur unconsciously as a consequence of "dark perceptions" or are consciously experienced as a clear and distinct chain of conceptions. "Souls follow their own laws, which exist in a certain development of their conceptions according to good and evil, while, for their part, bodies follow their laws, namely the rules of motion. Despite this, these two substances of quite different nature meet and correspond to each other like two clocks, which have been perfectly regulated in the

same way, even if they are of a completely different
construction. It is, in fact, this which I call prestabilized harmony" (Leibniz, 1705). The deeper sources
of activity lie, according to Leibniz, on the psychic
level and the reasons for each movement lie in the incorporeal series of conceptions. There is no such thing as
dead matter, for substance is built from "monads," which
possess an inherent "vis" as a principle of their
activity. The material changes in bodies follow the laws
of mechanism; thanks to the prestabilized harmony they
correspond at the same time to the ties as to content of
the perceptions. To these belong guidance. Consequently
there is a correlation between a leading *inner* (dark and
unconscious or clear and conscious) realm in the world of
souls and a parallel *outer* realm in the world of bodies.
Leibniz's doctrine can be called to a certain extent an
idealistic Naturalism. It is naturalistic in so far as
the causal legitimacy of corporeal things is considered as
given; it is idealistic in so far as the corporeal world
is an external view of demonstrating powers (Kuno Fischer,
1920, p. 569 ff). The system of Leibniz is reduced in
Plate I to a clear scheme; it shows the final linkage of
conceptions and outside, the chain of prestabilized co-
ordinated causal consequences or effective causes. In
this there is no effect from within to outside or from
outside to inside, there is no effect of the soul on the
corporeal processes or of brain processes on the soul.

If the teaching of Descartes did not create a
significant difficulty for the understanding of certain
prosaic observations, for example that the impulses of
the will move the muscles or that material sense stimuli
lead to psychic experiences (perceptions), this difficulty
is not removed by the Leibnizian law of motion. For if
the initiatives in the series of perceptions can be
analyzed perhaps for sleep and being awake, then it
becomes very difficult to understand those affects of the
soul which follow directly and suddenly on an external
action on the organism, for example pain from a wound, or
the dulling of consciousness through a slight brain
hemorrhage. "Should the disharmony of soul and body also
be prestabilized?" asks Georg Ernst Stahl, the opponent of
Leibniz among doctors in his "Negotium otiosum" (1720).
In any case Descartes and Leibniz brought the old naive

teaching of the reciprocal action between body and soul
thoroughly into question and all attempts to save them
have remained philosophically insufficient. Such
questions remain puzzling to the physician, interested in
principles, especially in a time like this, when so much
importance is laid on the role of the psychic in medicine.

Thus one can understand why physicians, philosophers,
and psychologists have always looked for an interpretation
of body-soul relations which are non-contradictory and at
the same time satisfy observable phenomena (cf. A. Busse,
1903; H. Rohracher, 1948; W.R. Hess, 1961). Since
Descartes and Leibniz the doctrine of reciprocal action is
no longer philosophically assayed as a solution. A
doctrine of body-soul unity (somewhat in the sense of L.
Klages) is not sufficient as an explanation; this unity is
certainly not disputed but again the actual experience is
divided for us into two series of phenomena. First of all
the two-fold aspect of unity must be explained, secondly
the fact that corporeal influences once seemed to produce
psychic experiences and on the other hand psychic
processes seemed to release corporeal manifestations.
Such differences in the unity and in psychophysical
dependence exist despite the absence of reciprocal action,
and cannot make the doctrine of unity comprehensible,
without attributing control to one of the two series. For
this reason I undertook (1963, 1963a) a new experiment.

BINOMIAL PSYCHOPHYSICAL PARALLELISM

Our new knowledge teaches us that corporeal manifestations follow the psychic, for example when a fright
paralyzes the muscles and makes the heart beat falter;
when intensive suggestions under hypnosis produce changes
in respiration, in heart beat, in blood pressure, in
secretion, and in muscle movement; when the will controls
the movements of our limbs, or when neurotic experiences
can result in abnormal disturbances. Complementing these
observations there is an abundance of experiences, in
which influences on the brain result in changes of the
psychic experience, for example, when sensory stimulation
of the eye and ear produce psychic perceptions, or when in
fever (typhus) so-called "exogene" disturbances of the

experience appear, or when experimental stimulation of certain regions of the exposed human cerebrum succeed in producing certain perceptual experiences (Penfield and Jasper, 1954), or when certain poisons and drugs produce intoxication and hallucination. Since Descartes, Leibniz and Kant the doctrine of reciprocal action as a solution has been left out of consideration. The new solution, called "binomial psychophysical parallelism," in contrast to the reciprocal action doctrine, asserts that such effects of the soul on the body represent self-deceptions. It supposes rather, that *the psychic is the manifestation of certain neuro-physiological series of outputs in experience.* It considers the consciously psychic as an inner view, as an *experiencing of the powers of integration of the central nervous system* (K.E. Rothschuh, 1963).

Such central nervous occurrences possess a closed, causal-lawful order, into which neither psychic immaterial parts can be inserted nor psychic motives can invade. The psychic experience is rather coordinated to these central nervous processes of integration. It is added to certain neurophysiological processes as inner side, as experience with both series running parallel to each other. This parallelism to the brain processes is not related to the physical-chemical elementary processes in the brain but to the quasi-intelligent series of outputs, which the brain, partly consciously, partly unconsciously, continuously extracts from itself. This solution, which was presented in detail in my "Theory of Organism," leads to the observation of life processes according to the two different sides which characterize them, the biotechnical and the binomial sides. The following was presented:

All life processes take place in a quasi-technical-causal setting of cause and effect relationships, but at th the same time they are bound to each other in such a way that organized powers of useful (binomial) individuality result from their specific arrangement and coordination. One and the same occurrence in an organism is at the same time biotechnically causal in the individual relationship and binomially significant in relation to the organization of the life processes or, in the language of von Bertalanffy, of the "System" of the organism. This

coordination doctrine is closely linked with Leibniz's
conception of the harmony of two series of phenomena, on
one side the active causes and on the other side the final
causes, with the one difference that it is one and the
same life process within.

Today we know more exactly than one did during
Leibniz's time the degree of succession output, even without psychic elements, can be accomplished without a pause
in the frame of material processes. The relationship
between living matter and the psychic is, in regard to the
inner structure and meaning, in narrower than one could
earlier have imagined. The central nervous system
unconsciously carries out innumerable *quasi-intelligent
outputs*, for example the cough reflex, equilibrium
regulation, thermo-regulation. The uncommonly complicated
adjustments of the eye muscles on the observed object
follow automatically and unconsciously from a system of
the central nervous apparatus. The central nervous system
(C.N.S.) has, moreover, the power of observation and
memory for movement series, respectively it "learns" e.g.
in sport training. The C.N.S. is also plastic; for
example it learns after the exchange of muscle groups to
form anew the proper coordination series, therefore
independently re-learning. *Innate patterns of behavior*
are already arranged in lower organisms, which are of a
specific kind and bequeathed according to predisposition,
thus constituting a "knowledge without experience."
Modern cybernetics, applied to the physiology of central
nerve outputs, shows more and more clearly, how much
"unanimated intelligence" is built into the organization
of living matter. The unconsciously executed significant
binomial output series of the C.N.S. are therefore in many
cases scarcely less complicated and less significant than
other conscious ways of behavior or experience. The many
analogies and structural relationships between life and
the soul give, according to this, the idea that the
psychic joined these highly integrated outputs of the
C.N.S. as an experience correlative and can thus be seen
as "Inner Side" of these integration outputs. If the
integrative production of the central nerve organization
reaches a certain level, then the psychic experience is
developed in the tree of life as a fresh and most
beautiful blossom. The parallelism between the psychic

and the corporeal in the sense of binomial partial
parallelism is therefore three-fold. The biotechnical and
the binomial side both belong to the course of life;
causal processes become binomial only if they fit together
usefully, that is, if balanced according to intensity,
pace and time. They cooperate, that is, if they are
organized. If this organization in the C.N.S. reaches a
high level in the integration of numerous nervous partial
processes, then psychic experience joins with their course
as consciousness and runs parallel with these output
series. This theory is not only admissible but also
fruitful. To make clear the meaning of "join" the
observation may be helpful that the control of our
respiration normally runs unconsciously. If respiration
is hindered, the intensity of the activity of the
respiratory center is continually increased by a multiple
number of freshly appearing stimuli; finally the
experiences join in shortness of breath. But this is
certainly no factor in the intensification of the central
nerve respiratory activity. After this introduction an
experience capacity will appear: for example, a perception will be experienced, if by flowing stimulations,
something from the visual system, especially composed
central nerve processes go into action. If the C.N.S.
disposes over a depot of memory contents, for example
after learning a language, then vocal sounds, vocal
movements are experienced and understood, while the
adequate notions join. The series of sleep and being
awake, of O_2-deficiency, of pharmaceutical substances on
the experience of the C.N.S. are thus easy to comprehend.
The experience of the will can be understood as an
experience of the activity of the motor apparatus of the
C.N.S. An affect is not primarily something psychic but
occurs at the same time with the adequate stimulation
processes (for example, the experience of fright on
noticing an approaching car). The present world and
environment are sources of continually different
stimulations, which the individual learns to recognize and
manipulate by constant training of the brain.

    Psychophysical binomial parallelism is made clear in
Plate 2. It supposes, as Leibniz did, a relation of an
incorporeal inner experience to a substantial central
nervous system external happening. With Leibniz, in

contrast to the above-mentioned theory, the roots of the activity lie not in the structure of living matter itself, but in a metaphysical source, in the "monads" and their inner processes, the series of perceptions and their strivings. This coordination is also thought of by binomial parallelism as prestabilized, for it hypothesizes the psychic as a peculiar form of existence which has been granted to living matter in its highest degree of succession. According to this the source of harmony lies in the living matter itself. "Organism" life moves into a new light and experiences a new essentially higher valuation than in earlier theoretical formulations.

In the final analysis it is "Theoretical Biology," the generalizations about behavior, derived from experiences of experimental laboratory research into life, which has yielded the data for this new Life-Body-Soul doctrine. The soul is stripped of its role as a primary cause and its role of the creative force, which the scholastics wanted above all. Organism possesses individual activity and is a highly organized causal system, whose central nervous system powers of integration proceed unconsciously into plurality or possess low brightness degrees. Only a small portion of a high integration le 1, chiefly in human beings, is experienced consciously as a psychic capacity. With this the idea of a continuous order of life form according to the growing level of organization and intensity of experience has remained in the Leibnizian sense. Thus the theory of binomial psychophysical parallelism effortlessly joins the development of Western thought.

POSTSCRIPT

After the completion of this essay the author received, through the friendly cooperation of the editor, Dr. von Bertalanffy's essay, "The Mind-Body Problem: A New View," *Psychosomatic Med.*, *24*, 29-45, 1964. In this essay Dr. von Bertalanffy arrives at conceptions similar to those which the author expressed in various publications since 1958. The convergence of views is confined not only to the rejection of the traditional dualism but covers also the road to the future. I suggested at the time, the exploration of the "Homologies" between the achievements of the central nervous organization and the psychic achievements. von Bertalanffy speaks of "isomorphism" when I speak about "Homologies." We also agree in our emphasis on the "auto-activity" of the organism instead of proposing a "stimulus reaction model". But I went a step further, by developing a suggestion which is more fully developed in the present essay. This suggestion concerns what I call "binomial psychophysical parallelism".

The author believes that this concept will be of interest to Dr. von Bertalanffy and dedicates this contribution to him, together with the best wishes for further fruitful work of synthesis in our fragmentalized world.

THE CONTINUING SEARCH FOR MEANING

ROY R. GRINKER, SR.

Director, Institute for Psychosomatic and Psychiatric Research and Training, Michael Reese Hospital and Medical Center, Chicago, Illinois ,U.S.A.

What has been written about Benjamin Rush the man, except by Carl Binger [1], does not contain enough information to constitute a valid biography from a psychological viewpoint. What we know about him comes out most clearly in his writings, the movements he sponsored, and the work he did.

I shall first briefly enumerate Rush's positive social accomplishments viewed from the framework of our current value systems. He signed the Declaration of Independence and wrote the first American textbook of psychiatry [2]. As a Quaker reformer he advocated temperance, abolishment of slavery, and better education for women. In his role as a physician he established the first free medical dispensary in the United States and formulated and modified procedures in all branches of

*Reprinted from *The American Journal of Psychiatry*, *127*, 725-731, 1970. (Copyright 1970, the American Psychiatric Association.)

This is an abbreviated version of the Benjamin Rush Lecture on Psychiatric History, read at the 123rd annual meeting of the American Psychiatric Association, San Francisco, California, May 11-15, 1970.

of medicine. For psychiatric patients, in imitation of
Pinel, he recommended clean cells, kind treatment,
qualified attendants, and work-occupation. He also asked
psychotic patients to write down their thoughts (called
"abreaction" today). In his attempt to improve and reform
prisons Rush advocated that housing and treatment of
prisoners correspond to a classification of their crimes,
whether from passion, habit, or temperament; he also
advocated a rational system of prison labor and indeterminate sentences.

Rush's psychiatric therapies included a
"tranquilizing" chair into which patients were strapped
until they were quiet, other mechanical restraints,
whippings when necessary, "shock" treatment by immersion
in cold water, and gyration to produce rushing of blood to
the head. In the first American textbook of psychiatry
(which lasted for five editions) he insisted that there
was one disease and one treatment for its etiology of
convulsive action in the cerebral capillaries. The treatment was severe purging and excessive bloodletting, which
Rush also advocated as a sure cure for yellow fever. In
1843, 30 years after his death, these treatments were
repudiated as "utter nonsense and unqualified absurdity."
In fact, they were condemned as "one of those great
discoveries which has contributed to the depopulation of
the earth".

When we see words such as "tranquilizer", "shock", or
aabreaction" and associate them with our modern procedures, we tend to consider that they represent
prescience or early discoveries. Nevertheless, for Rush's
day, and in stark contrast to his humanitarian attitudes
and his zest for reform, these painful and dangerous
treatments, including purging and exsanguination without
evaluations, were evidences of Rush's authoritative
nature. At least they represented a dualistic form of
thinking despite rationalizations for their use.

Several authors have been bothered by this conclusion
although they have not stated so explicitly. We find that
modern interpreters of Rush's thinking strongly disagree.
Farr [3] stated that Rush was an ambivalent and complex
character as evidenced by his need for support by

conventional upper-class society and, on the other hand, by his championship of novel ideas to help the poor and the sick. Shyrock [4] stated that Rush maintained a philosophical Cartesian dualism expressed clearly in his concepts of etiology and therapy. Adolf Meyer [5] completely disagreed, due to Rush's attitude about the interplay of mental and physical factors oriented toward a dynamic concept of life. Meyer may be correct on the basis of Rush's formal writings, but not if his behaviors are studied. This, however, does not imply condemnation of a man who revealed human frailties along with great achievements.

Benjamin Rush the man is repeatedly described as a controversial figure. He was unpopular, lacked resilience, and made few compromises. He was complex and devious and sensitive to the point of paranoia. Even his enthusiasm for what we call psychiatry was dogmatic, as exemplified by his statements that it is the most *important* branch of all sciences, it is the most *certain* of all kinds of knowledge, and the most *useful*. Perhaps, as Carlson and Simpson have done [6], some of us may term these statements somewhat over-optimistic or too sanguine.

Another way of viewing Rush is to recognize his contradictions and attempt to explain them. His dreams indicated a desire for supreme power and a recognition of his impotence. He preached and advocated humanitarian reform, yet did untold damage to his patients. He taught that clinical observations were the basis of medical sciences, yet he was dogmatic and unscientific in his writings about theory and practice. He disavowed history and repeated its errors. He urged the study of mathematics, yet he had no capacity to utilize its methods in thinking about or in producing scientific advances. Here then is my point of departure from Rush, whom I use as a prototype to this essay: a famous man who was afflicted with dualistic forms of thinking obvious in his ambivalent, contradictory, and impulsive behaviors, never synthesized by supraordinate control or regulation.

BIOLOGICAL PROTOTYPES OF DUALISTIC AND UNITARY THINKING

Before I amplify what dualistic and unitary forms of
thinking mean psychologically, it is important to realize
that they are soundly based on biological prototypes
understood by the great naturalists, who are now practically extinct. Coghill [7] traced individual development from undifferentiated forms or what may be termed
"early wholeness." The ensuing differentiation gives rise
to parts with specific functions. Conflict among these
parts, which are often functionally diametrically opposed
- as for example with catabolism and anabolism - is
controlled by supraordinate regulation in the service of
organization, which ensures survival behavior of the
whole. In terms of brain function Paul Weiss [8] states:
"It means the operation of a *principle of order* that
stabilizes and preserves the total *pattern* of the group
activity of a huge mass of semi-autonomous elements."

The early biologists saw in nature more than the
principles of stability or homeostasis. They undertook to
study goal-changing behavior as evolution, observable in
individual growth, development, and creativity.
E. Menaker and W. Menaker [9] expressed this as follows:
"Individual or societal disequilibrium as expressed in
human conflict is a by-product of man's ongoing psycho-
social evolution rather than a result of two separate and
irreconcilable aspects of his nature" (page 240). Indeed,
man has created and lives within superimposed systems of
controls, inefficient, unbalanced, and often disastrous
though they may be.

L.L. Whyte's [10] phrase "unity in diversity and
continuity in change" is exemplified by personality with
considerable freedom of choice within social patterns of
behavior to which it must at least partially conform. Yet
both factors together constitute an open system or network
with formative tendencies leading to change. Dualistic
thinking, on the other hand, is static and oriented toward
stability and permanence.

Our objective sciences tend to isolate parts of
systems and to observe, describe, and identify their
functions as if they were set as parts of a machine.

We gain a sense of security by "knowing" that what is will continue to be, even though our senses indicate that this is an illusion. Similarly, the background against which we view or focus on any part-function is considered to be steady even though it is constantly moving, albeit slowly. We try to keep our world in a "steady state."

Unitary thinking, on the other hand, considers that both parts and whole, both focus and background, are constantly changing but are regulated by some form of organization that prevents dedifferentiation, focal cancerous overgrowth, internal psychological confusion, social chaos, or anarchy. Our problem is to identify the ways by which the organizational principle operates.

The individual finds unitary thinking extremely difficult because it strips away the meanings of existence that he has set up to give himself a feeling of stability. Simpson [11] stated that religious faith is futile and that the world must be accepted as purposeless. "We must give up our childish dreams of a meaningful universe". This, however, does not mean that man does not have the power to choose and influence his future evolution. Others also believe that faiths, whether in philosophy [12], religion [13], political systems, psychoanalysis, or objective science, are expressions of man's quest for meaning and certainty. We want to grow and change but are fearful of giving up finalistic goals. Our· patients search for help, yet anxiously resist change and cling to their stable and uncomfortable patterns of adaptation.

Acceptance of a purposeless world, of existence for its own sake, and of the inevitability of death are among the painful consequences of unitary thinking. What Maslow [14] terms the "third force psychology" is concerned with higher needs of man for values of goodness, truth, beauty, perfection, justice, and order as part of his intricate nature - his "real self". This kind of existentialism is our modern delusionary system devised to alleviate the pain associated with the abandonment of certainty and meaning.

UNITARY THINKING

I presume that many unknown individuals have been able to overcome tendencies toward dualistic thinking. However, only the thoughts and actions of prominent or heroic figures in history can be scrutinized for the thesis of this essay. In his book, *The Next Development in Man*, L.L. Whyte [10] discussed the thinking of Heraclitus, Plato, Paul, Kepler, Descartes, Spinoza, Goethe, Marx and Freud. These outstanding historical heroes varied in their dualistic positions, but Whyte considered that only Heraclitus (the father of process thought), Spinoza, and Goethe really understood unitary concepts. In general, the Western world has continuously been under the domination of European dissociated thinking and its futile attempts at unification by beliefs in religion, myths, magic, and technology.

Thomas Mann, a modern writer who wrote, spoke, and lived a life devoted to unitary thinking wrote [15]: "We are interested in the whole, or we are interested in nothing". Gandhi has been described by Erikson [16], who interviewed those who witnessed his actions and studied records of his life. In a review of Erikson's book [17] I wrote:

> He describes a human with serious conflicts beset by struggles between internalized objects of mother and father, struggles between his erotic impulses and his ego-ideals, between his sadistic tendencies and his masochistic behaviors. In all this the totality of the god-like character is revealed to be the result of many divergent tendencies. The lesson here is that dualistic thinking at lower levels may become so integrated that at a higher perspective the totality of unitary thinking emerges.

> Gandhi had his failures during his life-time but, worse, his work did not persist for long. Indians are still violent and riot in their dissent. They fight with military might against the encroachment of neighbors. Their poor are even worse off today. Gandhi's emulator Martin Luther King, Jr., to whom Erikson's book is dedicated,

could not persevere in his nonviolence, but
brought violence wherever he went and finally
his own assassination. Like Jesus who preached
peace (the king of peace) the religion in his
name has increased violence in the world [18].

So few persons who are considered part of history
have encompassed unitary thinking that we have to ask why.
Those who did were often assassinated. Others did not
have what Margaret Mead [19] calls a small group of inter-
actionary individuals. Furthermore, the time has to be
"right" to utilize existing socially established behaviors
as a base line for inducing new insights. A new social
system cannot replace an earlier one without systematic
preparation. Thus we can conclude that change in thinking
can be taught successfully to the many only when an
extended field exists, at the least composed of particular
internal psychodynamics of a leader, his face-to-face
group of loyal followers, the appropriate nation, and the
times in which he lives. Up to now all personal successes
have been short-lived; nonviolence has bred reaction and
has been destroyed by violence and death. Even the basic
monotheism of Judaism has for centuries maintained a
particular tribal ritualism on which survival has been
dependent, in continuous antagonism with a spiritual,
universal attitude directed toward humanity at large [20].

SOCIAL UNREST AND REVOLUTION

Who will be the heroes leading to unitary thinking,
and when is their time? This question would not be raised
were it not for the current social revolutionary unrest in
the United States. It should be clear that we are
currently in the midst of *several* revolutions that are
confused with each other because of their common processes
of confrontation and sometimes resultant violence. What
we are witnessing are not actions toward the goal of
seizure of state powers or even the overthrowing of
political systems, although the slogans seem to be against
the establishment. We are, however, engaged in momentous
changes in social, economic, and racial environments and
in psychological goals, attitudes, and values. The confluence of these several "revolutions" with their final

common expression of violence gives an erroneous impression of mass effort based on a single cause.

There is a pattern that can only be compared roughly with the American revolution in which Benjamin Rush participated. Freedom to govern themselves was the ideal of the American colonies that led to independence. As Samuel Eliot Morison [21] stated, "All modern history proves that it is easy enough for a determined minority to pull down a government, but exceedingly difficult to reconstruct, to re-establish law and order on new foundations". The result is often tyranny instead of greater freedom.

Although each state developed its own constitution, our first American Constitution, without a bill of rights, became effective in 1781. This was the political regulatory system superimposed on the participating parts - the states. Although each state had its own bill of rights, it was only in 1791 (stimulated by the anti-federalists and Shays' rebellion) that the first amendment created a federal bill of rights. Each step concerned with developing a homeostatic social process from among parts of the whole was associated with bitter arguments, confrontations, and threats. That the resulting gestalt has survived for almost 200 years is no guarantee that it will not be drastically altered in the future.

All sorts of dogmatic pronouncements have been made about the cause(s) of what is called "revolution," depending on the so-called authority's bias. We hear that students are paranoiac, that they are struggling against prolonged adolescence, that they represent historically traditional violence of American life, that their value systems are products of an affluent society that requires new goals. One could name a dozen or more allocated single causes including the war in Viet Nam, life in the ghettos, or the over-population of involuntary students in our universities. But these are empirical propositions derived from observers' positions close to the scene. Causal explanations require distancing from the actual behaviors in order to discern patterns into which each fits.

Langer [22] states:

The seeds of civilization are in every culture
but it is city life that brings them to fruition.
Like every process of fruition, civilization
strains and drains the life which engenders and
supports it - the culture which reaches its
height in the development. Civilized life
establishes a new balance between conservative
and progressive elements and tips the scales of
feeling toward the venturesome personalistic pole
and away from piety and decorum. Such a shift of
balance does not take place, of course, without
flagrant exhibits of complete imbalance - lives
culturally lost, degenerated, the familiar
"criminal elements" and irresponsible drifters of
every big city in the world. (Page 90.)

Herein Langer describes one polarity of the mixture
of human reactions to civilizations. She could as well
have included the militant anarchistic polarity or the
severe character disturbances, among which is the borderline syndrome [23]. People with this disorder cannot
achieve or maintain close object relations; they withdraw
into a state of loneliness interrupted by unsuccessful
attempts to relate and in general are socially awkward.

We should not be misled by the group process that
assumes identity in highly polarized behaviors. Among
these are the drop-outs or hippies who give up, using
drugs and regressive pregenital drives to represent love.
Another polarity is the aggressive destructive youth who
wants to destroy the Establishment in order to change it
prior to the career choice he knows he has to make.

In both the black and student behaviors there are
current and historical similarities. The blacks have
achieved greater freedom, opportunity, and political
power; the student has been brought up in an era of
greater affluence, permissiveness, and pressures for self-
development and achievement. Each group has achieved more
freedom (although not so much or so fast as promised), and
individuals have time to think and to consider non-
materialistic values and the stupidities of our military
and industrial controls. These freedoms and opportunities

have increased, and at the same time social controls and excessive demands for social conformity have also increased. Each group, in addition, intensifies the reaction to changes in the other. The social dynamics, within which static dualistic forms have had some degree of permanence, are in a state of disequilibrium in which excessive demands for conformity and increased pressure for the rights of the individual to "do his thing" have reached a stage of explosive confrontation.

The personal internal task in developing unitary thinking is extremely difficult. Man tends to think in dichotomies, such as night and day and simple cause-and-effect relations. A transactional or reverberatory system of communication involves at least three-dimensional spatial perception and includes the setting and a temporal dimension. It demands a high level of control and regulation supraordinate to the conflicting parts of the system.

Even analytic ego psychology - although open and concerned with internal regulation - does not sufficiently involve the environment, loosely termed "reality". We need to understand, define and identify social and personal regulation as an ecosystem of a higher order. In brief, we need a term to apply to a supraordinate process that functions in integrating the psychological subsystems, including the ego, ego ideal, and superego, and at the same time organizes behavior into appropriate social roles. This may be called the "self-system", which is attained when multiple identifications permit socially adaptive transactions with many kinds of persons in many settings and when society recognizes the subject as a person [24].

Can mankind give up its reification of symbol systems that have a tendency to develop lives of their own? Can we recognize that organism and environment are parts of the same system, which means that both man's thinking and the social forms of control developed by him are in the process of change? Some stability is absolutely necessary for individuality and identity. Society and culture have always been the necessities for humanism, which implies that man can strive to choose his personal freedom in

accordance with his own nature only within the framework of
of a permissive and protective society.

The time, place, and populations engaged in a
struggle away from dissociated European thinking and
toward unitary concepts may be here and now. The process
is in a temporary phase of violence predicted many years
ago by Whyte, but no one can predict the results. The
possible range is from anarchy to oppression, which are
the polarities on both sides of the null position. At
present, repression and suppression go far beyond the
target of holding down human destructive forces;
aggressive striving for independence goes far beyond the
quest for reasonable individuality.

ROLE OF PSYCHIATRISTS AND SOCIAL SCIENTISTS

An uninformed layman could reasonably expect that
psychiatrists and clinical psychologists - who from their
education, background, and experience are deeply immersed
in the study of mentation - would understand and grasp the
principles of unitary thinking. Unfortunately, this is
not so. Modern psychiatry has been extended as a total
field as broad as life, giving more and more room for its
mad ride in all directions [25]. Some psychiatric groups
attempt to overcome this manic phase by fencing off a
limited space - the isolation of schools and ideologies
[26]. Others, as eclectics, wander aimlessly over the
entire pasture. A more common solution, persisting
through the ages, has been to assume either a reductionistic or a humanistic position with some lip service to
the other. The conflictual positions are analogous to the
differentiated parts of any biological, psychological, or
social system after primary pristine wholeness has been
lost.

What in the total field are the regulatory, control
controlling factors that maintain these parts in their
proper transactional positions? Indeed, this question has
plagued psychiatry since we became self-conscious that it
might become more than a medical specialty concerned with
diagnosis and treatment; in fact, a science. Some of us
have attempted specifically to study and discuss a unified

theory of human behavior [27]; others have concentrated on
isomorphism from cell to society including psychiatry as a
behavioral science. All of these may now be included
under the more general rubric of general systems theory
[28].

The need for an overarching, or what some may call
global, theory does not deny that operational or empirical
research may be inhibited by complacent satisfaction with
these big words. Nevertheless, research, no matter how
limited its focus, is aided by knowing what one is doing,
and where and when in a total system. This is especially
true now when social processes are rapidly changing, when
our nosological systems and diagnostic entities have been
clearly exposed as inadequate, when the behavioral
characteristics of neuroses and psychoses are changing,
and when homeostasis as an adaptive goal of living
organisms requires additional theory to explain evolution,
growth, development, and learning. However, it is
becoming imperative to view models for research, therapy,
and delivery of services less in isolation and more as
interrelated parts of a system.

We use the term "transactional" to mean a reciprocal
relationship among all parts of the system and not simply
as an interaction that is an effect of one system or focus
on another. It is a philosophical or theoretical concept
and yet has heuristic value as a means of analysis. If
one makes observations on multiple systems that involve
adjustive processes across boundaries, one can see a
sequence of change among several systems. There is not a
simple response to a stimulus, but a process occurring in
all parts within the whole field. All of this requires
organizational functioning by control and regulation.

We speak of the organizational principle in health
and sickness, especially of its failure in schizophrenia.
Yet we have not subjected this principle to operational
testing, and it remains, according to Weiss, one of the
main gaps in our knowledge of living nature - to account
for "order in the gross with freedom in the small".
Psychiatry is just beginning to establish an organizational principle in its own field, and it has a long way
to go. As this supraordinate, regulatory, controlling, or

organizational principle is defined better and investigated, and as more is known about the maturation of its time-regulated parts, we may achieve unitary concepts applicable to all of human thinking and behaviors.

The history of psychiatry and psychology in their search for meaning in human mentation in the health-illness continuum corresponds with the history of social dynamics and change and with the story of individuals as they struggle in their search for meaning. The psycho-biography of the heroes, of whom Benjamin Rush was one, gives a clearer understanding of the difficulties all of us have in developing a unitary system of thought.

There are cogent reasons why the scientific psychiatrist and psychologist and the social scientists should lead the way toward unified thinking in their research, translating its philosophical abstractions into concrete operations. It is just because our particular system of study has become greatly extended to include many parts - from biogenetics to culture - and has exposed many interfaces with other systems - from education to world organizations - that we have the responsibility of leadership. This requires abandonment of ideologies, polarizations, and limited focusing on conflicts. Instead we should develop an approach to systems and specifically concern ourselves with the properties and functions of organizational processes and their interfaces by employing unitary thinking, out of which our search for meaning may be furthered.

REFERENCES

1. BINGER, C., *Revolutionary Doctor: Benjamin Rush (1746 -1813)*. New York: W.W. Norton and Co., 1969.

2. RUSH, B., *Medical Inquiries and Observations Upon Diseases of the Mind*, 1812, 4th ed. Philadelphia: Grigg, 1830.

3. FARR, C.B., "Benjamin Rush and American Psychiatry", *American Journal of Psychiatry*, *100*, 3-14, 1944.

4. SHYROCK, R.H., "The Psychiatry of Benjamin Rush", *American J. Psychiatry*, *101*, 429-432, 1945.

5. MEYER, A., "Revaluation of Benjamin Rush", *American J. Psychiatry*, *101*, 433-442, 1945.

6. CARLSON, E.T. and SIMPSON, M.M.,"Benjamin Rush on the Importance of Psychiatry", *American J. Psychiatry*, *120*, 897-898, 1963.

7. COGHILL, G.E., *Anatomy and the Problem of Behavior*. London: Cambridge University Press, 1929.

8. WEISS, P.A., Living Nature and the Knowledge Gap, *Saturday Review*, *29*, 19-22, 56, November 29, 1969.

9. MENAKER, E. and MENAKER, W., *Ego in Revolution*. New York: Grove Press, 1965.

10. WHYTE, L.L., *The Next Development in Man*. New York: Henry Holt Co., 1948.

11. SIMPSON, G.G., *The Meaning of Evolution*. New Haven, Connecticut: Yale University Press, 1949.

12. LANGER, S., *Philosophy in a New Key*. New York: Mentor Books, 1948.

13. WATTS, A.W., *The Two Hands of God*. New York: Collier Books, 1969.

14. MASLOW, A., *The Psychology of Science: A Reconnaissance*. New York: Harper and Row, 1966.

15. MANN, T., *Thomas Mann's Addresses 1942-1949*. Washington, D.C.: Library of Congress, 1963.

16. ERIKSON, E.H., *Gandhi's Truth*. New York: W.W. Morton and Co., 1969.

17. GRINKER, R.R., Review of "Gandhi's Truth: On the Origins of Militant Nonviolence," by ERIKSON, E.H., *Arch. Gen. Psychiat.*, *21*, 766, 1969.

18. Reprinted with permission from the *Archives of General Psychiatry*, *21*, 766, 1969.

19. MEAD, M., *Continuities in Cultural Evolution*. New Haven, Connecticut: Yale University Press, 1964.

20. KAHLER, R., *The Jews Among the Nations*. New York: Frederick Ungar Publishing Co., 1967.

21. MORISON, S.E., *The Oxford History of the American People*. New York: Oxford University Press, 1965.

22. LANGER, S.K., *Philosophical Sketches*. New York: Mentor Books, 1964.

23. GRINKER, R.R., Sr., WERBLE. B. and DRYE, R.C., *The Borderline Syndrome*. New York: Basic Books, 1968.

24. GRINKER, R.R., Sr., "On Identification", *Int. J. Psychoanal.*, *38*, 379-390, 1957.

25. GRINKER, R.R., Sr., "Psychiatry Rides Madly in All Directions", *Arch. Gen. Psyhiat.*, *10*, 228-237, 1964.

26. GRINKER, R.R., Sr., "The Sciences of Psychiatry: Fields, Fences and Riders", *Amer. J. Psychiat.*, *122*, 367-376, 1965.

27. GRINKER, R.R., Sr., *Toward a Unified Theory of Human Behavior*, 2nd ed. New York: Basic Books, 1967.

28. von BERTALANFFY, L., *General System Theory*. New York: George Braziller, 1968.

THE COURT CLINIC AND COMMUNITY MENTAL HEALTH-GENERAL SYSTEMS THEORY IN ACTION

NICHOLAS D. RIZZO

Andover, Massachusetts 01810, U.S.A.

The court clinic represents a recently developed focus of community mental health interaction. In Massachusetts, the court clinic concept **was** first put into operation 20 years ago with the co-operation of several key persons and the temporary subsidy of a federal grant. Once the pilot project had demonstrated its effectiveness, a series of court clinics was established, and today there are 20 court clinics functioning in the Commonwealth of Massachusetts. The clinics are located in district courts, in one probate court, in the Boston Juvenile Court, and in the Suffolk Superior Court in Boston. The Lawrence District Court Clinic was opened on July 29, 1968, with a half-time psychiatrist who six months later assumed full-time duties as Director of the Court Clinic.

The reasons for the establishment of the Court Clinics Program are many and varied. Massachusetts, as well as nearly all other states, has witnessed a significant increase in crime, and programs for delinquency control

---

*This *chapter* has been adapted from a presentation made at the Seventh Annual John W. Umstead Series of Distinguished Lectures, February 6, 1970, in Raleigh, North Carolina. The lectureships were sponsored by the North Carolina Department of Mental Health, the National Institute of Mental Health, and the Institute of Human Ecology.

and reduction existing prior to 1950 were inadequate. It is an alarming fact that 18% of all crimes reported in the *FBI Crime Index for 1969* were committed by young people under the age of 17. More alarming still is the fact that juveniles, that is, persons under the age of 17 (*Juvenile Delinquency in Massachusetts*, 1968), accounted for 37% of class I offenses, those offenses classified as most serious. These are nation-wide figures and are not necessarily indicative of crime figures exclusively in Massachusetts. At the national level juveniles account for one million major offenses against the law annually, a staggering load for our society to bear and representing breakdowns in our traditionally cherished institutions: home, church, school, and community.

THE MASSACHUSETTS COURT CLINIC PROGRAM

Within recent years, the Massachusetts Court Clinics Program has become the largest system in the United States of America, and probably also the largest in the western world [11] for the out-patient psychiatric treatment of offenders. Two major services are performed by the court clinic. The first is chiefly consultative in matters of competence, psychiatric hospital commitment, assessing the dangerousness of certain offenders, in disposition and arranging for psychiatric treatment. "The court clinic is most effective in the role of *amicus curiae*, friend of the court, in its most literal sense [18]". A successful clinic becomes integrated into the court family and one judge has stated: "I no longer see as many familiar faces among the juveniles appearing before me every Wednesday morning". The second major service performed by the court clinic is the psychiatric treatment of the offender in the setting of the court. It must be clearly stated that the setting is authoritarian. Because of the defects of character formation in most offenders, the court setting is ideal. Offenders, as a rule, would not seek out psychiatric help on their own initiative. Maladaptive behavior, especially in the young, is symptomatic of underlying emotional, social, or educational problems. The offender's motivation to alter his behavior in a favorable manner when he is in conflict with the law and its consequences is assisted rather than impeded by being compelled to undergo therapy.

During 1970, there were operating in Massachusetts 20 court clinics serving 36 district courts [11]. More than 4,200 individual cases were evaluated or treated. The proportion of offenders receiving treatment is over 20% of the total number of cases seen. In each of the clinics treatment is either short term or long term and is, also, group therapy and family therapy.

The court clinic system in Massachusetts is administered through the Division of Legal Medicine of the Department of Mental Health. The clinics are staffed by psychiatrists, clinical psychologists, and social workers. Each month the court clinics hold conferences with visiting discussants. In the Lawrence District Court Clinic the monthly conferences have been attended by members of the public school systems, the Division of Child Guardianship, workers from the Protective Services for Children, many church groups, Boys Club workers, police officers, Key members of the fire department, judges, members of the probation staff, Mental Health Center workers, local welfare workers, and the volunteer probation officers.

In Massachusetts, especially, it has been evident for more than two decades that our public officials are demanding a concerted effort by all involved agencies toward the common goal of crime reduction and crime prevention. Rehabilitation, not punishment, is the theme. It was the unanimous opinion of the Massachusetts Attorney General's Advisory Committee [9, p. 34] that the court clinics had proved their value in the rehabilitation of offenders. Karl Menninger's recent and aptly titled book, *The Crime of Punishment*, has many interesting ideas on criminal behavior, but the one concept which runs through his writing is the great need for newer concepts, fresh models, and a different theoretical framework if one is to harness and direct the energies required to bring about the result sought. It is no less than the prevention of delinquency and the reduction of criminal behavior.

GENERAL SYSTEM THEORY IN ACTION

The present report will examine the reward-punishment
interfaces, not only through an interdisciplinary approach,
but through the application of selected concepts of general system theory. The district court is an ideal place
to examine the reward-punishment interfaces because, in
the court, the issues are concretized as well as codified.
One can, also, conceptualize the administration of criminal justice as a general system, or an open system, chiefly
because it has retained its character although innumerable
changes have occurred in its methods, content, and goals.
Most important, perhaps, the entire court system of our
country has demonstrated a continuing capacity to examine
itself and to make adjustments, modifications, and rever-
sals. It is this flexibility, or adaptability, which confirms its open system character. (See Escobedo, Miranda,
Gault, Gideon in [13]).

When one attempts to evaluate and treat an offender
in the court clinic, it becomes immediately apparent that
there are at least twelve interlocking, interrelated, and
interacting social systems. Each system claims to have its
own goals and procedural methods. This totality of social
systems comprises the organized complexity, the system,
whose avowed aim is to serve youth by performing a multitude of functions, such as to provide education, emotional
and medical care, and cultural conditioning. Many institutions are involved, institutions which, it is felt by
many, are crumbling and are very likely in the process of
losing their general open systems attributes. Some have
become rigid, strictly self-serving units, or isolated
power bases. Too often interdisciplinary studies, which
hope to achieve a unified approach to a given community
problem, end up with highly sophisticated but fragmented,
fractionated answers. They are doomed from the start
because of piecemeal methods or mechanistic, reductionistic frames of reference. The distinguishing feature
of general system theory [2, p. 51] is "the search for
developing basic principles" which are not limited to sub-
domains ever-increasing in number but decreasing in range
and scope. General system theory attempts to avoid the
ridiculous state in which the smallest fragment of learning becomes elevated to a separate discipline — even to the
status of a science!

General system theory has furnished scientists of all disciplines a set of postulates and assumptions, principles and guidelines, which have been derived by its founder, Ludwig von Bertalanffy, after nearly a half-century of tireless work in theoretical biology, in physics, in mathematics, in the philosophy of science, and, more recently, in psychology [4] and psychiatry [3]. Von Bertalanffy envisages a new science of man, one which is holistic as well as humanistic. It stresses the capacity for spontaneous activity as the distinguishing feature of the human being, rather than dealing exclusively with man's tendency to respond only when stimulated from without. There has been a popularized version of man within recent years which has bestialized him, in efforts to understand his less civilized nature. By contrast, general system theory regards man as the prototype of the general, open, living system and focuses its attention on his uniquely human traits rather than on those characteristics he shares with the lower species of the biological world.

CLINICAL MATERIAL

The Lawrence District Court serves the four communities of Lawrence, Methuen, Andover, and North Andover with a combined population of approximately 155,000. The District Court in Lawrence is one of nine district courts located in Essex County. Although the city of Lawrence has dwindled in population in recent years, the other three towns have more than made up for this loss by population gains. In the recent past, Lawrence suffered through a period of economic stagnation and the central city contained many condemned buildings and decaying, unsightly tenements. The current situation, however, is one of a city in transition. Old industrial plants have been modernized, there has been an influx of new business establishments, new housing, and attractive public buildings have been erected. Methuen spreads out over a larger land area than Lawrence and has many attractive residential sections. Andover and North Andover have always been considered among the most attractive towns in New England. Andover is the home of Phillips Academy and Abbot Academy and, together with North Andover, contains industrial plants representing several of the leading business firms of the nation. There is in the area a mixture of poverty and affluence.

Method of Referral: Offenders have been referred to the court clinic at various stages of the judicial proceedings, but usually after hearings have occurred in either the regular criminal or juvenile sessions. The judge may request an evaluation at any time, whenever he feels the findings would be helpful to the court. In the usual course of events pertaining to a juvenile offender, a probation officer makes a home visit and conducts a pre-trial investigation. His report covers a wide range of personal history including: family status, social, economic and housing conditions, school progress reports, and prior police record. Some of the schools make educational and psychological test reports available. Each offender is examined soon after the request is made, either on the same day or a day or two later. There is no waiting list. In matters of competency evaluations or in medical emergencies, the necessary consultation is provided as needed.

Psychiatric examinations are performed in an appropriate office housed in the court. The same provisions are made for privacy as in any medical consultation held elsewhere in the community. Reports are made directly to the judge and to the probation department with recommendations for treatment or other rehabilitative measures.

For the purpose of the present study, a cut-off date of November 30, 1969 was chosen and every patient evaluated and treated from the opening date of the Lawrence Court Clinic on July 29, 1968 is included in the present review. The Lawrence District Court is the twelfth largest district court in the Commonwealth of Massachusetts and, during the months under review, tried a total of 6,898 criminal cases. Of this number 6,373 were adults, that is persons beyond their seventeenth birthdays. There were 525 juveniles tried and of these 474 were males and 51 were females.

Fig. 1. Criminal cases tried in Lawrence District Court during 16 month interval ending November 30, 1969.

Percentage of Juvenile Offenders

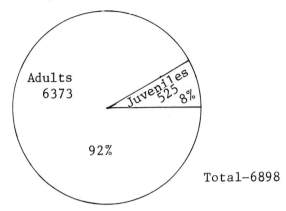

Sex of Juvenile Offenders

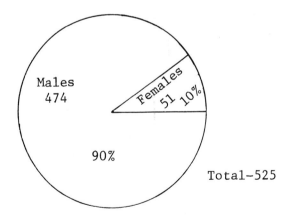

Among the juvenile criminal cases tried, the ratio of males to females is in the neighborhood of 10 to one, a fairly constant ratio in the Lawrence District Court and one which applies throughout the entire court clinic system. Figure i poses some interesting questions regarding the wide difference between boys and girls in their tendency toward anti-social acts. It is widely held belief that the

process of emotional growth and development is easier for
girls in our culture than it is for boys. In other words,
emotional maturity is more easily achieved by girls during
the early adolescent years. The presence of a weak, ineffec-
tual father, or the absence of any father in a home, is a
huge obstacle for a growing boy. He needs a masculine
model with whom to identify, rather than an over-protective
mother who may foster dependency instead of self-reliance
and independence. Apparently the determinants of emotional
maturity in girls are less affected in fatherless homes.

Fig. 2. Age and sex of 108 offenders evaluated in Lawrence
        Court Clinic 16 month interval ending November 30,
        1969

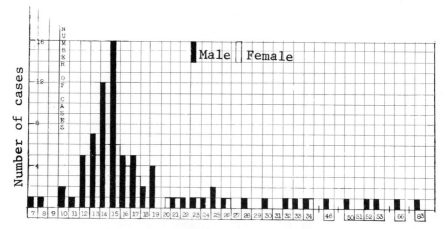

Age in years

Age and sex of offenders: The old adage about an ounce
of prevention applies to the group of offenders under study.
In the case of anti-socially inclined youngsters, the
earliest possible age is the optimal age for beginning treatment. Figure 2 shows that the average age of the offenders
is 15 years. If we combine the incidence at ages 14 and
15 years, we find that those are the years when most delinquency occurs. This is true not only of our rather small
group, but of the larger group seen in the entire court
clinic system according to collected statistics. It must
be kept in mind that we have charted only the age and sex
of the offenders who were referred to the court clinic and
this must not be confused with the 92% of the other criminal

cases noted in Fig. 1. The predominance of juvenile referrals reflects primarily the interest of the probation officers and the judges in the prevention of further delinquency and in the rehabilitation and re-education of the young offenders. In reviewing the case records of the 13, 14, and 15 year old offenders, one notices that the antisocial act is merely one symptom of a more serious organismic breakdown. Usually school failure and a major identity crisis are also present. These youngsters have continuing and serious difficulties in the area of impulse control and in dealing with authority at home, at school, or out in the community. When, in addition to these conflicts, they have to cope with a growing sexual drive and an emerging need for sexual identity it becomes too much for these young offenders to handle.

TABLE I. Offenders evaluated in Lawrence District Court Clinic during 16 month interval ending November 30, 1969

Juveniles		Adults		Total
71		37		108
Male	Female	Male	Female	
50	21	29	8	

Table I is self-explanatory. Seventy-one juveniles and thirty-seven adult offenders were evaluated during the first 16 months of the court clinic's operation. Of the 71 juveniles, 50 were boys, 21 were girls. There were 29 adult males and eight adult females.

Evaluation and treatment: Where evaluation ends and treatment begins is a difficult point to establish. For the purpose of the present study, "treatment" was recorded if four or more visits were made to the clinic by any offender. Even the briefest encounter necessary to establish a diagnosis, long before psychological and social dynamics begin to crystallize out, should be considered an organic part of the therapeutic process.

TABLE II. Frequency of visits of 108 offenders to court clinic.

Number of Offenders	Number of Times Seen
27	1
17	2
10	3
8	4
5	5
7	6
5	7
6	8
1	9
2	10
5	12
2	14
1	17
2	18
1	20
1	21
3	22
1	24
1	25
1	26
1	28
1	32
Total 108	

It can be seen from Table II that only 25% or 27 of the offenders were seen on a single occasion only, and that an additional 25% were seen in either two or three visits to the clinic. In 50% of the total group, or in 54 cases, active treatment has been recommended and furnished in the court setting. Clarification of the psychological problem, especially in the younger group of offenders with whom the major psychotherapeutic effort has been made, has had in many cases a salutary effect on the offender. The group sessions involving seven to nine boys, aged 15, 16, and 17, were characterized by frankness and honesty. The sessions were exceptionally well attended and were, undoubtedly, a source of psychological support to several ordinarily tight-lipped youngsters. One major difference between patients seen in private practice and those seen in the court clinic is the home structure and living arrangements from which the patients emerge. The homes which bred and brought up the offenders were, in general, grossly unsatisfactory and, in a majority of instances, though not all to be sure, could be characterized as being without a strong father figure, beset by poverty, lacking in any responsible home leadership, set up or managed by single women, and broken by divorce, death, or legal separation. In a small proportion of cases, offenders *surfaced* from homes of average means with both parents present. Apparently, the lack of sufficient guidance, the lack of adequate communication, or deep-seated emotional problems in any combination may account for anti-social acts under certain conditions. Naturally, it is desirable not to separate offenders from their next of kin, but, as one probation officer neatly put it, "He cannot be contained at home, in school, or in the community." It was necessary, therefore, in some cases to send offenders to corrective institutions.

TABLE III. Disposition of 108 offenders evalued at Lawrence Court Clinic during 16 month interval ending November 30, 1969

Disposition	Number of Offenders
1. Custodial Care	(23)
A. Medical	13
B. Correctional	(10)
1. Jail	1
2. Youth Service Board	4
3. Essex County Training School	5
2. Out-patient Treatment	(40)
A. In Court Clinic	30
B. By Private Physician	10
3. Probation or Suspended Sentence Without Recommended Treatment	(35)
Total	108

Table III presents the disposition of all offenders who were evaluated prior to November 30, 1969. The medical dispositions are the subject of Table IV and should be considered as a more humane method of managing sick people. The court sentenced to jail an 18 year old male who was guilty of repeated instances of petty and grand larceny. He was an attractive, personable young man, the product of a broken home, who had been using heroin for two or three years and refused to undergo necessary residential medical treatment. The referrals to the Youth Service Board and to the Essex County Training School were juveniles whose presence in the community and the public schools could not be tolerated because of repeated hostile, violent, or anti-social acts. More important, they were all the products of disorganized, broken homes where they had received the flimsiest guidance, discipline, and training.

TABLE IV. Medical diagnoses of thirteen offenders referred to hospitals

	Number of Offenders
1. Schizophrenic reaction	3
2. Organic brain syndrome	3
3. Acute drug intoxication	3
4. Acute nutritional disturbance	1
5. Acute or chronic alcoholic intoxication	3

Whenever possible, the court will respect the wishes of parents who prefer to engage the services of private physicians for the treatment of their children. In ten cases, treatment has been obtained away from the court clinic. It remains to be seen whether in these offenders the results of treatment will be comparable to those obtained in the court clinic.

TABLE V. Offenses committed in 108 cases evaluated at court clinic during 16 month interval ending November 30, 1969

Offense Committed	Number of Cases
1. Arson	6
2. Assault with or without dangerous weapon	6
3. Breaking and entering, day or night	9
4. Car theft	8
5. Chronic school offender, including truancy	12
6. Unnatural act	2
7. Cruelty to animals	4
8. Destruction of property	2
9. Disobeying court order	2
10. Disturbing peace	4
11. Drunkenness	9
12. Inhaling toxic substances (glue sniffing etc.)	3
13. Incest	1
14. Lewd, lascivious conduct	2
15. Poitering, obstructing public way	2
16. Setting off false fire alarms	1
17. Receiving stolen property	1
18. Sexual assault against child under 14 years	5
19. Stubborn disobedient behavior	17
20. Marijuana, other drugs	12
Total	108

Nature of offenses committed: In Table V are listed the major offenses committed by the offenders under review. The aim of treatment was not to work out the meaning of the specific offense in every case, but to discover why the individual, with his strengths and weaknesses, his hurts and disappointments, his aspirations and needs, reacted or acted out as charged. Two categories in Table 5, with a combined total of 29 persons under the age of 17, represent breakdowns in the home life and school adjustment of the included offenders. This group of 29 youngsters included 12 chronic school offenders under the age of 16, and 17 juveniles who were charged with stubborn, disobedient behavior. On closer scrutiny, these 29 offenders

were uniformly disinterested in school, rebellious, defiant,
and unable to submit to the rules governing school or
home — even in these days when permissiveness and laxity
seem to have replaced discipline and structure. In the
case of several among these 29 offenders, the parents were
actually terrified and tyrranized by their children. Some
parents gave in to their children's unrealistic, excessive
demands; others became unreasonably strict. Both
approaches frequently resulted in runaways from school
and home.

TABLE VI.   Current status of 30 offenders in treatment at
            court clinic

Attending school — Regular classes	20
Attending school — Special classes	3
In employment — Full time	4
In employment — Part time	3

Table VI simply shows how the group of offenders in
treatment at the court clinic were spending the business
hours of each day. "Special Classes" refers to an ungraded
school for slow learners and to evening classes provided
for dropouts who wish to continue high school studies for
credit. Several rather unusual facts about the school
systems were brought to light during the course of the
present study. All four communities permit the school
administration — that is, the bulding principals — to
suspend any student charged with an offense in the district court. Until the trial is held, the student is
barred from attending classes. Another item: there has
been in operation for several years a regional, technical
and vocational high school serving the jurisdictional area
of the court. It has now attained the earmark of many
modern institutions, a waiting list, perhaps equalling in
size the number of pupils in the school. A further item:
since the waiting list was created by popular demand for
places in the vocational school, the administrators now
will accept only applicants whose credentials are impec-
cable. They demand an average I.Q. as well as passing
marks in English, mathematics, and social studies. In
other words, the school is no longer accessible to the very
pupils it was set up to serve!

Diagnostic considerations: During the 20 years that Dr. Donald Hayes Russell has been associated with the psychiatric treatment of offenders, he has made numerous contributions to this exceedingly important area of clinical psychiatry. As the psychiatrist with the longest period of association with the court clinics in Massachusetts, he is largely responsible for the design and implementation of the Court Clinics Program.[*] Russell's efforts to

---

[*]
One must also mention the long years of meritorious and pioneering work performed by Mr. James M. Devlin, Liaison Agent, Division of Legal Medicine, Commonwealth of Massachusetts; formerly Chief Probation Officer, Norfolk County, Massachusetts. James M. Devlin, 1917- , was born in Boston and was graduated from English High in 1936. His father was for many years the Superintendant of The Massachusetts Training School, before its name was changed to The Youth Service Board. The elder Devlin's ideas were progressive, humane, and rehabilitative in orientation. James Devlin volunteered his services to the Boston Juvenile Court where he was an active volunteer probation officer for four years immediately preceding Pearl Harbor.

It is noteworthy that many of Devlin's immediate family entered the teaching and social service professions; doubtless the father's dedication to the rehabilitation of delinquent youngsters was an inspiration to his family. At any rate, James Devlin's entire life work has one common theme running through it, securing help for people in need. In 1947 he was appointed Chief Probation Officer for a newly created Juvenile Court District, serving 21 towns. Devlin was increasingly disappointed to discover that many juveniles, more than 90%, who were sent to psychiatric hospitals, soon returned to their original communities. The accompanying reports had a familiar, monotonous ring of sameness, "disturbed but not committable". From these early experiences and frustrations, Devlin conceived the idea of having psychiatric treatment carried on in the court house itself, for youngsters as well as adults. Treatment facilities were established to function in close relationship with the probation department. That psychiatric clinics are now established in 20 different courts is a tribute to this intuitive, far-sighted humanitarian. His vision of 25 years ago is now considered a cornerstone of the rehabilitative function exercised in modern courts.

categorize diagnostic classifications [17] have yielded a
singularly useful instrument with many practical implications for treatment, prognosis, and the extent of community involvement necessary for planning a statewide
rehabilitative program for offenders. The reader is urged
to become familiar with Dr. Russell's concise, clear, and
aptly phrased "Outline". By contrast, the most recent
edition of *Mental Disorders* (1968) seems vague and, in many
instances, not applicable.

TABLE VII.   Diagnostic categories of offender-patients

Diagnosis	*Percentages* Russell (11)	*Percentages* Laczko et al. (13)
1. Normal	9.0	—
2. Neurotic	13.5	2.5
3. Psychotic	16.1	16.8
4. Deprived	16.1	—
5. Character disorders	42.5	57.7
6. Organic psychopathic		
state	2.8	6.0
Mental deficiency	—	10.3
Transient situational		
reaction	—	6.4
No diagnosis	—	.3
	100.0	100.0

     Table VII presents the six major diagnostic categories
which Russell has been using during recent years, as well
as a recently published diagnostic scheme by Laczko, James,
and Alltop. Russell's diagnostic categories are based on
the co-ordinated efforts of 20 psychiatrists who had been
working in court clinics for more than five years and the
total number of cases included more than 5,000. All types
of offenses had been committed by the group under study.
By contrast, the offenders reviewed by Laczko and co-workers
had in each case committed felonies and were studied in
the forensic unit of a state hospital.

     The relatively large number of normal offenders evalu-
ated in the Lawrence Court Clinic were teen-agers scooped

up by the police for relatively minor offenses: such as obstructing a sidewalk or disturbing the peace.* Three or four were arrested for being in the presence of marijuana smoking. If, on psychiatric evaluation, the offenders were found to have basically good personalities it was so reported to the court. The neurotic acting-out offenders and the schizoid personality groups profited the most from therapy. Offenders with psychotic thinking disorders and the offenders from psychotic core families require a great deal of special help from other agencies in the community if they are to profit from therapy, usually in hospitals or special schools. Two frankly schizophrenic offenders, one a 17 year old boy with good academic potential, the other a 30 year old divorced man with excellent work habits, were kept in the community for one year while receiving psychotherapy. The 17 year old boy appears to be improving, but the adult required hospitalization a few days before the Christmas holidays. As a rule, the frankly psychotic offender should be hospitalized.

The deprived group are characterized by major quantitative ego defects because of their emotional, cultural, and educational handicaps. Because of their many needs, primitive and blatant, they usually get entangled in many diverse anti-social acts. Russell [17] makes a clear-cut distinction between two basic types of character disorders. He refers to the anti-social character disorder as that of the "hard-core" offender who commits offenses without regard for human values. The offender with a neurotic character disorder may do rather well in the court clinic, if treatment is carried on long enough to bring about appreciable repair to what is usually a qualitative ego defect reflecting early psychological influences. Borderline mentally defective offenders, as well as those with other organic psychopathic states, are seen either to determine competence to stand trial or, in some emergency situations, to arrange immediate hospitalization. Hospitalization, or other institutional placement, is ordinarily arranged for this group.

---

*For the first 108 consecutive cases evaluated at the Lawrence Court Clinic the diagnostic percentages were: Normal — 18%, Neurotic — 16%, Psychotic — 16%, Deprived — 11%, Character Disorder — 23%, Mental Deficiency and other Organic Psychotic States — 7%.

Results of treatment: A special effort was recently made to assess treatment results at the Lawrence Court Clinic*, despite the fact that there has been no statistical reporting in this vital area on a statewide basis. The same criticism, however, has repeatedly been made of all forms of psychiatric treatment. During the first 25 months of clinic activity a total of 138 offenders were evaluated. Of this number, 74 were seen at least four times, the critical number for recording the visits as treatment rather than simple evaluation. The therapeutic effort was classified as successful if the offender completed his term of probation without further difficulties reportable to the court or arrests. Terms of probation are usually six to twelve months long. The successfully treated group showed evidence that they had resumed growth and progress at school, or at work, or at both. In other cases they were leading productive lives in the community with the minimal guidance and supervision furnished by the probation department, or, in other words, they were staying out of trouble. In some cases treatment in the court clinic continued even after the probation term ended and, in a few instances, the court ended the probation term prematurely because of the unusually favorable progress made. Forty-eight offenders were therapeutic successes. In this group there were 39 males and nine females. The median age was 15 years. The average number of times seen was eight.

There were 26 offenders in the group who showed no discernible improvement. Of these, 20 were males, six females; median age was 15 years. The average number of times seen was seven. The criteria for failure included observations by probation officers as well as by the clinic staff that there had been no favorable changes in behavior or attitudes during the interval of treatment. In some cases there were additional anti-social acts resulting in

---

*The writer reviewed all cases evaluated and treated through August 31, 1970, and the resulting data have been presented to the American Correctional Association Centennial Meeting, Cincinnati, Ohio, October 13, 1970 (14). A similar presentation was made to the Massachusetts Association for the Psychiatric Treatment of Offenders one month later in Chestnut Hill, Massachusetts, entitled "Perspectives in the Court Clinic Treatment of Offenders".

further court hearings. Sixteen of this group of 26 were sent to correctional institutions; nine to the Youth Service Board, a detention center for juvenile offenders; six to the Essex County Training School*. Seven simply refused to enter into the treatment process, and one was sent to jail. Two other youngsters disappeared, and one moved away from the jurisdiction of the court. Of course it is too early to assess the permanence of the favorable results reported and whether recidivism will crop out later in life. Two case studies reported earlier [14] illustrate the handling of typical cases.

Case R 191. K.H. is a 14 year old boy, fifth born of seven children, son of living parents, both of whom are gainfully employed outside the home. This boy had four convictions in juvenile court in the two years preceding psychiatric referral. K.H. was known to fraternize with pimps, prostitutes, and drug pushers. It is not known whether he had used drugs himself. His parents appeared to be disinterested, took no corrective measures, and finally K.H. simply refused to attend school. Examination of the boy was most revealing. He was an undersized, undernourished, courteous, happy-looking youngster who promised to change his school attendance habits, his associations, and his attitudes toward the law, all within the next two or three days. Of course, nothing of the sort happened. He persisted in his old ways and one week after the psychiatric consultation he was committed to the Essex County Training School. Two months after the commitment, this youngster seemed healthy, had gained some weight, and was adjusting to the routine of his new home.

Comment: K.H. was headed for even more serious trouble and incarceration. His family seemed either unable to help or disinterested in his problems. Now the boy is acquiring wholesome habits of living in a therapeutic environment. His freedom to roam the streets has been taken away temporarily, but he is permitted to visit his family and they are permitted to visit him.

---

*A tax-supported institution for boys between six and 16 years, guilty of truancy or of being chronic school offenders.

Case R 150. P.C. is a 17 year old son, third born of five children, in a home where both parents were Italian immigrants and the mother speaks no English. P.C. had two older sisters, and two younger brothers. Both parents were employed outside the home, as were the two older sisters. P.C. was involved in a series of adventures with stolen automobiles at about the same time that his father was stricken with an ineradicable cancer. It was assumed that P.C. did not know the nature of his father's illness, but P.C. frequently told his friends and immediate family that his father was becoming less strict, passive where he had been active and self-assertive, resilient where he had been inflexible before. P.C. was referred for psychiatric evaluation and treatment by a probation officer who was aware of the many inconsistencies in the boy's story and history. P.C. spoke good English, seemed of at least average general ability, yet on the tenth grade intelligence tests he earned IQ scores of 80 to 85. All the members of his immediate family liked P.C., but did not approve of the friends he chose. Financial poverty was not a family problem.

On examination, P.C. was a clean, attractive, rather thin boy, properly dressed, and appearing his stated age. Immediately, it became apparent that he was embarrassed, remorseful, full of shame. He cried as he told the therapist "what a bad son" he had been to his parents. He admitted to many more misdeeds than he had been charged with*. In the next three or four individual interviews a recurrent theme was the low esteem P.C. held of himself. Many times he said to the doctor, "How can you be so nice to such a rotten person? I really feel rotten to the core". He was reassured that he was more than just a bundle of problems, that he would receive help with some of his reality problems, and that he would be expected to meet

---

*As a rule, in routine cases such as P.C., the court does not expect psychiatric testimony to be given. An evaluation of the chief features of the offender's personality, an assessment of rehabilitation potential and dangerousness to himself or others, and any specific therapeutic suggestions or treatment plans make up a typical report to the court.

the conditions of probation, namely the resumption of school (night time or continuation school) and to find full-time employment. One year later he had completed the requirements for the eleventh grade in high school and was employed full-time. He participated actively in group therapy sessions and was especially helpful to one offender younger than himself. When his own younger brother was caught violating the law, P.C. tried to be of assistance. Fifteen months after referral to the court clinic, the court took him off probation so he was able to get an automobile driver's permit and, therefore, earn higher pay. Approximately five months later P.C.'s father died of cancer and P.C. became, in fact and deed, the man of the family.

Appointments at the court clinic have been faithfully kept, the attendance record being higher than 98%. The obvious reason is that the court orders it. Court clinic attendance by the offender is a condition attached to continuance of the case without a finding, suspension of a sentence, or extension of probation. Nowhere is the reward-punishment value system so clearly experienced as at this very juncture. The loss of freedom, even for a short period of time, makes most people stop and ponder. Unwelcome as it may be for some, talking with a psychiatrist is preferable to 90 days in jail. It is the collective impression of court clinic therapists that a much larger number of persons can be carried in treatment in the court clinic than is the case in private practice or in outpatient clinics. The offender need not be seen as often as other patients. There are several reasons. The authoritarian setting and the cooperative participation of the probation department assure the psychiatrist that appointments will be kept.

OFFENDER PATIENTS AND PRIVATE SCHOOL PATIENTS

Because the author has served as a consulting psychiatrist to two private boarding schools during the past 15 years, it is possible to make several interesting comparative observations. The offenders as a group do not seem as disabled medically as a series of patients evaluated and treated in a special counselling unit which serves two private schools. It is obvious that the only factors common to both groups, that is, the offender patients and the private school patients, are age and sex. The consulting psychiatrist examined and treated 4% to 6% of the total private school student population [16] during a 15 year interval. In the private school group, all of high school age, there were suicidal gestures or severe psychophysiological reactions in almost 15% of the boys referred to the consultant.

TABLE VIII [16]. Reasons for Referral

Reason	Number of Boys
1. Poor marks	94
2. Disciplinary problems	56
3. Disorganized living habits	26
4. Withdrawn behavior	19
5. Social immaturity	17
6. Disruptive, destructive, impulsive behavior	16
7. Psychosomatic disorders	14
8. Sexual problems	14
9. Suicidal thoughts, gestures	13
10. Dislike of school, strong wish to leave school	5
11. Philosophic-religious problems	5

TABLE IX [16]. Severe Emotional Disturbances

Disturbance	Number of Boys
1. Major disciplinary problems	10
2. Delusional thinking	9
3. Suicidal preoccupation, gestures	8
4. Sexual problems	8
5. Psychosomatic disorders	7
6. Depressive reaction	4
7. Chronic drinking	2
8. Impulsive, destructive behavior	2

Psychiatric consultation experience with a private school for girls has indicated that the same general type of emotional problems occur in girls, with one exception. A higher proportion of the girls make suicidal gestures. In any case, the offender study group data has not revealed a single suicidal gesture and only two youngsters with transient peptic ulcer symptoms, one a 16 year old boy arrested for being drunk and the other a 15 year old girl with ulcer symptoms who was brought into court for chronically disobeying her mother and skipping school. The court clinic group appears healthier, it seems, because aggressive feelings are not bottled up but are, instead, acted out and unmistakably expressed through acts of hostility and resentment against parents, peers, teachers, schools, and communities.

Several additional statements should be made concerning the two groups of teen-agers. The private school students are, in most cases, highly motivated, have strong intellectual defenses, and are required to repress many of their instinctual needs. Behavior of the sorts listed in Table V would, ordinarily, result in dismissal from school or in being placed on probation. The family background of most of the school group is, typically, of higher socio-economic status. The offender patients are notoriously poorly motivated toward school work and, frequently, search out easy gratification through the medium of the anti-social act. Their hostile acts are the products of many social, economic familial, and psychological factors. Their anti-social behavior cannot be truly appreciated if one believes only in straight-line or single factor causality.

ENFORCED PSYCHOTHERAPY

The successful functioning of psychiatric clinics in courts of law affirms the contention that it is possible to carry on psychiatric treatment with non-voluntary patients. Actually, from one standpoint, all patients in psychotherapy or in psychoanalysis are forced by compelling motives from within the self, such as the removal or amelioration of symptoms, the existence of curiosity, or the need to fulfill a professional requirement. The severely disturbed psychiatric patient and the offender before the law are examples of persons for whom psychiatric intervention

may be ordered without the consent of the patient. Directed
psychotherapy in the court setting has a sound theoretical
basis and, if certain conditions can be met by the therapeutic milieu, such as a skillful therapist with the necessary practical approach, favorable results can be expected.

Schmideberg [20] and Whiskin [21] have recognized the
problem of motivating treatment in some offenders stating
that once "the heat of the trial" was removed many initially
compliant, co-operative, submissive patients became resistive
to the process of psychiatric treatment. The results present
in this *chapter* strongly suggest that to motivate offenders
before the law to change their behavior is not a hopeless
task. Far from it! Many offenders, when faced with the
legal consequences of their misdeeds, gradually made the
necessary behavioral adjustments to live within the law.
In the patients who have experienced remorse or other
depressive equivalents — such as the wish to be caught and,
therefore, be helped, stopped, or punished — therapeutic
progress occurs much the same as it does outside the court
setting. The patients who harbor fantasies of omnipotence
and those for whom criminality has become an adaptive and
ego-syntonic way of life present immense obstacles. Also,
the offenders who somehow maintain emotional equilibrium
in the presence of obvious ego defects because of severe,
early, and persistent deprivations represent treatment chal-
lenges of great magnitude.

Many social problems in growth and development are
optimally dealt with, as well as understood etiologically,
as breakdowns in various systems, and more specifically,
at one or more of the interfaces of the multiple interlocking systems involved. Certain basic isomorphies exist,
whether we are dealing with delinquent adolescents in court
or poorly motivated, prankish, mischievous children attending selective schools. Maladaptive behavior is a temporary
organismic breakdown at a crucial interface between systems,
and directed psychiatric intervention aims at no less than
repairing the human organism involved through psychotherapy.

Psychotherapy in its broadest dimensions includes clarification, psychological support, a continuing process of
reality testing and assessment, and, eventually for some
patients, the development of insight. Offenders before the
law are made aware that the court will not countenance

anti-social acts or behavior which is either self-sabotaging (school truancy in minors) or injurious to the self (glue sniffing, heroin use). Destructive or aggressive behavior toward other persons, or against property, is also prohibited, as well as the violation of laws and regulations whose purpose is to serve the public welfare. It is precisely when a conflict occurs between the public long-range interest and the individual immediate interest that certain laws are broken. The need for immediate gratification overwhelms the psychic controls which usually inhibit illegal behavior. Then there may occur an acting-out of hostile impulses against authority, society, property, or even against self. This illicit behavior, which momentarily overwhelms the internal regulators, is in the service of the drive for immediate gratification. It is during the initial interviews, when the therapist is formulating the dynamics of aberrant behavior, that he must evaluate the offender's potential for surmounting his behavioral misadventures. At this point he must substitute his own moral, psychological, or human standards as guidelines for the offender. He takes sides, as it were, with the court, with the community, and with society. He hopes the offender will adopt a measure of the thinking and feeling which will temporarily get him to abandon criminality in favor of a fairly liberal conformity which society expects. Often, two opposing systems of gratification are too far apart and therapy gets off to a slow start. In some of these cases, especially with young offenders, temporary removal of the offender from the community has had a sobering and realistic impact. In effect, we say to the patient, "We cannot accept this aggressive behavior. For a while the community *and you* are going to be protected from your misdeeds. We expect you to do better on your return". The court takes a firm stand in favor of reparative socialization and, in the majority of cases, emotional growth, behavioral improvement, and a progressive reduction in destructive activities has become evident.

DISCUSSION

     Although general system theory is a relative newcomer to scientific theory and the interaction between general system theory and psychiatry is even younger, a considerable literature on the subject has already appeared. Mention should be made of *General System Theory and Psychiatry*

(1969), *General and Social Systems* (1968), and the fundamental, basic contributions of Ludwig von Bertalanffy.
General system theory is a broad domain and so is its relevance to modern psychiatry and its many spheres of implementation. The immediate problem is to choose a relevant
sector of this wide-ranging theory as it is being applied
in court work by psychiatrists. It would be rather pointless to develop an exhaustive list of interfaces in the
application of general system theory to the highly complicated and varied structures involved in the court and
its clinic. There is a special direction of growth that
occurs if one can be both psychiatrist and general system
thinker and be flexible enough to be favorably influenced
by the theory. The basic distinguishing features of general system theory require a reappraisal of man: what he
is, what he can do, and what he must do to survive. According to the most popular versions of psychology being taught
today, and according to the most influential psychologist
of our times [7], man has been "robotized" and "animalized".
The tragic aspect of conditioned-response psychology is
that it works as far as it goes and that it forms the core
of many empirical disciplines based on psychology. Teaching machines do work, robots can function in situations of
awesome complexity, and brainwashing techniques such as
modified "Mao-think" tricks and ruses are being used in
treating mental illness. That a large and influential segment of our society is dedicated to the inexorable pursuit
of materialistic goals and affluence, no serious student
of the current American scene can deny. Mass media appeals
are made to the mechanical aspect of man, not his higher,
more rational, mental functions. It is a sad truth that
if one treats man as a robot, or as a machine, in many
cases he will eventually be just that — a machine. If one
deals with a young person as a stupid dolt, the young victim, sooner or later, responds in kind. By contrast, general system theory leads of necessity to a more humanistic
approach because the core of this newer theory is man,
rather than a discipline or process. Another special point
is that in the court one may witness in full operation many
systems other than the law, medicine, and psychiatry. In
the court clinic there appears to be a very special aspect
of systems congruence, or what Buckminster Fuller has
referred to as "synergy".

The court clinic, as a recently conceived and developed area for serving urgent community mental health needs, has continued to demand an approach which cuts through many disciplines and has yielded some new truths as well as affirmations of older principles. It is imperative that the focus of attention in each discipline be the human being to be helped rather than an organization, or a function, or a department, to be perpetuated or strengthened.

An important, and heretofore unreported, clinical finding has been presented and substantiated in the comparison of the offender group and the private school group of patients. The finding strongly suggests the dynamics of symptom formation and the hidden meaning of the anti-social act. It has been obvious to the writer for some time that the high-pressuring and "stretching" of young adolescents for more and more distilled academic performance misses the point, in just as serious a manner as the structureless, undisciplined, overcrowded, fatherless home from which emerge many young delinquents. Excessively high standards of performance applied to some young learners without due regard for the young person's total individual needs is hazardous, especially when the major emphasis is on extraneous values.

The theoretical speculations as to why the court possesses the characteristic of synergy lead us to believe that there has been overlooked in the past one chief aspect of courts and the law, namely its function to promote socialization and reparative socialization. Law is the only area where behavior has been historically codified over the centuries, and where earlier codifications have been frequently reviewed. Working within the court system has led several psychiatrists to see the continuing codifications of legal processes as open, general systems. The judge, who accepts the court clinic as an added modality for the rehabilitative treatment of offenders, is in effect placing the human being above all other considerations.

BIBLIOGRAPHY

1. BERRIEN, F.K., *General and Social Systems*. New York:
    E.P. Dutton & Co., Inc., 140, 1968.

2. von BERTALANFFY, L., *General System Theory*. New York:
    Braziller, 1968.

3. von BERTALANFFY, L., "General System Theory and Psy-
    chiatry". ARIETI, S. (ed.) *American Handbook of
    Psychiatry*. New York: Basic Books, *3*, 1966.

4. von BERTALANFFY, L. *Robots, Men and Minds*. New York:
    Braziller, 1967.

5. *Crime in the United States*. Uniform Crime Reports,
    1967. F.B.I., U.S. Dept. of Justice, Washington, D.C.
    Available from Sup't. of Documents, U.S. Govt. Print-
    ing Office, Washginton, D.C. 20402.

6. *Diagnostic and Statistical Manual of Mental Disorders*.
    Washington, D.C.: American Psychiatric Association,
    second edition, 1968.

7. EVANS, R.I., in: *B.F. Skinner; The Man and His Ideas*.
    New York: E.P. Dutton & Co., 140, 1968.

8. GRAY, W., DUHL, F.J. and RIZZO, N.D., (eds.), *General
    Systems Theory and Psychiatry*. Boston: Little, Brown,
    446, 1969.

9. *Juvenile Delinquency in Massachusetts*. Governor's
    Committee on Law Enforcement and Administration of
    Justice. State House, Boston, 1968.

10. LACZKO, A.L., JAMES, J.F. and ALLTOP, L.B., "A Study
    of Four Hundred and Thirty-five Court Referred Cases".
    Journal of Forensic Sciences, 15, No. 3, 311-323, 1970.

11. *Massachusetts Court Clinics*. Monograph published by
    the *International Journal of Offender Therapy*. London,
    20, 1970.

12. MENNINGER, K., *The Crime of Punishment*. New York:
    Viking, 1968.

13. POWERS, E., *The Basic Structure of the Administration of Criminal Justice in Massachusetts*. Massachusetts Correctional Association. Boston, 5th ed., 1968.

14. RIZZO, N.D., "Il Principio Fondamentale Della Psicoterapia Non-Volontaria". Presented at the International Congress of Psychotherapy, Milan, August 27, 1970. To be published.

15. RIZZO, N.D., RUSSELL, D.H. and GRAY, W., "Theoretical and Practical Aspects of Enforced Psychotherapy". Presented at the Centennial Meeting of the American Correctional Association, Cincinnati, Ohio, October 13, 1970. To be published.

16. RIZZO, N.D., GRAY, W. and KAISER, J.S., "A General Systems Approach to Problems in Growth and Development". GRAY, W., DUHL, F.J. and RIZZO, N.D.(eds.), *General Systems Theory and Psychiatry*. Boston: Little, Brown, 1969.

17. RUSSELL, D.H., "An Outline of Diagnostic and Treatment Categories". *Journal of Offender Therapy, 9*, No. 2, 48-50, 1965.

18. RUSSELL, D.H. "Law-Medicine Notes: Court Clinics in Massachusetts". *New England Journal of Medicine*, 276, 46-7, January 5, 1967.

19. RUSSELL, D.H. Unpublished data, 1969.

20. SCHMIDEBERG, M., "Reality Therapy with Offenders". *International Journal of Offender Therapy, 13*, No. 3 , 152-158, 1969.

21. WHISKIN, F.E., "Enforced Psychotherapy". *Massachusetts Court Clinics*, Offender Therapy Series, APTO Monographs, No. 1. *International Journal of Offender Therapy*, London, 1970.

BASIC CONSIDERATIONS ON BIOLOGICALLY ORIENTED NEUROPSYCHIATRY ON THE BASIS OF BERTALANFFY'S GENERAL SYSTEM THEORY

ALFRED AUERSPERG*

*Formerly Professor of Psychiatry,
University of Concepcion, Chile*

ACTIVE SYSTEM VERSUS PASSIVE SYSTEM

The split of the science of the biology of the nervous system into static-anatomical morphology and energetic-dynamic neurophysiology has led to a strange *dualism* in the conceptions of neurophysiological thinking. The nervous system as defined in its anatomical structure is considered by physiologists as a "given" and hence appears to be the objective substratum of neurophysiological processes. Reflexology in the broadest sense, as well as cybernetics, interpret the structure of the nervous system as a complex switchboard system or, to use von Bertalanffy's term, as a passive system. The biologist von Bertalanffy has recognized that this dualistic conception which degrades man to a robot is artificial, and not only excludes the essential reality of direct experience but even mistakes the actual physiological structure of the nervous system. Neurophysiology considered from the biological viewpoint has to take into account not only the morphological-anatomical structure of the nervous system, but must include what we call "physiogenesis" of these structures.

In his interpretation of the nervous system, von Bertalanffy replaces a static concept with the concept of a

---

*   Deceased.

process which is maintained in a steady state. Consequently, what appears as the anatomical stability of an organ actually is the result of the equifinality of such a "physiogenetic" process. Yet homeostasis, including physiogenetic morphostasis, is only a limiting case of equifinality. The meaning and essence of human life become clear only when the notion of equifinality is expanded to the original area of personal identity. In this broadened sense of equifinality, personal identity means that the person, after action is completed, returns to itself enriched in experience or knowledge. Whether a physiological or biochemical correlate of mnemonic traces (Hyden) can be established is presently unknown. The primary order of personality, however, must be sought in an *active system* realizing its spontaneous activity by equifinally reversible brain processes. This leads to overcoming the anatomical-physiological dualism indicated above.

Von Bertalanffy's biological monism starts with the spontaneously active system of personality and seeks physiological conditions of personal self-realization. Two of these conditions are homeostatic and morphostatic equifinality. Further conditions will be mentioned in the following section. In this progressive determination, Goethe's way of biological thinking is re-established; he expressed it by saying that the phenomenon "has to be stopped" or "to be narrowed down" ("ein Phänomen zum Stehen" or "in die Enge bringen").

THE COMPLEMENTARITY OF ACTIVE AND PASSIVE SYSTEM IN THE CYCLE OF PERCEPTIVE ACTIVITY AND ACTIVE PERCEPTION AS A CONDITION FOR RESPONSIBLE RELATEDNESS

Consistent with Goethe's biological thinking, von Weizsäcker, some 40 years ago, established his theory of the *Gestaltkreis* ("perceptive cycle") and so transcended the dualism of perception and action, thus, under inclusion of the time dimension, re-establishing Goethe's original four-dimensional conception of the gestalt in primary perception. In contrast, the Kantian dualism of space and time is applicable only to the conceptual universe created according to Newton's axioms. It is not applicable to primary perception. It is in this sense that Einstein should

be understood when he stated that the difficulties many have
in conceiving four-dimensional space are inconceivable to
him.

Although we know that our perception and action originally are *animalistically* centered; that is, is in the service
of personal interest, the theory and method of *gestaltkreis*
limits itself to exploring ways and means under which *technologically* defined tasks of perceptive activity and active
perception are fulfilled. In this sense Weizsacker opposed
the conductivity principle (*Leitungsprinzip*), which established the mode of function of switchboard models of passive
systems. His novel performance principle (*Leistungsprinzip*)
which describes the regulatory function of the nervous system followed from its nature as an active system in the
sense indicated by von Bertalanffy.

This limitation of the *gestaltkreis* approach to performance has the advantage of elucidating what is meant by
"activity" of a system, namely, its originality (in the
sense of non-reducibility, according to Goethe) and its creativity. Von Bertalanffy uses this grand word only with conscious restraint, realizing that it may easily be abused in
the area of the psychology of mental faculties, as when the
"creative faculties" of the baby or infant are discussed.
Such misuse of the word "creative," need not be feared within *gestaltkreis* research. What is meant here are automatisms which, by definition, are largely unconscious and
hence not to be ascribed to the subject as the author of
their creation [1].

The *Gestaltkreis* method is interested in the "correspondence of coincidentals" (i.e., the determination of timing
of teleologically controlled automatisms with respect to a
physically defined task (See below). In the following we
shall try to show, by this phenomenon of "timing," the relationship between the active and the passive conceptions
of the nervous system.

A. *Coincidental Correspondence*

"Timing" of an act of perspective activity and active perception is not concerned with the uniform infinite time wherein mechanical processes are described, but rather with finite time.

A mechanical process is described, in the sense of Newtonian axiomatics, as a predetermined and continuous sequence of effects. As a continuous sequence of effects, mechanical processes have neither a beginning nor an end. The time in which such process is adequatelt described, in the sense of Laplace's determinism, we therefore call "infinite" (endless) time. This does not apply to the time in which an action is realized. By definition it is limited by a start and an end. "Actual genesis" is therefore accomplished in finite time, as may be illustrated by the following example: Suppose one grasps some object. In this very moment a hypothesis about the object to be grasped is produced. We have called it "the schema of the touchable object of "the principle of tactile experience progressing from the indeterminate to the determinate." For even if one cannot name the tactile object at this moment, the sequence of touching movements is determined by the tactile schema to the extent that the object is not allowed to slip out of the hand. As Leipmann says, "The brain knows what I do not yet know." We have called the sequence of tactile movements in its perceptive function the "principle of progressive ascending development." Only when the object is named has this sequence ended and the tactile object found its final definition. Finite time, has the following structure: by seizing an object, anticipative potentialities are awakened with in the sequence of touching are step by step confirmed or refuted, until the object has arrived at a final determination and the time course of "actual genesis" is terminated.

One may also call finite time "teleological" if the anticipative meaning of finality is complemented by "retrogressive determination." Retrogressive determination is the provisional confirmation or refutation of anticipations determining every step of "fingering" which comes to a close in the final determination of the object by the touching movement as a whole. This comparison of finite and infinite time, we believe, at the same time elucidates the difference of time within the active system (finite time) and passive system (infinite time). The teleological "principle of performance" can thus be understood as the mode of regulation within an "active system." The "principle of conductivity," in contrast, is a model construct in the sense of mechanistic causality and thus concerns a "passive system."

In summary, our considerations, intended to clarify the relation of the nervous system as an "active" or "passive" system, start from "coincidental correspondence," i.e., the fact that the *teleologically* controlled automatisms at the same time correspond with the mechanic-*technologically* defined conditions of their realization.

B. *"Intended" versus "Intentional"*

The described automatisms that are common to man and animals are primal, that is, irreducible in Goethe's sense, and related to a world of objects. In Brentano's terminology they are *intentional*. Since the invention of tools and weapons it has become clear that the human being is aware of the effects it may intend and reach within concrete reality. The fact that the human creature may consciously influence intentional automatisms, as noted by Brentano, was called "magic" by Karl Jaspers. Plessner characterizes this human privilege of planned and deliberate action in contrast to the situational bondage of all other living beings, as man's "eccentric position." The man in the street finds this fact of deliberate obvious.

C. *Limits of the Applicability of Mechanistic Modes of Thinking*

According to Newton's axiomatics, further elucidated by Kant, it becomes clear that the mechanistic mode corresponds to constraints imposed by our categories of thought. This epistemologic statement, in the generalization of Newtonian axiomatics finalized by Laplace, became a metaphysical contention of the causally defined predeterminism of all natural events. This generalization became limited, however, in contemporary micro-and mega-physics. Laplacean causality is applicable only to the realm of macrophysics directly accessible to man.

D. *Complementarity of the Nervous System as Active and as Passive System*

Up to now we have discussed the self-maintenance of animal creatures within the concrete world, including intelligence which enables that "deficient creature" (*Mangelwesen*), man, to deliberately cope with reality. We have, in this way, bypassed the essential meaning of life and experience. One does not experience only to maintain life, rather life is maintained to enable the human being to experience. Von Bertalanffy has reviewed the manifestations of *joie de vivre*, from the curiosity of a rat spontaneously exploring its environment, to the human enjoyment of a work of art. It is common to all *joie de vivre* that it gives itself to excitation by the "new." It is just this new or novel that distinguishes artistic creation from plagiarism. All human encounters and conversation live on the stimulus of the new, which one partner may communicate to another.

According to cybernetic information theory the stimulus of the new equals the unexpected, and hence is proportional to information content. This is hardly acceptable to the biologist. In application to human encounter, the bridegroom will expect from his bride a repetition of the well-known, but with changing nuances, without which she would soon become a bore. But completely unexpected behavior (proportional to a high information content) would scare him away rather than please him.

However the "new" may be defined [2], what interests us in this connection is the fact that our senses communicate "news," that is data which were not included in the anticipative programming of perceptive activity ("prolepsis"). We find, first, a stimulus-dependent behavior of the organismic system which permits us to infer a mode of function corresponding to a *passive* system. However, as we shall see in the next section, this appears to be completely in the service of the *active* system.

Even though the requirement of the "new" characterizes interpersonal relations, fulfillment of this function is possible only within the coincidental correspondence of the apersonal *gestaltkreis*. We have called the relation of the passive and active system "complementarity" [3]. Phenomenologically, the point, in its spaceless spatiality, appears as negation of a negation: a datable point of time can be indicated only as a starting or end point of a temporal extension.

Within Newtonian axiomatics, finite time of "timing" of the immediately given, or *natura naturans* ("becoming") is bracketed out in favor of *natura naturata* ("being").

In present exact science the modi of infinite and finite time appear as complementary modi of determination. Waves propagating uniformly are conceived of in "infinite" time, but the impulse is determined at a point of time. Here, I would like to raise the question of whether it is not backsliding into animistic-mechanistic thinking when the impulse is thought to presuppose a corpuscle, and a complementarity of wave theory and corpuscle theory is spoken of.

It appears that the *gestaltkreis* of perceptive activity and active perception is to be understood as a *multivariable system*, in von Bertalanffy's language. In coping with reality, suitable voluntary action depends upon four mutually independent variables. These are:

1. A technologically suitable control of automatisms;

2. The voluntary usability of these automatisms;

3. A physical structure of the world which corresponds to its conceptual structure according to the laws of our thinking;

4. The complementarity of neurological function as passive system and the integrating control of the nervous system as an active system.

The convergence of these four mutually independent conditions constitutes the presupposition of responsible interaction between man and world. If these seemingly obvious but actually most complex presuppositions of practical action did not exist - for example in a world of unforeseeable miracles - responsible action would be impossible.

THE PRIMACY OF THE ACTIVE SYSTEM

It is now time to transcend the methodological limitations of the *gestaltkreis* approach and to envisage its results within horizons both more primal and more comprehensive.

First, let us remember that the investigations of *gestaltkreis* research are within the area of intentionality, according to Brentano. Intentionality, however, is not a "free floating" fact but is determined by motivation. Is it possible to determine motivation itself? I answer: no. Nevertheless motivation can be historically deduced from actual moral life values which the faithful consider to be eternal and prescribed by the highest authority.

If even in the realm of intentional interest magic and the amazing complementarity of the cerebral function modi of the active and passive system are apparent, the problem of the ultimate and essential "Worum-Willen" (the ultimate *why* of life - Heidegger) pertains to the Numinous, In consideration of the Numinous, we are referred to our Judeo-Christian traditions in order to procure "support from above," in Teilhard de Chardin's words.

At present this tradition appears to be represented in the purest by M. Buber. We interpreted Buber's notion of "Zwischen" ("between") as "inter-esse." Introducing the notion of "inter-esse" in Buber's sense, we transcend the presupposition of the *gestaltkreis* approach as the latter pertains to the subject-object relation, and we enter Goethe's conception of the "primal" where "the light" has essential reality, although this reality can realize and manifest itself only in its action. It is to be understood in this way when Goethe perceives colors as "deeds and sufferings of the light," when he says that through light "total nature" speaks to us - here (as in the Erfurt Fragment: *Die Natur*) he means the *natura naturans* or creative nature.

The preceding section was concluded with a reference to "relate to" (In-Antwort-Stehen); this relatedness pertains to total nature, that is, the revelation of creative nature through our senses, especially sight. Then we will also

understand the last words with which Goethe reportedly ended
his life - "mehr Licht," or "Let the Light increase."

The area of creativity is the domain of the poet; Heidegger
emphasizes that the essentially creative is beyond the philosopher's competence. Yet the doctrine of "life" in the broad
sense cannot "bracket out" primal experience and fudamental
creativity, and hence is referred to the poet. Goethe's notion of "total nature" is a personification of the all-em-
bracing, creative principle of *natura naturans*. But how is
persona to be understood?

In the original meaning, persona is the mask through
which the voice of the actor resounds; in J. Zutt's expression, it is the "phenomenal body" which speaks to me. Person, as a present phenomenon, originally is someone else
whom we have met. This is apparent in the baby's relation
to the mother, and even more in the relation of master and
dog [4]. Speaking of mother and child, master and dog, it
becomes clear that "person" must not be identified with
"individual" although it appears only in individual representation. The "person" of the emperor at the same time
represents his dignity; Faust's Gretchen is all bridal
charm, the eternal female.

If *gestaltkreis* theory deals with *intentional interest*
in Brentano's sense, in interpersonal behavior we encounter
motivating interest. As von Bertalanffy posits personality
as the highest active system, and as motivating interest
affects the area of interpersonal encounter, we may expect
that motivating interest in its regulating function controls
intentional interest.

Intentional interest has its mnemonic centers of learning, knowledge and know-how in the neocortex. In contrast,
the mnemonic development of motivating interest, of personal
experience, of sympathies and antipathies as well as of the
vital appetences seems to be manifested by the palencephalon, especially the cingular system.

The influence of this sympathetic system, via the re-
ticular system and neighboring centers of moods and attitudes and accessory fibres (e.g., gamma fibers), reaches

down even to the receptors. E.g., in H. Peon's "neuronal afferent habituation" the effect of a series of acoustic stimuli (registered in the N. cochlearis) depends on the motivating meaning gained in the previous specific experience of the animal.

In other terms, the afferent excitations flowing towards the centers which cooperate in the realization of intentional interest, take place, after identical physical stimuli, with correspondence to the individually motivated meaning which this stimulus has acquired in previous experience. This is a significant reversal of the common opinion that *gestalten* are first perceived "more geometrico," and only in a second step evaluated in view of their experience-based meaning for the individual.

The supposition that apersonal experience precedes personal experience is based on the fact that objective reality is interindividually perceived in the same way; and this is apparently verified by *gestaltkreis* research. However, in discussing the "stimulus of the new," we have found that the interindividually corresponding, coincidental correspondence already presupposes the complementarity of the principles of "conductivity" and "performance." In the following we shall further discuss the complementarity of motivating and intentional interest, of personal and apersonal order, in order to further confirm the primacy of the active system.

THE RELATION BETWEEN BIOLOGICALLY ORIENTED NEUROPSYCHIATRY AND TECHNOLOGICALLY DEFINED ORDER IN NEUROLOGY

With the invention of tools and the possibility of directing attention to certain phenomena within the perceived world (a faculty common to me and my dog), a certain area differentiates within the perceivable which, in Goethe's terminology, we have called the ascertainable (*das Feststellbare*).

Human scientific exploration is directed at the establishment of the "ascertainable;" human technology is based on it. The ascertainable is a specific mode of conscious knowledge in abstract, meaningful relations which as yet is closed to animals.

Obviously it cannot be denied that animals, in "technologically" differentiated and highly specialized performances, often surpass man to the extent that anthropological
considerations (originating with Herder) have labeled man
a "deficient creature" or *Mangelwesen* from the viewpoint of
maintenance biology (i.e., preservation of the individual,
or of the species).

In the modes of self-maintenance in the concrete world,
in the coincidental correspondence of technologically defined automatisms to a mechanically defined reality. higher
mammals, including man, may be considered uniform or isomorphic in their performances. The difference between the
mode of existence of man and that of highly organized animals is expressed in Teilhard de Chardin's sentence: "L'animal sait, mais l'homme sait qu'il sait". (The animal knows,
but man knows he knows.)

The isomorphic coincidental correspondence of technologically defined performances in perceptive activity and
active perception has, moreover, an eminent organismic meaning: the majority of morphologically defined lesions of
the nervous system entail disturbances of the sensorymotor
coincidental correspondence, but they do not seriously affect
the personal order, whose disturbances are the concern of
the psychiatrist. If this were not the case, there would
not be an area distinct from that of psychiatry, namely,
neurology.

Previously we have based our comments upon recent results
of neurophysiological research, and have emphasized the primacy of the sympathetic system which operates from the cingular system via the *substantia reticularis* by means of
accessory fibres reaching the extreme periphery. Hence the
above fact (i.e., the distinction of neurological and personality disorders) can only be interpreted by way of a
hierarchical order which takes the laws of technologically
defined performance into its service.

This hierarchical order of control functions is accounted for in von Bertalanffy's general system theory, where
personal order is considered to be that of an active and
creative system. Only from this point of view can the

deviations of personal order and its relativity in a common environment be investigated in their "physiogenic" becoming or their "adjustment," using Adrian's term.

From this biological point of view which transcends
somatophysiological dualism, psychiatry becomes a biologically oriented neuropsychiatry at various hierarchical levels.
From the point of view of active system, the etiological
differentiations of classical psychopathology - organic,
exogenic, endogenic, psychogenic, receive a new meaning and
refer to different levels of "order":

1) *Organic*: The integrity of maintenance metabolism
of the brain, or "physiogenic morphostasis," has to be acknowledged as a necessary condition for ordered performance
and realization of specific modes of behavior.

By and large, as already mentioned, neocortical forma-
tions are concerned with the realization of specific performances. (We are especially thinking of aphasias, agnosias,
apraxias, etc.) In contrast, defects of the palencephalon
entail perversions of behavior, memory disturbances, etc.;
the latter, however, are not related to specific performances
of learned knowledge, but rather, as in Korsakow's syndrome,
of a general nature in context with the life history.

So far as organically caused psychiatric syndromes are
concerned, we owe decisive progress to clinical experience
with psychomotor epilepsy and to experimental results of
operations on the cingular system, localizing areas of disturbance in personality disorders.

2) *Exogenic*: When investigating the physiogenic function of an exogenic toxic factor, we must take into special
consideration the humoral sensitivity of functions regulating the general status (including consciousness) of the
substantia reticularis; for it decisively influences consciousness, as "le présent sensuellement représenté" (H. Ey),
enables us better to discern between disorders of personality and of consciousness; for instance, between the para-
noid persecution mania as a failure of interpretation and
the alcoholic manic delirium as an immediate disturbance of
consciousness (A. Cid).

The variations of consciousness which are controlled by periventricular centers (e.g., sleep-waking, vital appetences and disappetences) should be considered, from the viewpoint of general system theory, as manifestations of the physiogenic spontaneous activity which can be modified by habituation.

From the biological point of view, neuropsychiatry, in consideration of the peripheral expansion of the sympathetic nervous system, cannot be restricted to the disturbances of consciousness. H. Pluegge attempted to relate organically defined diseases to concurrent disturbances of mood and consciousness. In my work, *Pain and Painfulness* [5], I have tried to distinguish between interoceptive viscerogenic pain [6] in its specific physiogenic condition as a disturbance of mood, and extreroceptive pain which should be considered a cognitive, sensory function.

3) *Endogenic*: Endogenic, too, is to be considered a function, i.e., a deviation in the physiogenesis of the brain, in the sense of *maturation*, the word being understood in the broadest sense. The organism has to pass critical phases, especially puberty and climacteric.

The majority of psychoses are endogenic; family history hints at genotypical dispositions to typologically definable deviations of personal order within physiogenic maturation. Tellenbach calls the constitutional disposition towards variation of personal development the "endon."

Up to this point, all attempts have failed to base schizophrenia on anatomically definable deviations of the morphogenesis of the brain, or to explain endogenic maladies as an innate disturbance of metabolism leading to toxicosis.

Research into the biochemical causes and inter-relations in the physiogenesis of the processes of maturation, its pathological deviations (with sickle-cell anemia as a paradigm) may be fundamental for elucidation of the physiological causes of endogenic psychoses. We have, of course, always to consider that genetics only concerns potentialities whose realization depends on the historical context of life. Thus we come to the last point, psychogeny.

4) *Psychogenic*: As far as the so-called psychogenic means what is motivated by experience, we are confronted with the neuropsychiatrically fascinating problem of the mnemonic and functional development of the brain. So far as the neocortex is concerned, this is learned knowledge; in the paleocortex, it is experience in the order of life history. Seen from this viewpoint, the development of so-called psychogenic disturbances seems to be primarily due to the paleocortex.

In the totality of mnemonic functions, the theory of information may be able to give decisive insight. The school of V. von Weizsaecker developed, in 40 years of effort, a theory of information on a physiogenic basis, derived from the *gestaltkreis* principles. At present it is beginning to profit from the technologically highly specialized cybernetic theory of information.

It becomes clear that from the biological viewpoint, the notions "organic," "exogenic," "endogenic," and "psychogenic," which originally signified nosologic entities, become factors in a multivariable system in von Bertalanffy's sense. They all are to be considered in every case of pathologic disturbance of the personal order. In this way, the rigid systematics of nosologic entities become a "mobile order" in the sense of Goethe's biology. Such order, because of its mobility, makes a mutual understanding within the broad horizon of comparative psychiatry possible, in the sense of von Bertalanffy's "perspectivism."

NOTE

The above considerations are a continuation of conversations with L. von Bertalanffy. I realize that the notion of the personal here presented, which originated in a *phenomenology of the encounter*, has its own history. However, in view of the difference of approach (which lead him to his "general system theory") a continuation of our discussion is highly desirable, even imperative.

My meeting with L. von Bertalanffy was made possible by a grant from the H. Werner Reimers-Stiftung fuer anthropo-

genetische Forschung (Frankfurt), for three months' work in
Europe.

(Editor's Note: Continuation of the discussion, as was
hoped for at the end of this contribution, was unfortunately
terminated by the untimely decease of Professor Auersperg.)

REFERENCES

1. Even learned performances, e.g., the acoustic-motoric
    gestaltkreis of piano playing, are based on automatisms
    which, in this example, are modified for aesthetic pur-
    poses.

2. From the point of view of creative originality the "new"
    is the unfamiliar which integrates into the familiar,
    the unknown which integrates into the known. AUERSPERG,
    Alfred und zu OETTINGEN-SPIELBERG, Therese, *Poesie und
    Forschung*, Chapter 11, Stuttgart: F. Enke, 1965.

3. The complementarity of finite and infinite time can be
    conceived as a function of the isomorphism which, accord-
    ing to von Bertalanffy, is to be presupposed in the
    psychophysical problem. In the previous section we have,
    with von Bertalanffy, conceived physiogenetic morpho-
    stasis as steady state and hence a process in time.
    Now, via the fact of coincidental correspondence, it ap-
    pears that the process of "timing" of actualization in
    perceptive activity and active perception, extends into
    the dimension of physicochemically defined processes,
    which take place in "infinite" time. It appears impos-
    sible to transcend from the infinite time of predeter-
    mined processes to the finite time of actual realization.
    Infinite time may, however, be conceived as an empty
    limiting case of finite time. This way was already
    indicated by Leibniz in his infinitesimal calculus.

4. The same applies, *mutatis mutandis*, to the mutual rela-
    tions between animals even down to the very primitive
    forms, as we may see from the brilliant panopticum of
    animal behavior presented by LORENZ, K. in his book,
    On Aggression.

5. AUERSPERG, Alfred, *Schmerz und Schmerzhaftigkeit*, Berlin, Göttingen, Heidelberg: Springer, 1963.

6. "La douleur maladie" (Leriche).

BEYOND PLURALISM AND DETERMINISM

VIKTOR E. FRANKL

Professor of Neurology and Psychiatry, University of Vienna Medical School, Austria

Professor of Logotherapy, United States International University, 1, Mariannengasse, Vienna, Austria 1090

It is the contention of the present author that the two perennial issues philosophy has been wrestling with, namely the problem of body and mind and the problem of free choice, are unsolvable. However, what appears to me to be possible - and what I attempt here to do - is to show the reason why the two problems are *necessarily* unsolvable.

As to the first problem, the body-mind problem boils down to the question: How is it possible to conceive of man as a unity in the face of the diversity constituted by the physiological and psychological aspects of the human reality? And who would deny that, as Konrad Lorenz puts it, "The wall separating the two great incommensurables, the physiological and psychological is insurmountable. Even the extension of scientific research into the field of psychophysics did not bring us closer to the solution of the body-mind problem" [1]. As to the hope that future research might bring a solution, Werner Heisenberg has arrived at an equally pessimistic statement in contending that "we do not expect a direct way of understanding between bodily movements and psychological processes, for even in the exact sciences reality breaks down into separate levels."

As I see it, we are living in an age of the "pluralism of sciences" [2] in that the individual sciences depict reality in such different ways that the pictures contradict

each other. However, it is my contention that the contradictions do not contradict the unity of reality. This
holds true, also, of the human reality. In order to demonstrate this, let us recall that each science, as it were,
cuts out a cross section of reality. Let us now follow the
implications of this analogy borrowed from geometry.

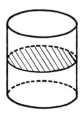 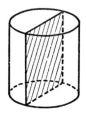

If we cut two orthogonal cross sections from a cylinder,
the horizontal cross section represents the cylinder as a
circle whereas the vertical cross section represents it as
a square. But as we know, nobody has managed as yet to
transform a circle into a square. Similarly, no one has succeeded as yet in bridging the gap between the somatic and
psychological aspects of the human reality. And, we may add,
nobody is likely to succeed, either, because the *coincidentia
oppositorum*, as Nicholas of Cusa has called it, is not possible within any cross section but only beyond all of them,
in the next higher dimension.

It is no different with man. On the biological level,
in the plane of biology, we are confronted with the somatic
aspects of man; and on the psychological level, in the
plane of psychology, with his psychological aspects. Thus,
within the planes of both scientific approaches we are facing
the diversity but missing the unity in man because this unity is available only in the human dimension, and must necessarily disappear within the cross sections through the human
reality as they are used by biology and psychology. Only in
the human dimension lies the *unitas multiplex*, as man has
been defined by Thomas Aquinas. And this unity now turns
out to be not really a "unity *in* diversity" but rather a
unity *in spite of* diversity.

What is at stake, however, is not only the oneness of
man, but also his openness.

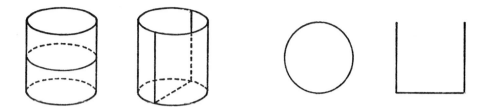

Going back to the cylinder, let us now imagine that it
is not a solid but an open vessel, say, a cup. In that case,
what will the cross sections be like? While the horizontal
one still is a closed circle, in the vertical plane the cup
is now seen as an open figure. But as soon as we realize
that both figures are mere cross sections, the closedness of
one figure is perfectly compatible with the openness of the
other.

Something analogous holds for man. He, too, is sometimes
portrayed as if he were merely a closed system within which
cause-effect relations are operant, such as conditioned or
unconditioned reflexes, conditioning processes or responses
to stimuli. On the other hand, being human is profoundly
characterized as being open to the world, as Max Scheler,
Arnold Gehlen and Adolf Portmann have shown. Or, as Martin
Heidegger has said, being human is "being in the world".
What I have called the self-transcendence of existence [3]
denotes the fundamental fact that being human means relating
to something or someone other than oneself, be it a meaning
to fulfill or human beings to encounter. And existence fal-
ters and collapses unless this self-transcendent quality is
lived out.

Let me illustrate this by a simile. The capacity of the
eye to perceive the world outside itself, paradoxically
enough, is tied up with its incapacity to perceive anything
within itself. In fact, to the extent to which the eye sees
itself, for example, its own cataract, its capacity to see
the world is impaired. That is to say, in principle the
seeing eye sees something other than itself. Seeing, too,
is self-transcendent. With regard to the self-transcendent
quality of existence, however, it is understandable that

the self-transcendence of the human reality, the openness of being human, is touched by one cross section and missed by another. Closedness and openness have become compatible. And I think that the same holds true of freedom and determinism. There is determinism in the psychological dimension, and freedom in the noological dimension, which is the human dimension, the dimension of human phenomena, the "symbolic level" in terms of Ludwig von Bertalanffy's general systems theory.

As to the body-mind problem, we wound up with the phrase "unity in spite of diversity". As to the problem of free choice, we are winding up with the phrase "freedom in spite of determinism". It parallels the phrase once coined by Nicolai Hartmann, "autonomy in spite of dependency". As a human phenomenon, however, freedom also is all too human. Human freedom is finite freedom. Man is not free from conditions. But he is free to take a stand on them. The conditions do not completely condition him. For within limits it is up to him whether or not he succumbs and surrenders to the conditions. He may as easily rise above them and by so doing open up and enter the human dimension. As a professor in two fields, neurology and psychiatry, I am fully aware of the extent to which man is subject to biological, psychological, and sociological conditions. But in addition to being a professor in two fields I am a survivor of four camps - concentration camps, that is - and as such I also bear witness to the unexpected extent to which man is capable of defying and braving even the worst conditions conceivable.

Sigmund Freud once said, "Let us attempt to expose a number of the most diverse people uniformly to hunger. With the increase of the imperative urge of hunger all individual differences will blur, and in their stead will appear the uniform expression of the one unstilled urge." Actually, however, the reverse was true. In the concentration camps people became more diverse. The beast was unmasked - and so was the saint. The hunger was the same but people were different. In truth, calories do not count.

A statement made by von Bertalanffy epitomizes this is state of affairs: "Will is not *determined*, but is *determinable*" [4]. Wittingly or unwittingly, man decides whether

or not he will let himself be determined by the conditions
that confront him. Ultimately, he is not subject to these
conditions; rather, the conditions are subject to his decisions. He decides whether he will face up or give in.
Of course, it could be objected that such decisions are
themselves determined. But it is obvious that this results
in a *regressus in infinitum*. A statement by Magda B. Arnold
lends itself as an apt conclusion of the discussion: "All
choices are caused but they are caused by the chooser" [5].

The compartmentalization of science is counteracted by
interdisciplinary research. Interdisciplinary research covers more than one cross section; it prevents us from one-
sidedness. As to the problem of free choice, it prevents
us from denying, on the one hand, the deterministic and
mechanistic aspects of the human reality and, on the other
hand, the human freedom to transcend them. This freedom is
not denied by determinism, but rather by what I am used to
calling pan-determinism. In other words, the alternative
really reads pan-determinism versus determinism, rather than
determinism versus indeterminism. And as to Freud, he only
espoused pan-determinism in theory. In practice, he was
anything but blind to the human freedom to change, to improve when he once defined the goal of psychoanalysis as
giving "the patient's ego the freedom to choose one way
or the other" [6].

First of all, it is lack of discrimination that causes
pan-determinism. More specifically, "causes" are confounded with "reasons". What then is the difference between
them? If you cut onions you weep. Your tears have a
"cause". But you have no "reason" to weep. If you do rock
climbing and arrive at a height of 10,000 feet, you may
have to cope with a feeling of oppression and anxiety.
Oppression has either a "cause" or a "reason". Lack of
oxygen may be the "cause". But if you know that you are
badly equipped or poorly trained, anxiety has a "reason".

Heidegger has defined being human as "being in the world".
I would say that the world includes beings as well as meanings. What is even more important, the meanings form reasons, and the reasons, in turn, form those motives by which
man lets himself be determined. But reasons and meanings
are excluded if you conceive of him in terms of a closed

system. What is left are causes and effects. The effects are represented by conditioned reflexes or responses to stimuli. The causes are represented by conditioning processes or drives and instincts. Drives and instincts push but reasons and meanings pull. To be sure, if you conceive of man in terms of a closed system you notice only forces that push but no motives that pull. Consider the front doors of a hotel. From within the lobby you notice only the sign "push." The sign "pull" is noticeable only from without.

Man has open doors, as does a hotel. He is no monad without windows. Indeed, psychology degenerates into some sort of monadology unless it recognizes man's openness to the world. This openness of existence is reflected by its self-transcendence. The self-transcendent quality of the human reality, in turn, is reflected in the "intentionality" of human phenomena, as it has been called by Franz Brentano. According to Edmund Husserl, the human phenomena point to "intentional referents." Reasons and meanings do represent such referents. They are the *logos* for which the psyche is reaching out. If psychology is to be worth its name it has to recognize both halves of this name, the *logos* as well as the psyche.

On the other hand, once the intentional quality of the human phenomena, the self-transcendence of existence, has been denied, existence itself is also distorted. It is reified. Being is made into a mere thing. Being human is de-humanized. The person is de-personalized. And, what is most important, the subject is made into an object. How is this enacted?

I would say that it is characteristic of a subject that it relates to objects. And it is characteristic of man that he relates to objects in terms of intentional referents. In other words, man relates to values and meanings which serve and function as reasons and motives. His is a "will to meaning" [7].

If self-transcendence is denied and the door to meanings and values is closed, reasons and motives can, and must, be replaced by conditioning processes and the like. It then is up to the "hidden persuaders" to do the conditioning, to

manipulate man. For it is reification that opens the door
to manipulation. And vice versa. If one is to manipulate
human beings he has to reify them, in the first place, and,
to this end, to indoctrinate them along the lines of pan-
determinism.

No one has put it more aptly than von Bertalanffy, who
says: "The expanding economy of the 'affluent society'
could not subsist without manipulation, Only by manipulating
humans ever more into Skinnerian rats, robots, buying auto-
mata, homeostatically adjusted conformers and opportunists
can this great society follow its progress toward ever increasing gross national product. The concept of man as robot
was both an expression of and a powerful motive force in in-
dustrialized mass society. It was the basis for behavioral
engineering in commercial, economic, political, and other
advertising and propaganda" [8].

Videant consules.

REFERENCES

1. LORENZ, Konrad, *Uber tierisches und menschliches Verhalten,*
    362, 373, Munich, 1965.

2. FRANKL, Viktor E., *The Will to Meaning: Foundations and
    Applications of Logotherapy*, 22, New York and Cleveland:
    New American Library World Publishers, 1969.

3. FRANKL, Viktor E.,"Beyond Self-Actualization and Self-
    Expression." *Journal of Existential Psychiatry, 1,* 6,
    1960.

4. von BERTALANFFY, Ludwig, "General System Theory and
    Psychiatry", *American Handbook of Psychiatry, 3,* 717,
    ARIETI, Silvano (ed.), Toronto, Canada: U. of Toronto
    Press, 1966.

5. ARNOLD, Magda B. and GASSON, J.A. (eds.), *The Human
    Person,* 40, New York: The Ronald Press, 1954.

6. FREUD, Sigmund, *The Ego and the Id,* 72, London: Hogarth
    Press, Ltd., 1927.

7. FRANKL, Viktor E., *The Will to Meaning: Foundations and Applications of Logotherapy*, 22, New York and Cleveland: New American Library World Publishers, 1969.

8. von BERTALANFFY, Ludwig, "General System Theory and Psychiatry", *American Handbook of Psychiatry*, 3, 706, ARIETI, Silvano (ed.), Toronto, Canada: U. of Toronto Press, 1966.

GENERAL SYSTEMS AS AN INTEGRATING
FORCE IN THE SOCIAL SCIENCES

KENNETH E. BOULDING

Institute of Behavioral Science, University of Colorado, Boulder, Colorado, 80302, U.S.A.

General systems is not so much a body of doctrine as it is a point of view or even an intellectual value orientation. In the original "manifesto" of what later became the Society for General Systems Research, a general system was defined simply as any theoretical system which was of interest to more than one discipline [1]. The value orientations are towards putting a high value on the conceptual unity of knowledge, on breaking out of the narrow confines of particular disciplines, on learning from those with whom we do not ordinarily associate, and on a simplification of the general learning process.

A strong preference for the conceptual unity of knowledge has been important in developing the whole scientific revolution. Pre-scientific explanations of the world tend to be *ad hoc* particular causes for particular phenomena without any unifying principle. Science has constantly been characterized by the discovery of great unifying principles such as the theory of gravitation, the atomic structure, the chemical elements, and the theory of relativity. These would not even have been looked for in the first place if there had not been a dissatisfaction with fragmented explanations and a constant hunger for a unifying theory. In this sense the general systems approach merely continues a very ancient tradition in science. It is a tradition, however, which has been constantly modified by the still more fundamental tradition of careful observation and measurement, prediction, and empirical feedback. A theory is not judged to be better merely because it unifies a larger area, if this unification does not meet the empirical test of predictions fulfilled. Scientists, indeed, and social scientists in particular, have some reason to be wary of the great unifying vision which does not really pay off and which tends to divert attention from evidence which is contrary to itself. The scientific imagination is quite rightly suspicious of the grandiose. Aristotle, Bacon, Spengler, Marx, and Toynbee all went far beyond what was testable in their manic drive for unity. No amount of failure, however, can destroy this drive itself. The rage for order which moves the scientist as well as the poet is a rage which can ultimately be mollified only as things fall into place in a single pattern, a pattern which persists both in space and in time.

The motivation to break out of the confines of particular disciplines which is also characteristic of the general systems movement seems to have two principal sources. The first arises from the practical needs of those who are studying a particular empirical phenomenon which simply refuses to be confined within the conventional disciplinary limits. I can trace back my own interest in general systems to the fact that I became involved in the study of industrial relations, starting off as a very pure economist, and discovered very soon that if I was to get anywhere with the study of this empirical field I had to acquaint myself with some of the methods and findings at least of sociology, psychology, and political science. In spite of the fact that industrial relations was traditionally in the Economics Department, I very soon discovered when I began to study it that economics is probably not more than 20% of the field, although a very crucial 20%. Similarly, anyone who studies a practical problem such as pollution, flood control, or war and peace will soon find that no discipline can contain him. If we study air pollution, for instance, we need to know something about chemistry, biology and all the social sciences. No single discipline or even group of disciplines can encompass the interaction of the atmosphere, the hydrosphere, and the sociosphere.

The second motivation for getting into other disciplines is simply that of curiosity, a pure interest in what lies beyond the intellectual fence within which one has been raised. Indeed, general systems might be described by its

enemies as a kind of intellectual voyeurism, if indeed this
mild and low-keyed enterprise had ever produced any enemies.
As scientists, however, we should not be ashamed of idle
curiosity, for this is one of the great motivations of science, and a disinterested interest in the affairs of other
disciplines should not be undervalued. Curiosity, however,
like any other virtue, can have pathological forms, such as
dilettantism, and it seems to be most healthy when it starts
from a solid base in the particular discipline and goes
through holes in the fences into adjoining disciplines.

The organizational aspects of breaking out of one's
discipline consist in organizing communications with those
people in other disciplines with whom we do not ordinarily
associate. Even within the structure of a university, which
is supposed to be universal, this is a more difficult problem than might be thought at first sight. Political power
in universities tends to lie with the departments and the
disciplines, and the prime loyalty of a professor is to his
discipline rather than to the university at which he happens
to teach. Interdisciplinary activities, however, are not
supported by any "interdiscipline" in the world outside them.
They tend to have to rely on what is often a transient interest on the part of transient faculty members. The care
and feeding of faculty interest in other disciplines, which,
one might argue, should be the main concern of university
administrators, is usually left almost entirely to chance,
and will not take place unless there happens to be what might
be called a general systems type of entrepreneur in the
vicinity. The importance of this intellectual entrepreneur-
ship function can hardly be overestimated, although its rewards are somewhat uncertain. General systems enterprises
usually have to be disguised under other names, and even
other purposes, such as Mental Health, or Conflict Resolution, or Education in High Schools, or Educational TV, and
I know of no instance in which a university has propagated
an organization for general systems by that name and for this
purpose. Perhaps it will change in the future as the Society
for General Systems Research acquires members and prestige
and the university will respond to pressures outside it.

A final value orientation of general systems is towards
the simplification of the learning process. In the long run

this may turn out to be the most significant of all the
fruits of general systems and it will not be the first time
that something which may have originated largely in idle
curiosity may turn out to have certain practical ends. For
the educator, especially, faced with the exponential growth
of knowledge to increasingly unmanageable levels, the practical end of the simplification of the image of the world
which has to be learned is of very great importance and it
could well be that general systems could make a vital contribution towards this. If indeed there are certain patterns
in the empirical world which repeat themselves in discipline
after discipline, it is a waste of time for the student to
have to learn these, often in different languages, as he goes
from discipline to discipline. It also arouses student interest and creates intellectual awakening when he perceives
that things which he previously may have thought of as unrelated and disparate are in fact related.

As I have tried to teach general systems [2], I have
found that a good deal of the content of the course consists
of an attempt to interpret certain very simple mathematical
and logical concepts and operations as descriptive of a variety of empirical worlds. Such concepts, for instance, as
sets, sequences, dimensions, identities, inequalities, differences and differential equations, exponential growth,
graph theory, maximization, the minimax, and so on, all have
reference to a large number of empirical fields and if the
student can be made to perceive this he is a long way towards
perceiving the fundamental unity of the world. There are
also certain processes which it is harder to reduce to mathematical form, but which also are descriptive of many different empirical fields, such as the ecological equilibrium of
interacting populations, the mutation-selection process in
evolution theory, the principle of optimum scale in organizations, the relations of growth to form and function to structure, the problem of nucleation of organizations, and so on.
Each of these processes has examples in both the natural and
the social sciences and it is not too difficult to make the
student perceive that there are patterns which persist through
widely different empirical referents; that, for instance,
the architecture of an insect is related to that of a building, that social evolution is in a very real sense a continuation of biological evolution with less random mutations,

and that the automobile is a species very much like an animal
but with a more complex reproductive process.

The source of all these generalities in the empirical
world is the fact that the whole empirical world, physical,
chemical, biological, and social, is a structure in the four-
dimensional continuum of space-time. It has microstructures
down to the neutrino and macrostructures up to the total universe, and they all participate in the common quality of
being part of the space-time pattern. The predictive power
of knowledge of any sort consists in our ability to perceive
regularities and patterns in this space-time continuum.
These may be of four kinds. The simplest patterns are those
which can be described by differential or difference equations,
such as celestial mechanics, hydrodynamics, simple econome-
tric dynamics, and so on. The success of astronomers in predicting eclipses and even the somewhat less spectacular success of economists in predicting next year's gross national
product derives from the same principle, that if we can detect in the past a stable relationship between every today
and its corresponding tomorrow or between today, tomorrow,
and the day after, then starting from Monday we can find out
what Tuesday is going to be like and on Tuesday we can predict Wednesday and so on. If astronomers have been more
successful than economists, it is only because they have more
stable constants in their differential equations.

A second type of pattern in the space-time continuum is
what I call the wallpaper principle. If we see a wallpaper
with a regular pattern of roses on it we predict with some
confidence that the roses will continue behind the mirror
where we cannot see them. Similarly, if we perceive clusters
of patterns in the space-time continuum and we perceive the
beginning of one of them at the present we have some confidence that it will project into the future. The best example of this is the life pattern of living objects from conception to death. All members of a single species age in
very much the same way, and if the pattern is not interrupted
by death it can be predicted with some confidence. Population projection, which is a dynamic with very universal applicability to anything which depends on a "lifecycle,"
whether this is man, mice, automobiles, or even ideas, is
a combination of the first and second principles.

A third pattern which we perceive in the space-time continuum is that of evolution, that is, a pattern of mutation
and selection, which is a pattern followed not only in biological evolution but in social evolution and also in human
learning and even perception, where modern theory suggests
that even the senses select from the array of mutations which
the imagination creates. Evolutionary theory has much less
predictive power than the first two, and for a very fundamental reason, that any process which involves the creation
of information structures, that is, the development of less
and less probable organizations, must contain in it an element of what I call fundamental surprise [3]. We cannot
predict the course of evolution for the very same reason that
we cannot predict the results of a research project. If we
could predict the results we wouldn't get any money for the
research, and we wouldn't have to do it. Nevertheless, the
evolutionary pattern is a vision of a structure in space-
time of enormous importance, and one that will almost certainly turn out to have great practical importance in the
study of human learning.

Perhaps even a fourth pattern in space-time can be de-
tected. This might be called the decision tree. Individuals
in their lives come to points where decisions have to be made
on alternative images of the future. The shuttle of the
present weaves the pattern of the past; only one out of many
potential futures is actualized. Nevertheless, we may be
able to say something about probabilities here, and the pattern by which the learning process of the past leads into
the decisions of the present, which in turn lead into the
actualities of the future. At a very simple level, cybernetic control systems are systems which insulate a part of
the total empirical world against the randomness of the rest
of it. The more cybernetic machinery we have, the more the
regular patterns occupy the center of the great four-dimensional web and the random elements are pushed to the edges,
at least from where the observer sits.

Equilibrium systems, of course, are simply special cases
of the four-dimensional matrix in which Monday produces a
Tuesday that is the same as Monday. There are also equilibrium systems which are heuristic devices, intellectual step-
ping stones, as it were, to the perception of dynamic realities, but which have no actual place in the empirical world.

It is quite possible that general systems will have a much greater impact on the content of the social sciences than on the natural sciences, and that it will operate not merely to call attention to similarities and regularities in already developed theoretical systems, but that here it may be the actual producer of a more integrated social theory. My principal reason for believing this is that the social scientists study an empirical system which is itself highly unified; the physical and natural scientists are to some extent separated from each other by the fact that they study different orders of systems, and while there may be many processes which are similar in the different orders of systems, the empirical fields themselves are fairly distinct. A crystallographer, for instance, does not really have to know very much about the anatomy of the sawfly, because he operates in an empirical system which is fairly self-contained and separated, as it were, by an order of systems from those around it. The different social sciences, however, are not really separated from each other by any fundamental difference in the order of the systems which they study. All the social sciences study the same social system, but from somewhat different points of view. The social system itself is very much of a unity, with a sociosphere which may be defined as all human beings on the surface of the globe in their capacities as actors in roles, as participants in organizations and as an interaction with each other. This is a total system to the parameters of which, of course, certain physiological systems or even physical, chemical, geographical and geological systems are relevant, but which nevertheless is strictly separated from these other systems by its degree of complexity.

The divisions of the social system, however, such as economics, political science, sociology, psychology, and so on, are not divided from each other by differences in the order of systems, but are all aspects of the total social system. Thus, economics studies those aspects of the total social system which are particularly governed by the institution of exchange, and those social institutions which operate primarily in an exchange environment. Political science, similarly studies those aspects of the social system which are concerned with legitimate coercion and those institutions, such as the state, which are more particularly

concerned with this social form. Sociology is especially
concerned with those aspects of the social system which relate particularly to the integrative system - that is, to
such relationships as identity, community, loyalty, friendship, legitimacy, and their opposites, - and similarly tends
to concentrate on those particular institutions which operate mainly in the integrative system, such as the family,
the church, the school, and so on. Psychology is such a
heterogeneous collection of almost unrelated disciplines
that one almost hesitates to call it a social science. At
one end it finds itself in biology, in the study of animal
behavior and physiology of the human nervous system; at the
other end it finds itself in clinical psychology and psychoanalysis, where it really belongs to the medical rather than
to the social sciences. Insofar as behavior of the individual human organism, however, is the building material out
of which the whole social system is built, obviously psychology is highly relevant. Social psychology, along with
anthropology perhaps, have come closest to studying social
systems as a whole, though they have tended to confine themselves to rather small systems. Geography has strong claims
to be a social science, studying mainly those aspects of the
social system which are related to location. History, of
course, in the broader sense of the word, including archeol-
ogy, is a study of patterns of social systems in time and
of the deposit of the records of social systems. It is, as
it were, the paleontology of the social sciences, and as
such is the indispensable raw material from which any theoretical structures must ultimately be developed and by which
they must be tested. History as it is usually taught as a
separate discipline is a much narrower concept than the
above and confines itself largely to what might be called
the public record.

The question is, therefore, if the total social system
is in fact a unity, could it not produce a unified body of
theory? If, indeed, it should, we might expect the general
systems interest in this case to produce not merely the
transfer of suggestive insights from one field to another,
but a radical restructuring of the existing body of theory
into a general social science. There are a good many indi-
cations, I think, that this is happening. In the first
place, we have something that might be described as economics

imperialism. This is the expansion of the methods and concepts of economics into other social sciences. Oddly enough, this is not being done for the most part by the economists themselves, who seem to be for the most part in a rather isolationist mood and are very quietly minding their own parameters. The imperialist forays, if that indeed is what they are, are being conducted for the most part by fifth columns in other camps who have been impressed and perhaps over-impressed by the skills and the successes of economics. We see this movement reflected in sociology in the work of people like Homans [4], Peter Blau [5], or even Talcott Parsons [6], who see the generalized concept of exchange as the key to practically all social relations. One sees it in political science in the work of people like Anthony Downs [7], Buchanan and Tullock [8], Riker [9], and Lindblom and Dahl [10]. Here again the concept of exchange has been used as an explanatory factor of substantial power in explaining the phenomenon of political life. The rise of game theory itself can be regarded as to some extent an expansion of economics, and it is certainly no accident that the classical work in game theory is by a mathematician, Von Neumann, and an economist, Morgenstern, and is called, indeed, *The Theory of Games and Economic Behavior* [11]. I must confess, even, that my own work, *Conflict and Defense* [12], is to a considerable extent an application of the economic theory of oligopoly to the problems of the international system. The methods and concepts of economics have perhaps made the least impact in psychology, though even here in the work of men like Clyde Coombs [13] we see a certain impact of the economic theory of utility, decision-making, and exchange.

In spite of what looks like a considerable success for economics imperialism, it is by no means the whole story. The contributions of psychology and social psychology to the study of economic and political institutions, or rather to institutions which are usually regarded as the prerogative of economists and political scientists, such as banks, households, or governments, has been of considerable importance. As between economics and psychology, indeed, the terms of trade may very well have been running in the favor of economics, with psychology giving a good deal more than it has received, especially through the work of men like George Katona [14], who has greatly enriched the study of the household by both theoretical and empirical methods

which have been largely brought in from psychology, and by
the work of Cyert and March, whose *Behavioral Theory of the
Firm* [15] has enriched what used to be the pretty thin soil
of formal economic theory with a rich deposit of complexity
derived in part, at least, from certain psychological models.

The anthropologist likewise has been trying to break out
of his disciplinary ghetto among the so-called primitive people and apply his methods and techniques to more complex so-
cities, though it is perhaps a little too early to judge the
success of this enterprise. It is the great virtue of the
anthropologist that he is trying to perceive a culture and
a society as a whole. The anthropological spirit as applied
to the larger and more complex society, such as, for instance, Ruth Benedict's work on Japan [16], yields a breadth
of insight which excuses a good deal of possible inaccuracy
in detail. The Society for Applied Anthropology has done
good work in expanding the anthropological vision to large
societies, and the main obstacle to this expansion seems to
be the difficulty which many anthropologists have in appre-
ciating the special contribution of other disciplines. One
wishes, indeed that anthropologists would approach the other
social sciences with the eagerness and thirst for the learning of other languages and cultures which they apply in
their own specialized work.

A possible reason why it seems to have been economics
rather than anthropology which has made the main imperialist
thrust into other sciences is perhaps that there is within
the social system a real difference of system levels in subject matter between large systems and small. Anthropology
and social psychology on the whole study fairly small systems of human interaction, whereas economics, sociology and
political science tend to study the large systems. Economics
has been the most successful of the social sciences in developing both theoretical techniques and information collection
and indexing for large systems, such as a big national economy. The economic models of J.M. Keynes, and before him of
Irving Fisher, coupled with measurements of the large aggregates and averages of the system, such as national income
and the price level, have given economists a certain skill
in handling these large total systems which the other social
sciences still in part lack.

The success of economics imperialism, therefore, may be a rather accidental phenomenon, depending on the particular stage which economics and the other sciences happen to have reached. I would myself argue strongly that the phenomenon of exchange, which is so central to the economic abstraction, is by no means the only social organizer. Any attempt to explain society exclusively in terms of exchange will leave out some very important elements, such as the threat system, and what I have elsewhere called the integrative system, which deals with such relationships as love, loyalty, legitimacy, community, identity, and so on, which ordinarily have been regarded as somewhat the preserve of the sociologist, but which it is clear apply to all social relations and have been very much neglected by economists and political scientists. At the moment, indeed, I am inclined to advocate a sociological imperialism on the grounds that it is the integrative system which really dominates the larger dynamics of the social system. In this country especially we are in grave danger of supposing, for instance, that wealth and power legitimate themselves, which they do not, and of neglecting the all-important element of the system of legitimation without which both wealth and power are virtually useless. The dynamics of legitimacy acquires its importance from the fact that without legitimacy no continuing operation or organization can be carried on. A bandit using a illegitimate threat can establish a temporary role structure with his victim. If he is to rob a man every week, however, he must turn himself either into a landlord or a tax collector. Similarly, wealth, that is, purchasing power, which loses its legitimacy, is in grave danger of expropriation.

Another good example of the need for integrative theory is in the field of community and organization. Game theory may be able to explain why people form coalitions against the common enemy, though it doesn't even explain this very well. What game theory does not explain is why communities take shape in the way they do, and why people band together into societies not merely out of common fears and hatreds, but out of mutual love and loyalty. The structure of organization, to be sure, has something to do with economic payoffs, but it has also something to do with the capacity of organizations to become communities and to attract the gifts and sacrifices from those associated with them. It is a

structure of gifts and sacrifices, which is part of what I
have elsewhere called the "grants economy," which is the
principal evidence for the existence of an integrative system and is a first approximation measure of it.

One may perhaps concede something to those who are arguing for the primacy of exchange as a social relation, in
that it is possible to put both the threat relationship and
the integrative relationship into a form which looks something like exchange. The bandit says, "Your money or your
life." You give him your money, he gives you your life.
This looks superficially like exchange, although it is the
exchange of a positive "good," your money, for a negative
"bad," not taking your life. Negative bads are not the same
as goods, and the threat system which is concerned primarily
with bads has many different properties from the exchange
system which deals mainly with goods. Nevertheless, the
similarities are great enough so that it is not wholly un-
reasonable to regard the threat relationship as a rather
peculiar form of exchange.

In the integrative relationship, likewise, even though
in the gift a good passes from one person to another without
anything apparently going in return, it can be argued that
there is a generalized good which is returned for a gift. I
refer here of course to genuine gifts, not to gifts which are
merely disguised exchanges, as many of them are. If I give
to a beggar, presumably he gives me in return a sense of
satisfied pity or of identity with him even at a very low
level. If I give to my children, it is because they give
me the status of being a parent. Nevertheless, between the
specific good or service which constitutes the gift and the
generalized good that constitutes status, there is a profound
difference, and if we want to put the integrative system under exchange we have to recognize that it is a very peculiar
form of it. Even the exchange of gifts, that is, reciprocity, is not the same as contractual exchange and has very
different consequences. Reciprocity or the unconditional
exchange of goods and services creates and sustains an integrative system in a way that contractual exchange does not.
Thus, even if in the exchange of Christmas gifts there are
certain "terms of trade" and, as it were, a price structure,
the gifts are theoretically unconditional, that is, given

whether anything is received or not, and they reinforce the
integrative system of the family or the friendship group.

A further thread which unites all the study of society
insofar as it is concerned with dynamic processes and development is learning theory. It has become very clear that
the developmental process in society is essentially a process
in human learning, about which, unfortunately, we know very
little. Thus, economic development is essentially a process
by which man acquires new skills and new ways of doing things
which are associated with the creation of new forms of capi-
tal, that is, human knowledge imposed on the material world.
Political development consists in the acquisition of new
skills in the management of conflict, both internal and external, in the development of community, and in the developing of forms of organization and communication which will
make wise decisions on the part of the powerful more probable. Ethical development consists in the learning of new
value systems which not only increase the probability of economic and political development, but which enrich the quality of human life and experience itself.

If, then, we really are to understand the dynamics of
society, especially the dynamics of the total social system,
we must look at what might be called the macro-learning process, especially the process by which the noosphere or the
total cognitive content of all human minds is transmitted
from one generation to the next. Perhaps the most significant single factor in human existence is that all knowledge
is lost every generation, for all other aspects of the social system are ultimately based on knowledge, that is, the
total structural content of human minds. Hence the transmission and the expansion of knowledge is the key to social
dynamics. There are four major transmission belts, the family and the groups that center around it, the institutions
of formal education, that is, schools, colleges and universities, the peer groups, especially in childhood and youth,
and the mass media. A change in the methods of child-rear-
ing may easily be the most important key to transforming
the dynamic parameters of a total social system, though the
family, in the absence of impact from outside, is apt to be
a highly conservative institution tending to reproduce in
the children the values and skills of the parents. The formal educational system again has often been conservative,

but in the transition from traditional to modern societies
is often a major source of change. It may well be indeed
that the greatest changes are those which originate somewhere within the system of formal education and are then
transmitted into the family. The peer group, especially the
"youth culture" which in many societies is conservative, has
now become a very significant agent of change, perhaps because of the growth of mass media, especially television, and
the increasing economic independence and affluence of youth.

What seems to be happening today is a certain tendency
for the traditional disciplinary barriers to break down in
all the sciences. This is particularly noticeable in the
social sciences. It has become harder and harder to identify
the discipline of anybody who is working on the frontiers
of knowledge. Whether this process will eventually result
in restructuring of the present disciplines, only the future
can tell. The existing disciplines have a strong dynamic of
their own, and a strong set of vested interests, which make
them highly self-perpetuating. It may be, therefore, that
one of the roles of what might be called general social systems will be to provide a larger matrix within which the
existing disciplines can continue without doing too much damage. Within this framework we can perhaps also foresee the
development of a new disciplinary structure which cuts across
the older disciplines, dividing up the subject matter somewhat according to the level of systems involved. At the
level of mechanical and correlational systems, for instance,
we have econometrics, and the newly developing field of po-
liticometrics, which have developed rather similar techniques
for perceiving mechanical regularities in social quantities
in the space-time continuum. At another level we have the
development of what might be called social cybernetics, the
study of feedback systems ranging from the family through
all social organizations into the study of business cycles,
peace and war cycles, cultural and fashion cycles, even
cycles of civilization itself. At still another level we
find a discipline emerging in the study of organization and
organizational behavior involving open systems and growth
systems at all levels, and the dynamics of deviation-ampli-
fying feedback. This restructuring of the disciplines according to systems level rather than according to historical
accident or particular forms of abstraction are not likely

to replace the existing structure of disciplines and departments, but if it can be laid across the old structure it
will greatly enrich the present conceptual framework.

The implications of all this for teaching, especially
at the level of general education, may be quite considerable.
It may well be that we should now devote a substantial amount
of energy to developing a general social science curriculum
not only in the Freshman and Sophomore years of college,
but down into the high schools or even the grade schools,
following the excellent example of Dr. L. Senesh of the University of Colorado. Only thus, I expect, can we ensure
that reasonably sophisticated concepts of the social system
will be sufficiently widespread in the population so it can
respond politically to the increasingly difficult decisions
that lie ahead.

The implications of general systems for teaching go of
course far beyond the social sciences. One would like to see,
indeed, the development of a core curriculum centering the
whole process of formal education from kindergarten right
through to college around the concept of what I have called
the "total earth," that is, the planet as a total system.
I would certainly not want to exclude the rest of the universe, and indeed earth has to be placed in its setting in
the solar system and in the universe as a whole. Nevertheless, it is earth which is going to be man's home for a long
time to come. One of the major objects of formal education
should be to develop the concept of the earth as a total
system of interacting spheres. We could start indeed with
the lithosphere, with the hydrosphere and the atmosphere,
and go on to the biosphere, the sociosphere, with constant
attention to the way in which each of these spheres inter-
acts with the others. As suggested earlier, each of these
spheres must be considered in the four-dimensional continuum
in time as well as in space. All the disciplines which describe the empirical world can be fitted easily into this
framework. Those that do not fit so easily might be called
the language disciplines which not only include the human
languages themselves, but also mathematics and logic which
constitute as it were the specialized language of relationship. To think of these as part of the communications network of the noosphere, or sphere of knowledge, in no way

diminishes them; it makes, indeed, for a richer appreciation of their significance. Even though a large part of
the task of formal education in this field has to be the
acquisition of skill rather than the perception of significance, it will surely motivate people towards the acquisition of skill if the larger significance of that skill is
perceived. Similarly, with the creative arts, with philosophy and with religion, to perceive these as an essential
part of the total system in no way diminishes them but again
makes for the deeper appreciation of their significance.
The vision of the universe indeed as a total system extending
magnificently through time and space and with equal magnificence towards the infinitesimal structure, and towards the
immense complexity of the inner space of the human mind, is
an experience which we need not be ashamed to call religious.
We are capable indeed of perceiving and knowing only a small
part of this magnificence, but he who has not sensed it however dimly as a totality is deprived of the greatest of
human experiences.

REFERENCES

1. General Program - Directory of the Berkeley Meeting,
    American Association for the Advancement of Science,
    281, December 26-31, 1954.

2. I have taught a course entitled "General Systems" in the
    College Honors Program at the University of Michigan
    designed mainly for Honors Seniors for a number of years.
    See BOULDING, Kenneth E., "An Interdisciplinary Honors
    Course in General Systems," *Superior Student*, *4*, 31,
    Jan.-Feb., 1962.

3. BOULDING, Kenneth E., "Expecting the Unexpected: The
    Uncertain Future of Knowledge and Technology," *Prospec-
    tive Changes in Society by 1980*, 199-215, (Reports Pre-
    pared for the First Area Conference), Denver, Colorado,
    July, 1966.

4. HOMANS, George C., *Social Behavior: Its Elementary Forms*,
    New York: Harcourt, Brace and World, 1961.

5. BLAU, Peter M., *Exchange and Power in Social Life*. New York: John Wiley, 1964.

6. See especially the impact of Alfred Marshall in Talcott PARSON's *The Structure of Social Action*, Glencoe, Illinois: Free Press, 1949.

7. DOWNS, Anthony, *An Economic Theory of Democracy*. New York: Harper and Row, 1965.

8. BUCHANAN, James M. and TULLOCK, G., *The Calculus of Consent*. Ann Harbor: University of Michigan Press, 1962.

9. RIKER, William H., *Democracy in the United States*. New York: Macmillan, 1953.

10. DAHL, Robert A. and LINDBLOM, Charles E., *Politics, Economics, and Welfare: Planning and Politico-economic Systems Resolved into Basic Social Processes*. New York: Harper & Row, 1965.

11. von NEUMANN, John and MORGENSTERN, Oskar, *Theory of Games and Economic Behavior*. Princeton, N.J.: Princeton University Press, 1944.

12. BOULDING, Kenneth E., *Conflict and Defense*. New York: Harper and Bros., 1962.

13. COOMS, Ckyde H., *A Theory of Data*. New York: Wiley, 1964.

14. KATONA, George, *The Mass Consumption Society*. New York: McGraw-Hill, 1964.

15. CYERT, R.M. and MARCH, J.G., *A Behavioral Theory of the Firm*. Englewood Cliffs, N.J.: Prentice-Hall, 1963.

16. BENEDICT, Ruth, *The Chrysanthemum and the Sword*. Boston: Houghton, Mifflin, 1946.

INDETERMINACY AND GENERAL SYSTEMS THEORY

FRED E. KATZ

*State University of New York at Buffalo,
Department of Sociology, Amherst,
N.Y. 14226, U.S.A.*

Ludwig von Bertalanffy has focused attention upon open
systems. This involves interactions between different systems. During the interaction the structural components of
the systems are apt to undergo change while, in a fundamental way, remaining intact. Thus, in biological systems
there is apt to be a "continuous inflow and outflow, building up and breaking down of the component material of the
systems" [1]. Bertalanffy sees orderliness in this process
by focusing on the relation between different system levels.
He notes that

> ... what appears to be persistent at one level is in fact
> maintained in a continuous change, formation, growth,
> wearing out, and death of systems of the next lower
> level: of chemical components in the cell, of cells in
> a multicellular organism, and of individuals in a (spe-
> cies) ... [2]

and ...a living organism is an object maintaining itself in
> an orderly flow of events wherein the higher systems ap-
> pear persistent in the exchange of the subordinate ones
> ... [3].

In short, von Bertalanffy suggests that what may be in
flux at one level is really fairly stable when viewed from
another level. The implication is that the system that exhibits flux contains instability and, therefore, at least
some amount of indeterminacy in the activities of its component structures. Yet there is also continuity (or a

steady state, to use von Bertalanffy's term) exhibited by
the fact that the system is continually being reconstituted
so that the structure remains virtually identical to the
earlier state. Cells are forever wearing out and being replaced in essentially the same form as before, while they
are engaged in interaction with other cells as they perform
their work in the animal body.

The question that arises is whether one can conceptually
find a way of handling the flux, the indeterminacy existing
in a system, as well as the continuity of that system without taking refuge in the next higher system where there is
no evidence of flux [4]. A truly *general* systems theory
should not require one to vacillate between a system-in-flux
and a system-in-stability. Thus, one should not need to
consider separately the breakdown of cells from the stable
life processes of mature cells. One should be able to devise a way of picturing the internal structure of systems
that simultaneously accounts for the existence of indeterminacy as well as determinate, stable structures.

It must be obvious, for example, that the breakdown of
cell structure - and the emergence of entropy- has to take
place within a context that retains some stability, if new
cells are to re-emerge. This implies that the *total* system
does not succumb to anarchic flux. Yet indeterminacy persists. In physics, engineering, and mathematics one can
discern the rudiments of a perspective that accommodates itself to a measure of persisting indeterminacy among orderly,
stable structures. In physical systems one finds acceptance
of a kind of indeterminacy in subatomic levels of activity.
The Heisenberg Uncertainty Principle suggests that, at the
subatomic level, measurement techniques will themselves interfere with the things being measured. Hence, one must
agree to accept a degree of indeterminacy. But this is not
fatal since, for many purposes, probability mathematics
enables one to calculate the structures with adequate precision. Here, then, is a way of coping with indeterminacy
created by measurement problems.

In the Heisenberg formulation one assumes that the actual
subatomic physical systems are determinate; it is merely a
matter of not being able to devise measurement strategies
that can capture them in their naked form. This assumption

is unsatisfactory. By describing the behavior of the particles in a gross manner – because this can be done by probability mathematics – it claims to describe a system of behavior of individual particles. This is postulating something
about one sector of a system while describing another. For
present purposes, however, the most important point is that
a way was worked out for accepting and coping with indeterminacy. This represents the stand that scientific precision
can be preserved even under conditions of uncertainty.

A slightly different perspective toward indeterminacy
exists for man-made physical systems, such as machines, where
one finds deliberately built-in "tolerance" patterns that imply acceptance of a degree of imprecision in actual systems.
The degree of acceptable imprecision is likely to depend on
cost considerations, on the state of technology, and on the
tasks that the machine is expected to perform. At any rate,
a degree of imprecision (or indeterminacy) is frequently acceptable. Indeed it can be quite necessary. For instance,
a wheel that turns vertically on a horizontally placed shaft
is usually allowed some small amount of horizontal motion
(by not regulating its place of rotation on the shaft)
with infinite precision. This allows for lubrication to be
introduced and distributed by the sideways motion of the
wheel. It also allows the wheel to "adapt" to the presence
of particles of dust or other minor obstacles: (It can move
the particles aside or it can avoid them) by moving away from
them. If the wheel's place of rotation were fixed with utmost
precision – if there were no indeterminacy in the location of
the wheel – then the wheel (and the rest of the machine)
would break down each time some particles of dust appeared
on the shaft where the wheel rotates. Obviously, however,
the wheel cannot have unlimited horizontal movement if it is
to remain connected with other parts of the machine. Typically one finds collars on the shaft on each side of the wheel
that prevent the wheel from moving horizontally beyond specific points. The limits of horizontal movement are thus
controlled rigidly.

The main point that emerges from the preceding discussion,
especially in relation to man-made machines, is that, although
imprecision implies a lack of certainty about the exact nature of certain sectors of the system, the *limits of*

*imprecision that a system can tolerate are usually stated
very precisely.*

A corollary to the presence of indeterminacy in empirical systems is the fact that mathematics, probably the most
determinate of analytic systems, also contains indeterminacy.
Gödel's famous proof that some components of mathematics are
unprovable constitutes an elegant example. He demonstrated
that "it is impossible to establish the internal logical consistency of a very large class of deductive systems - elementary arithmetic, for example - unless one adopts principles
of reasoning so complex that their internal consistency is
as open to doubt as that of the systems themselves ..." [5].
Gödel thereby showed the obstinate and irreducible presence
of indeterminacy within mathematical systems. Such indeterminacy appears to contradict the fully determinate nature
of mathematics. Perhaps the indeterminacy is based on the
inherent limitations of man - that man does not have the
ability to build fully determinate mathematics. On the other
hand, perhaps the present limitation is merely a temporary
condition, subject to future "improvements" that may result
in elimination of all indeterminacy. Or it may be, as I
shall propose, that there necessarily exist spheres of indeterminacy in all systems, including various sectors of formal
mathematics. At any rate, returning to Gödel, the rest of
mathematics does not seem to be undermined by the indeterminacy demonstrated by Gödel.

I suggest that both Gödel's proof concerning mathematics
and Heisenberg's Uncertainty Principle concerning small-scale
physical systems are an indication of what is perhaps a more
general theorem: *For each system - and each structural component of a system - there exists a specifiable level of
indeterminacy.* It is important to note that the indeterminacy
levels (the limits of indeterminacy) are themselves struct-
tural properties of systems. This line of thinking emerged
from a consideration of social structures and social systems.

SOCIAL STRUCTURES

Sociologists often operate on the basis that social structures are made up of *expected* behavior. Thus the physician, when treating a patient, is expected to use objective scientific knowledge, whenever it is available; he is expected to refrain from personalized emotional involvement with the patient. Personal likes or dislikes are taboo, even when he does not approve of the patient's morality; he is expected not to take advantage of the patient, financially or emotionally. Similarly, there are expectations that apply to the patient. He is expected to obey the physician; he is expected to withhold no information that is relevant to his illness. Sociologists combine such items into clusters that are called roles. They then study role-based interactions between persons and between composites of many roles that make up institutions.

Returning now to the doctor-patient interaction, it must be noticed that the expectations do not state what the *specific* doctor in a *specific* situation actually does. Is he jovial and out-going or quiet and reserved? Is he doggedly efficient or hopelessly disorganized? None of these questions are answered by the underlying expected-behavior themes. Yet all are quite legitimate *as long as they do not transcend the limits* that are incorporated in the expectations. When efficiency becomes brutality, when joviality becomes irresponsibility, the limits have been transcended and the physician's behavior is regarded as illegitimate; and the entire system of interaction of medical personnel and patients is endangered. In more abstract terms, the expectations are statements of limitations within which behavior must fall. The expectations typically have some tangible and sensible relation to the fundamental task at hand. In the case of the doctor-patient situation, they are geared to relatively orderly deployment of medical knowledge [6].

Here one must notice that, being *limits*, the expectations do not specify each and every item of behavior. This is a great advantage. It makes for flexibility. The doctor can, for example, adapt himself to the particular patient and the particular immediate circumstances in which he and the patient find themselves. Since medicine is a long way from being an exact science, this room-to-manoeuvre is absolutely essential. Hence, a degree of indeterminacy in the physician's role has very practical significance.

The illustration of indeterminacy in the smallest social building-blocks, the expected-behavior-in-roles, shows that in a fundamental way such social structures contain determinate ranges of indeterminate behavior. This offers distinct adaptive advantages for these structures. Let us now consider built-in indeterminacy patterns in larger social structures.

SOCIAL SYSTEMS [7]

I shall use the concept of "structured autonomy" as the sociological equivalent of indeterminacy. The following points are proposed:

1) "Structured" autonomy differs from randomly occurring autonomy in that it can be clearly located and its limits are known.

2) The autonomy of parts of systems constitutes a measure of indeterminacy within systems. One can, nonetheless, regard structured autonomy as a property of social systems that one can incorporate into models of social systems.

3) Structured autonomy has distinctive functions that can be discovered, alongside other structural characteristics of social systems.

4) As a strategy for developing theory, the structured autonomy construct can:

a) improve one's ability to explain specific social interactions and relationships (e.g., I shall discuss an improved explanation of the place of workers in factories);

b) improve some existing theoretical models (e.g., I shall discuss the revision of the formal-informal dichotomy and the model of organizational adaptation to its environment);

      c) open the way for a more explicit theory of the
separation and fusion of social structures - where acknowl-
edgement of where and what sort of indeterminacy exists may
lead to increasingly precise theories of how social structures are linked.

The term 'autonomy' is in common use in the English language, particularly in the psychological sense, meaning personal freedom. It is also used in sociological treatises,
as in Gouldner's work on functional autonomy in bureaucracies
and Eisenstadt's work on functional differentiation of institutions in societies [8]. My work essentially shows how
autonomy is an integral part of the structure of social systems. I define structured autonomy to mean the relative
intractability of the component parts of social systems,
i.e., the relative absence of control of one part of a system by the other parts of that system. The basic assumption
is that, despite the interdependence of the parts of a system, the parts also retain a measure of separateness that
is not completely eliminated by their interrelatedness with
other parts of the system. But the systemic character is
not eliminated, because the autonomy is often clearly locatable and its part in the operation of the system can be
understood quite precisely.

A guiding assumption, then, is that the task of the social system theorist - or, for that matter, any system theorist - is to ascertain two things: (1) the kind of inter-
relatedness among the component parts of systems; and, (2)
the kind of separateness, the autonomy, that the component
parts retain while operating as parts of the system.

In a book on autonomy [9] I illustrated ways in which
autonomy is built into the structure of modern organizations,
and how this in turn plays a part in the way these systems
work. For example, I have already mentioned that in modern
hospitals physicians must have certain spheres in which they
can exercise professional judgment. To be effective in
their medical work they must have a sphere of discretion
where they are not closely supervised. They must even be
permitted to make guesses and to act when they are *not* absolutely certain about the patient's condition. In a particular situation such doctor autonomy may lead to disastrous

errors that adversely affect a patient's health, even his
life. But such risks are accepted. The reason is that only
when the physician has some autonomy will he be able to use
his professional judgment for harnessing and selectively
using available medical knowledge for the particular patient
he is trying to help.

In modern medical care, one assumes that the physician
must actively intervene rather than let nature run its course.
This requires considerable autonomy for the physician. Here
autonomy is a socially accepted device for reaching socially
accepted goals. In practical terms, as one tries to understand what goes on in a hospital, the doctor's autonomy means
that the specifics and details of his behavior are not pre-
dictable by those around him in the hospital. However, the
location of the doctor's autonomy (within his sphere of "medical competence" can be pinpointed quite precisely.

A more complicated use of structured autonomy is provided
by the well-known informal subcultures of workers in factories (or those of inmates in prisons, or enlisted men in
the military, or children in schools). Here built-in autonomy helps an organization adapt to its environment and, at
the same time, achieve a degree of internal cohesion. Also,
the autonomy construct offers a lead for a unified theory
of organizational structure.

Let me elaborate. The factory worker typically has a
technical job in which he has little autonomy. Beyond his
technical job, but still within his life in the factory, the
worker has a considerable sphere of behavior in which he has
autonomy from official surveillance. Ordinarily the worker
uses his autonomy to bring into the factory many of his working-class customs and concerns that are central to his life
outside the factory. This comes out in what he talks about
to his neighbor on the assembly line, what he jokes about,
much of what he thinks and daydreams about. Over these matters - the "informal culture of the worker" - the official
factory rules ordinarily exercise little control. The behavior patterns that emerge are often alien to the upper-
middle class culture of the factory's bureaucratic, manage-
rial staff. Yet, as long as they do not seem to create too
many problems, they are allowed to exist. By bringing

workingclass culture into the factory, the worker is bridging the gap between his life in the factory and his life in the community. The factory benefits since, by the same process, it is obtaining a bridge between itself and its environment. But by allowing some of the worker's culture to intrude, the factory is accepting the coexistence of "two cultures" with its inevitable problems of communication and presence of disparate values. It is accepting a form of internal cohesion based on a cultural and social pluralism, where workers have considerable leeway to work out by themselves what their social relationships, their commitments, and their forms of participation in the factory will be.

Let me now inject a note about the distinction between formal and informal organization. One of the curious phenomena in the sociological study of complex organizations is that generations of sociologists have accepted the dichotomy between formal and informal patterns as a legitimate *theoretical* distinction. They have insisted that some phenomena must be studied at one theoretical "level" and certain other phenomena must be studied at another "level." The distinction came about on empirical grounds as researchers repeatedly discovered that there exist both officially stated, normative patterns of social organization and actual ongoing behavior that often departs from the official, "formal" scheme. The early studies of factories were sponsored by management to investigate and, frequently, to bring under control the actual behavior of workers. The "formal" structure tended to coincide with the responsibilities and rights that were set forth by officials of the organization. The actual behavior of officials was usually ignored and so were the responsibilities of officials set forth by workers. This suggests a methodological bias in favor of discovering "deviance" in blue-collar workers' informal patterns simply because the researchers sought out a good deal of realistic detail about the actual behavior of the blue-collar workers. They did not, at the same time, study the actual behavior of officials except at the lowest level, that of foremen [10].

The formal-informal dichotomy refers to non-comparable phenomena. It is as though a chemist said that a particular substance consists of molecules and heat. It is difficult to see how the dichotomy was ever accepted as *a* theory of

organization. A second generation of researchers on work
organizations, notably Peter Blau and his students, expanded
the scope of research by looking at the actual behavior of
professionals and other middle-level persons. They, too,
rediscovered "informal" innovations that were essentially
deviant from the official prescriptions. It is safe to predict that if one observed the ongoing behavior of senior executives, he would also discover the "deviance" from officially stated rules.

There is need for one conceptual baseline - i.e., one
set of concepts - that explains the phenomena usually included under both the formal and informal headings. Using
the assumption of clearly locatable "structured autonomy,"
one can devise a scheme that comes close to developing just
such a baseline. Let me reiterate, the worker's technical
role contains little autonomy. But in the rest of his life
in the factory he has considerable autonomy. He has much
autonomy "external" to his tasks but internal to his existence in the factory. He may thereby perpetuate a very
minimal commitment to the organization in which he works.
In contrast to all this, the administrative official, the
organization-man, has relatively great autonomy in his technical organizational role; his work ordinarily involves
exercising considerable discretion. But autonomy external
to this role is severely limited since his organizational
responsibilities and affiliation are defined very broadly.
For the organization-man the organizational role "spills
over" into his life outside the factory. He cannot easily
shed his organization role as he leaves the factory. He
thereby helps the factory export its ethos and diminish the
autonomy of its social environment.

The following model emerges: the internal structure of
the factory may be divided into (1) the administrative
sector and (2) the manual labor sector. (A possible third
sector, the "staff," need not concern us here.) In the
first, the administrative sector, there is a high level of
autonomy internal to one's task role in the organization,
but low level of autonomy for one's role outside the organizational task roles. The person's organization roles
dominate his other roles. In the second sector the situation is reversed. Within the manual labor sector, there is

a low level of autonomy within one's task role in the organization, but a relatively high level of autonomy in one's roles outside the task role. As a result, the organization tends to "export" its culture (the familiar organization-man pattern) through its administrators; it imports working-class culture through its manual laborers. Within the organization there tends to be rather rigid discontinuity between the administrative and manual-labor sectors. In the ensuing "two cultures" there is minimal communication beyond technical task matters. There is little career mobility between the two levels. This "autonomy" of each sector prevents a true circulation process of the imported working-class culture within the factory or a full diffusion of the organization-man culture within the organization or an amalgamation of the two.

I shall not go into greater detail. I hope I have done enough to show that a model on the *location of autonomy* offers a common conceptual baseline for looking at both formal and informal patterns. The *location of autonomy* also shows how complex social organizations adapt to their environment by selectively employing both separation and fusion of structures.

CONCLUSION

The thesis of this paper has been that systems contain built-in indeterminacy. This thesis is stated in a general way in the first part of the paper. In the second part it is developed more fully in relation to social systems. Here socially structured autonomy is examined.

Built-in indeterminacy contains two important features: (1) it can be clearly located within systems; (2) its limits are specifiable. Indeterminacy is regarded as a structural feature that performs vital functions in the operation of systems. This view of indeterminacy differs from the traditional views (illustrated by the Heisenberg Uncertainty Principle) that regard indeterminacy as an impediment to accurate scientific description.

Built-in indeterminacy also implies two refinements of open-systems theory: (1) systems contain a degree of *internal* openness (stated differently, openness can be regarded as an internal structural attribute of systems); (2) the degree of openness of a system and the spheres in which the openness exists are specifiable.

Open systems theory has traditionally relegated flux and stability to different analytical levels of general systems. Similarly, open systems theory in sociology has dichotomized formal and informal structures. In contrast, I am suggesting that if structured indeterminacy (autonomy) is appropriately utilized in one's explanations, separation of these levels becomes superfluous.

When I suggested the general theorem that *all* systems contain specifiable indeterminacy I was perhaps more bold than judicious. Yet it must be recognized that the presence of specified indeterminacy is already implicit in many, if not most, scientific formulations. When the cellular biologist does not consider the submolecular level of activity he is, in effect saying: I am holding the determination of submolecular action in abeyance provided it does not operate at the cellular level. This means that he is specifying the limits of indeterminacy at a particular point. I am suggesting that every scientist necessarily draws such limits. He cannot allow himself the luxury of attempting to deal with all aspects at the same time. When the physicist makes formulations that link mass and velocity but omits atmospheric conditions, when the chemist makes formulations about molecular combinations but omits considerations of subatomic motion, each is limiting himself to a sphere of operation. He is saying that what is outside his sphere can be left indeterminate provided that it does not intrude into his chosen sphere of inquiry. I am here saying that most scientific formulations thereby contain an implicit formulation of the limits of *acceptable* indeterminacy. Focus on a set of interdigitated parameters implies that other possible parameters are excluded and the corresponding behavior is left indeterminate provided that it does not set in motion behavior that is measurable by the accepted parameters.

All this may suggest that indeterminacy is *outside* the chosen system that is being studied. This is precisely the assumption that I have attempted to challenge. I have tried to show that indeterminacy, when it is random and when its limits are precisely specifiable, is an attribute of parameters *within* systems.

If this paper appears to be a criticism of the very fruitful concept of open systems developed by von Bertalanffy, it should be noted that one can pay no greater respect to an exciting scholar than by taking his ideas seriously and wrestling with them.

REFERENCES

1. von BERTALANFFY, Ludwig, *Problems of Life*, 125, New York: Harper, 1960.

2. Ibid., 124.

3. Ibid., 134-135.

4. The problem has its analogy in a long-standing philo-sophical dispute: Can one step into the same river twice? (without taking recourse in the notion that the river's banks remain stable even though its water is in flux).

5. NAGEL, Ernest and NEWMAN, James R., *Gödel's Proof*, 6, New York: New York University Press, 1960.

6. This does not mean that the expectations were deliberate-ly designed with this in mind. They may have evolved accidentally or by trial and error over a period of time.

7. This section is an adaptation of a paper given at the 1970 Annual Meetings of the American Sociological Association in Washington, D.C.

8. See GOULDNER, Alvin W., "Reciprocity and Autonomy in Functional Theory," *Symposium on Sociological Theory*, 241-270, GROSS, L. (ed.), Evanston, Ill.: Harper & Row, 1959. Cf. EISENSTADT, S.N., *The Political Systems of Empires*, London: Free Press of Glencoe, 1963. Gouldner's view

implies that autonomy os system parts is apt to produce
tension and stress. He has done research on the process
of *asserting* autonomy. Here, of course, tension is very
likely to occur. Also, Gouldner views an autonomous
part as one that has relatively little need of the other
parts of the system. This, too, differs from the view
I am adopting. I am defining autonomy as the relative
absence of external control. A part of a system may not
be controlled by the remaining parts of the system. Yet
it may still be influenced by other parts of the system.

9.   KATZ, Fred. E., *Autonomy and Organization: The Limits
     of Social Control*, N.Y. : Random House, 1968.

10.   A postscript on factory structure: In contrast to the
     existing distinction between formal and informal structure on
     can conceive of the following components of factory structure

     I.   The actual behavior
          A.   Of workers
          B.   Of officials
     II. The normative prescriptions (the rights and respon-
          sibilities)
          A.   as set forth by officials concerning
               1.   Themselves
               2.   The blue-collar workers
          B.   as set forth by blue-collar workers concerning
               1.   Themselves
               2.   The factory officials

For the sake of simplicity I am leaving out white-collar,
middle-level people and professional "staff," who are
not strictly in the administrative hierarchy.

The "formal" patterns traditionally cover only IIA1 and
IIA2; the "informal" patterns cover IA. Some of the
sophisticated studies of informal patterns did touch on
IIB1.

THE BIORRHESIS OF CULTURAL SYSTEMS

LUDWIG VON BERTALANFFY'S CONTRIBUTIONS TO HUMAN ETHOLOGY AND CULTURAL ANTHROPOLOGY

FRIEDRICH KEITER *

Hamburg, Germany

In appraising L. von Bertalanffy as a productive writer
in human ethology as well as cultural anthropology, attention
may first be attracted to his newer contributions which continue Cassirer's approach to man as a symbolizing animal and
Heinz Werner's approach to psychic development as a process
of gradual differentiation. But to quote these newer facets
of our author's multidimensional work is by no means enough.
In a much broader and wider sense human ethology and cultural
anthropology have to learn from the findings of von Bertalanffy. They are fully comprised in the long list of fields
which are deficient in basic understanding if general system
theory, equifinality, von Bertalanffy's theory of growth,
etc., are not used.

Instead of discussing this statement theoretically it
seems more adequate to the writer to give a report of an
(unpublished) scientific work which clearly shows the deep
influence of von Bertalanffy in all these directions. We
are concerned here again with the old intriguing Oswald
Spengler quest for cultures as organisms. It will be an attempt to continue Kroeber's *Configurations of Culture Growth*
(1941), which is mostly an empiric answer to the quest.
Kroeber ended his endeavour earlier than necessary. He was
never fully aware of modern biology and statistics. Even
von Bertalanffy's *Theoretical Biology* was already available
in 1941. This is the reason why, after twenty-five years,
a successor and continuer of Kroeber's grandiose opus may

*Deceased

not seem inopportune, so that the universal data collected
by Kroeber will not remain only partially used.

In the theory of historical processes three aspects must
be distinguished: *cultural systems*, *social structures*, and
populations as the sum of the human individuals to whom such
systems and structures are an essential part of their environment and identification. The general category of growth
and aging can be applied to all three aspects. Too often
these have not been separated clearly enough. Our topic is
cultural systems. Kroeber used the method of counting geniuses and famous or well-known men. He relied for that on
encyclopedias, etc., which he did not name. His counts on
the "ledger of geniuses" are the most universal ever accomplished. Not less than 45 different cultural systems and
processes are included. Philosophy, science, painting,
sculpture, music, drama, literature of all European and non-
European nations which left sufficient mark are listed. His
most important finding was that cultural history is not a
perpetual flow but is very discontinuous in its periods of
flowering and lying fallow. Cultural productivity is always
"clustered". So far Spengler has been justified by Kroeber.
But these clusters of geniuses more often correspond to
special partial systems rather than the total cultural life
system of their nations, as Spengler taught; and the lifetime of the clusters or systems is not uniform, but can differ very much. Cultural systems in this sense are not individuals of the same species, but very different "organismic"
species.

Kroeber has given in his diagrams only the *historical
duration* of the systems without working out from his lists
the *statistical distribution* of the "geniuses". This is the
point where the present writer slipped in. To each name in
Kroeber's list a certain point in a historical 20-year-scale
has now been designated as his "floruit", as the estimated
central point of his activity. A more exact regard for the
duration, the overlapping, and the changing intensities of
the productive lives would have been prohibitive for statistical evaluation.

By this procedure we get in nearly all 45 cases very
good approximations to symmetrical normal Gaussian

distributions of the incidence of "genius" through time.
This article is not the place to unfold all the data critically. Certainly these normal distributions are best approximated if the respective system can develop freely and
with little clash with or disturbing influence from other
systems. Italian painting, German painting, French and German literature, Islamic science, and Occidental philosophy
are outstanding examples of this regular Gaussian distribution, some of them with recurrent florescence within the
same geographic area.

The relative number of good, normal distributions can
be taken as a calculus of the degree of isolation in cultural history allowing such independent development. Estimated by this calculus, the multi-chambered, pluralistic-
monadic character of cultural history is very pronounced.

How can it be possible to reduce extremely complicated
historical events to such simple mathematical models? To
take whole systems without analyzing their single parts and
to ascribe to them characteristics of great simplicity leading to unexpected results of unusual interest was perhaps
von Bertalanffy's most original adventure. We must remember also how tough a model the normal distribution model is.
Many partial distributions, usually in superposition, give
a total normal distribution again. As long as normal distributions which have averages of a distance of not more
than two sigma are superposed, a common normal curve without
bimodality or signs of beginning bimodality is the outcome.

A total separation of two normal distributions on the
same scale needs a distance of at least six sigma between
the two means. In Kroeber's data for Occidental philosophy,
for example, we find a sigma of 36 years for the medieval
cluster and of 75 years for the modern cluster. This example clearly demonstrates, incidentally, how different the
sigmata (the lifespans of cultural systems), even of the
same kind (i.e., philosophy), can be: the means of the two
clusters are situated at the years 1246 and 1765. This is
a distance of 519 years or 9 times the mean of the two sigmata. So one should not be surprised that there is little
disturbing interference in the development of medieval and
modern philosophy.

As a case of total confluence of three (if not more)
partial systems with widely different geographic and mathematical parameters, Islamic science may be mentioned. Old
Arabic, Persian, and Spanish-Maghreb waves are distinguish-
able in Islamic science, but the generalized distribution
is completely uniform. The sigma of this common distribution is as high as 131 years. A total curve for all ancient
literature and science between 500 B.C. and 500 A.D. is uniform also, but skewed to the left, as if the decline were
slowed down compared with the rising tide. But as the climax is in the time of Pericles at 400 B.C., the corresponding point to 500 A.D. is 1300 B.C., or perhaps the time of
the advent of the Greeks in Hellas. In any case since our
curve lacks the greater part of the "rising tide", its skewness is totally artificial.

If Greek, Hellenistic, Roman, and provincial geniuses
are counted together, the prominence of the Hellas of Pericles is preserved, but it is much less unique than our scholastic ideas imply. Anyway, scaling of statistical distributions of geniuses makes sense even in compilations of a
thousand years and longer cultural "supersystems" (Sorokin).

The most practical measurement of symmetry and skewness
of Gaussian distributions seems to this writer to be the
separated calculation of the sigma for the lower and higher,
earlier and later, left and right, wings of the curve with
the mean as separator. Therefore, for medieval philosophy
we get 37 and 35 years, for Islamic science 124 and 138
years, for modern philosophy 84 and 66 years. But if the
definite end of "modern" philosophy will not be before 2017,
the distribution will be symmetric in this still incompleted
cultural system. The year 2017 is at a distance of 3 x 84
from the mean of 1765. Modern philosophy has certainly been
in decline for a long time, so its end soon after 2000 is
not unsubstantiated by fact. At least we can use the case
as an example for historic prophecy based on statistical
grounds, on the laws of normal distribution. As daring and
tentative as such a prophecy for cultural systems may look,
it is less so than similar guesses used (but often poorly
fulfilled) for some time in demography. Populations are
less bound to follow intrinsic conditions in growth than
are new inventions and arts. In the terminology of Kroeber,
the latter are structured by special cultural patterns, a

phenomenon not extant in general demography. Within the
same investigation, evidently as an effect of this reason,
Sorokin has found very consistent development in the history
of inner values, philosophy, art and religion, but inconsistent oscillations in the frequencies of wars, revolutions,
and politics.

If "modern" philosophy may linger along until the beginning of the 21st Century only, modern science, according to
Kroeber's data, has so steep an ascent that today it can not
be more than halfway in its curve. If we take 1900 as the
definite mean, the "end" of modern science will not come
earlier than 2300. This calculation also does not seem unsubstantiated by the facts. At any rate, it must be remembered that such calculations can make sense only if the general conditions remain the same. For the future of scientific discovery, that means the total mass of discoverable facts
is so immense that discovery may not come to a premature end.
The adventures of great voyages of discovery have been stopped not by inner conditions, but by the finite size of our
planet. A new era of great flights of discovery is just
dawning now.

The symmetry in the distribution of the numbers of geniuses in time is so striking that any difference in the time
needed for the rise and decline of such processes seems lacking. The writer's expectance, it must be confessed, was a
slower decline than rise. This guess was influenced by the
fact that organismic systems need a much longer time for involution than for evolution. Man is adult at twenty, but
he may not be dead at a hundred! But are the curves described
until now life cycles, biorrhesis from birth to death, at
all? Oswald Spengler doubtless thought so. With Kroeber,
it is not quite clear if he has grasped fully that this interpretation is a gross error! The present author for de-
cennia has stressed that the "civilizations", which follow
the "cultures" as their old ages or petrifactions, in Spengler's
thinking do not mean high age at all, but nothing other than
sheer adultness after the end of the period of growth!
Spengler's melancholic pessimism on the decline of the west
is like the nostalgia of a teenager who cannot understand
that life can be worth living after twenty. Schwidetsky,
in her book on the death of nations (1954), takes the same
stand on this question.

To demonstrate this in a mathematical way a little trick
is sufficient. If we do not count geniuses for single periods in time but sum up the total number of such men counted
from the beginning to this period, we have at the end of the
development not a re-decline to zero, but a maximal total
number. Gaussian distribution is necessarily transformed by
this procedure into the typical exponential curve of growth.
So in our 45 cultural systems we now have as many typical
growth curves ending at the point where man is about twenty
years of age and the cultural systems end their growth also,
as we had Gaussian distributions beforehand. It is not at
all new, of course, that cultural growth sometimes follows
the exponential curve (cf. Lotka for the American Railway
System). But it *is* new that balancing of geniuses causes a
slight transformation of growth curves, and that these curves
so prevalently are regularly exponential.

It is the writer's fond hope that L. von Bertalanffy will
again enjoy reading that simple mathematical models generally
fit so well in the complicated behavior of the immensely complicated systems of cultural history. These developments, in
their wide and general form, are no more conscious of the
men acting them than are molecules in a chemical reaction.
(Later we will stress that human beings are able to see at
least the obvious conditions of their actions and therefore
a certain difference between human actions and the blind behaviour in chemical reactions is obvious.) But cultural systems are not enigmatic or mystic entities beyond human intellectual grasp. We have not arrived at the solution to
the question of souls of the cultures, but we have found
strict mathematical facts and rational laws of systems.

Still there is the question as to what inferences we have
to make regarding cultural history to explain *why* our mathematical findings are obvious consequences of necessary premises. Gaussian distribution is always the outcome of the
chance combination of many co-acting factors. So we have to
infer now *that* many factors in a unordered, stochastic way
are co-acting in the growth of cultural systems. This is a
strong formal check on all monocausal ideas on historical
effects. Kroeber has given the term "cultural pattern" to
the unknown reasons for the strong tendency to cluster he
found everywhere in cultural history. He did not attempt
more exact statements on the nature of these cultural patterns but preferred to delay the problem. Now we see that

they cannot be an ordered *unity*, a *single idea*, if Gaussian distribution presupposes the *multicausal* character of historic developments implicating chance combination of many factors. This is a very formal, but nonetheless important, point.

As Kroeber has seen clearly, the discontinuous, clustered structure of cultural systems is a very strong argument against a too direct biological explanation of cultural rise and decline by rise and decline in the genetic giftedness of the population. Such theories have been proposed often indeed. But the giftedness of a population cannot rise and decline within so few generations and in so very regular a form. It can not even rise and decline more than once within the same population, as cultural climaxes sometimes are twofold or even threefold in the same nation. But the other theories, which lay all stress onesidedly on the cultural patterns and the cultural systems embodying them and give them full independence from the men as biological substrata of the process, are exaggerated also. If a large number of factors are working, then biological factors may well be as efficient as other factors. If we take the cultural pattern primarily as the structural core of the cultural growth-processes, more or less giftedness of the population or other biological factors may, at least, have an accelerating or retarding effect. The predicament of a culturology which claims full independence of human behavior for cultural processes has been chastised by Morris E. Opler (1964), not without reason. Lastly, our mathematical findings must be a consequence of human behavior in general and may also imply every form of difference in human behavior.

Another factor regarding the biological substratum of cultural development is that men of prime importance - high geniuses - are not concentrated typically in the earlier or later parts of the historicalgrowth-curves. Kroeber himself has indicated by asterisks which men he ranges first class and second class. We are not arbitrary in this classification. So we have, in high genius, the constancy across the change of historical conditions. This is to be expected if biological giftedness is not changing or is changing slowly. The same forces which make possible the manifestation of cultural production at all do so with genius production also. Still another observation may be added. The greatest of all

men, e.g., Jesus, Confucius, Shakespeare, Dante, Goethe, and
Beethoven, all have appeared near the climax of cultural developments. None of them is isolated historically. Dante
had the whole medieval spirituality and a youthful poetry
around him. Homer was early, if seen from the "historical"
times of Hellas, but in the midst of many epic singers. If
Homer and Dante are deemed to be the climax of Greek and
Italian literature, but situated near the beginning of them,
this is certainly a perspectival error. So, the greatest
of all men do not seem to owe their greatness to their biological gifts only, but are lavishly furthered by the point
in history where they appear.

The symmetry of the distribution in Gaussian curves or
their exponential transformation is again due to the chance
combination of many co-acting factors. But, it is still
completely enigmatic to the author why the steepness of ascent and descent mirror each other and why such strong symmetry has been found empirically. We have already seen that
the speed of the development, even if philosophy is the field,
may be so different that the sigma for modern philosophy was
75 and for medieval philosophy only 36 years. Why then,
within the same curves, are the sigmata for ascent and descent, rise and fall, not very different also? The mathematical consequence is that the positive, furthering factors
in the average must strictly mirror the effectiveness of the
negative retarding factors within the same growth and system.
But who can propose a good hypothesis to explain this fact?

As we have seen, our curves of the numbers of geniuses
in time are growth-curves, not life cycles (biorrhesis from
birth to death). But the number of geniuses or of productive works (Sorokin prefers this indicator) is a very incomplete picture of the process of growth. Here L. von
Bertalanffy's theory of growth and the life cycle as a balance of assimilation and dissimilation, of structuring and
de-structuring, of gain and loss, is an unavoidable and
inevitable corrective. At all moments of cultural growth,
as in organismic growth, the production of a new substance
is accompanied by other processes lowering the total amount
of "substance" accumulated. In culture, this loss of substance is devaluation, wear, forgetting of products and the
man producing them. This process is neverceasing. If we

could also get these counteractions into our model, the total
amount of growth would lessen, but the general form would
not be altered.

The situation is much worse for Kroeber's or Sorokin's
indicators if the life of cultural systems is to be followed
beyond the point of adultness - of the end of growth. Invo-
lutions could only stand out in this model if negative numbers of geniuses or work could also be counted. As this is
obviously impossible, this method definitely stops at the
point of adultness and must be replaced by another one. We
have already seen that L. von Bertalanffy's model is perfectly
able to follow both decline and involution. Another question
is where may we find a feasible source of cultural data for
the application of von Bertalanffy's model to empirical research in cultural life-processes, as simple counts of geniuses or of works were useful to Kroeber and Sorokin. The
writer has some suggestions as to where to find such data
but, unfortunately, he has not yet offered any empirical
work or experience in this area. Therefore only delibera-
tive deductions regarding the outcome of applications of the
model of balancing gains and losses in the study of cultural
biorrhesis can be tried here.

If the applicability of Kroeber's model ended with "cultural adultness", von Bertalanffy's model has no major restriction from following cultural systems until their end.
The fact that evolution in organisms is always much shorter
than involution (aging and death) can also be clearly explained by von Bertalanffy's model for cultural systems.
If growth is gradual stabilization, then successful stabilization may be very capable of resisting dissolution much
longer than its evolution could.

In biological organisms the high stability of the adult
state is, of course, warranted by the genotype which is selected for this stability over millions of years. What then
is the guarantee of such a stability in culture? The cultural pattern in Kroeber's sense, one may answer. But what
is such a cultural pattern? One answer to this is: just
as much an exceptionally fruitful and consequential structure of behavioral possibilities as an ideal entity; a
"sachlogisches Ordnungsgebilde", to put it in German. The
productive and selective acts of men are led by the ever-

lasting search for the more valuable, the better form of
life and culture. These men are not blind, but when acting
they have only restricted understanding and foresight. Even
restricted, as these abilities are, they can be the tool
which enables history to select stable cultural structures
in a hundred years which resemble the stability of the organismic genotype selected by blind nature after million of
years. Such an acceleration, as an effect of the human intellect and consciousness, compared with the extremely slow
blind selection of bodily traits is by no means unlikely.
Man, in this respect, is not unique at all. Every action
of an animal is already immensely speeded up in equifinality
and efficiency compared with organismic growth of genotypic
evolution.

Cultural systems as a whole are *not* foreseen by the men
producing them. But, in man's never-ending search for betterment, some of the trials are more successful and rewarding
than others, some make more money, some more glamour, some
more lust, some more intrinsic satisfaction, and in this way
are reinforced. Every action is a structured system in itself and has a structuring effect on all things related to
it. If such effects concentrate and become consequential
around the central "success", then the gradual unfolding of
a far-reaching, total system can follow - be it industrial-
ization, the gold rush in South Africa, the Gothic style,
the Holy Roman Empire, painting able to imitate the perception of nature, or painting consciously abstaining from such
imitation, etc., etc. Then, step by step, consciousness may
also radiate from single experiences to a more and more total
survey of the style, the atmosphere, the spirit, the "ethos"
of the evolving cultural system. Sooner or later reflection
also begins. As in all religions, scholastic and dogmatic
interpretation can be found which is secondary in time to
the immediate emotional appeal of the new god, the new pro-
phet or creed. Such reflections and definitions usually are
still very incomplete compared with the total dynamic reality of the system. Many cultural systems never reach even
such a partially conscious state at all.

Many languages are spoken for thousands of years without
the construction of a grammar. The structurology in modern
cultural anthropology (Levi-Strauss, etc.) is concerned mostly
with living systems which existed and were fully efficient

without any of the people living it being aware of them at
all. As Alois Dempf has stated, any feeling for the total
cultural supersystem, within which men are acting and functioning, can not be found in the history of the human spirit
earlier than in the Western 18th Century.

This is a very short and incomplete sketch of the ways
which lead cultural developments within some generations of
productive human animals, endowed with limited ability for
prevision and a surveying understanding for their situation
to a degree of systemic stability, warranted in organisms
only by the blind selection of stable genotypes. Today
perhaps no problem in natural science is less well understood
rationally than the ontogenesis of the body. So it is still
much more premature, of course, to expect a full theory of
the analogous events, which lead to the stable realization
and embodiment of cultural systems today already. Kroeber
certainly had been sympathetic with this attempt, but he has
not tried it himself. Spengler even hated rational explanation in these matters not of nature but of history. History
for him, as for many others, had to remain outside science
on ontological grounds.

It may even be that the rational elucidation of cultural
patterns will make better and quicker progress than the same
task in organismic ontogenesis. The behavioral building
stones of cultural systems certainly are more immediately
understandable to us than the building stones of *living
organisms* and their behavior.

If we speak of cultural systems, it must be understood
that a congeries of independent single goods, tools, and
ideas is within them. A German literary writer some years
ago has described 50 cultural items flowering 50 years ago
in the Occident and the very different reasons for their
devaluation and decline (Christian Ferbers Flohmarkt, marche
aux pouces, 1959). This is a charming demonstration of the
fact that every cultural item has its special fate, like
every human individual, in spite of both being interwoven
with many structural and systemic conditions.

What may happen to cultural items, e.g., to the knife,
to the car, to the piano, or to the stage, after having arrived at an adult, ripe stable state in their history?

Three main possibilities must be taken into account:

1) *Unlimited stability* forever hence. The knife was invented in paleolithic times and is still used by every one of us today. During the Iron Age the knife was perfected and, since then, alterations to it have been stylistic rather than technical. But we must understand that even definitely stable cultural items are stable only in their ideal core while embodied differently according to the special tendency of time and people. Though "the" knife is paleolithic, each single knife is an individual.

2) *Aging* from inner grounds: a negative balance of gains and losses. So a stage play is stable (point 1) if it is played again and again through all time as Sophocles, Shakespeare, and Schiller are. Even this stability is likely not to be linear, but to include temporal oscillations, going of and again coming into fashion. It is definitely declining if is performed a lesser number of times in the succession of years. Historic forms can be stable in the sense of the stone, so a certain knife and every material cultural object is. They must be recreated every day if they imply human behavior, as the *idea* of the knife or the performance of a stage play. In this sense their stability is the attainment of a steady state (Fliessgleichgewicht). If such steady states are not supported by a certain amount of continued productive activity, they are always in danger of declining: Wern rastet, rostet; rest is rust. Very often in history we find in such aging cultural systems an adaptive retreat into hyperstable states which make the system as much like a stone as is possible. Selection of a canon of classics, definite dogmatization, pedagogic use in schools, ritualizations, taboos against change and against newcomers have very often effected preservation without further growth. The whole world of primitives is full of such hyperstabilizations counteracting the weakness of the stabilizing factors in small illiterate groups. However, such hyperstable cultural forms are *not* bare of inner life. Even if the pattern of our Christmas feast is hyperstable, every single Christmas feast is a wonder to children, adults, and the aged anew. Aging of cultural forms is not aging of human life. But the ability to resist final decline certainly is weakened by aging and hyperstable cultural patterns.

3) *Negative selective differential*: cultural forms and systems which have grown by positive selective value in man's search for betterment are due to be overcome sooner or later in their turn by other forms and systems, which are still "better" again. For some time the victory of the railway over the mail-coach seemed warranted, but in the meantime the car became superior and perhaps it is finding its master as well.

It is clear that the unfolding of technical values is relatively unidirectional, while the values of play, fashions, and inner satisfactions are much more unstable. Sorokin has investigated the change of such untechnical and unstable values in 2600 years of Western history and has found very long cycles beyond the minor fluctuations. These cycles are so long that they are too few - indeed not more than two "religious" and two "worldly" ages in nearly 3000 years - to be interpreted as representing a general law of sine waves for unstable values in cultural history. At any rate, history wave-cycles are caused by reversible changes in the selective value of cultural items from positive to negative and vice versa. Sorokin has already begun to appraise the results of his gigantic work in the light of certain concepts of a sort of system theory. This is not the place to continue this task.

One cannot guess at what time an existing cultural pattern will become selectively inferior to a "better" one. It is only unlikely that such an uncanny event will never come. However, it may be some consolation that a high percentage of older cultural patterns are not totally obliterated by the newer one. In cultural history, as in the animal kingdom, subdued forms very often find a deviating or special ecological niche to help them survive along with the newcomer.

What may be the interplay of our three points (unlimited stability, inner aging, and negative selective differential) in reality? Empirical proof can only be found if data are available on the fate of many cultural items in a long series of historical crossections - four or five in a century perhaps. Aside from this, it can be stated that *all three* sorts of processes are very frequent in cultural history. This means that most single histories will show a combination of more than one of them. During growth-times of

cultural systems one can suppose a positive co-working of
stabilizations, rising adultness and positive selective dif-
ferentials. But, at any rate, it is likely that after fin-
ishing growth, one of the other of these factors may become
prevalent. At least at the present time it seems premature
to the writer to think that the whole biorrhesis, the *whole*
life-cycle and life-process of cultural systems, will be
open to simple mathematical formulations because evidently
growth and rise of such systems are surprisingly uniform in
this sense.

   As this writer understands the standpoint of system theory, it can be described as a complementation of the atomistic
procedure of natural science. Complicated wholes are not
explained by describing some building stones within them
whose combination must produce the total system, but are investigated by describing general cahracteristics of the whole
system as parameters whose behavior is elucidative. This
way is adequate wherever a system is so complicated that its
atoms cannot say enough on the total structure; e.g., as
the stones and their qualities cannot explain a cathedral.
Every biological organism is such a system. The behavioral
world of man is another. As a conclusion to this article,
an experiment of the author to describe the behavioral world
of man may be quoted (cf. F. Keiter, *Verhaltensbiologie des
Menschen auf kulturanthropologischer Grundlage*, Munchen,
1967). In this book 18 prime contents, great themes of human life, are listed, which have the deductive necessity of
being the things which cannot fail to be important in the
life of every rational mammal, as man is. Then, in 30 different literatures representing a sample of all narrative
literature in man's history, 1000 notes of the themes which
are alluded to in these stories have been taken. With these
30,000 data, general statements on the behavioral world of
man have been worked out statistically. These statements
describe the total system and are not the outcome of atomistic summations. It could be seen that the 18 prime themes
were never absent in any narrative literature and are sufficient for describing the thematic content of all of them.
It was seen that the varying frequencies of the themes from
literature to literature are ordered in the sense of mono-
modal symmetric Gaussian distributions. There is always a
noticeable center of the distribution - a mean, which well

represents the medium man or average behavioral humanity.
There are lower and upper ranges of frequencies which do not
exceed $\pm$ 3 sigma. The historic variation of basic human behavior is by no means unlimited but follows strict laws of
statistic distributions, which are different for everyone,
of the 18 prime themes. It can be said that each of them
has a certain amount of instinctive urge, of behavioral dynamics, behind it. The frequencies of the single themes in
history can vary only so far as the counteraction of all the
other themes makes allowance for them. Man cannot live by
bread alone, for he needs orientation also; not be in search
of lust alone, as he needs safety; not so sexual as to loose
social status and honor; not too interested in reading to
forgo necessary action; etc. If we split up the 18 prime
themes of human life further into 217 secondary themes, other
observations can be made which again are assertions about
the whole of the system of the behavioral world of man and
its variation in geography and history, without having been
based and derived from atomistic assumptions and their superposition and summation.

These short quotations from another work of this writer
may further elucidate how the deep and far reaching influence
L. von Bertalanffy's revolutionary accomplishments in rational
scinetific method applied to the most complicated phenomena
in reality are suited for ethological and cultural anthropology also - and have indeed has an influence on the thinking and work of this writer.

THE IMPACT OF GENERAL SYSTEMS THEORY ON ORGANIZATION THEORY

ERWIN GROCHLA

University of Cologne, 5 Köln-Lindenthal, Albertus-Magnus-Platz, Germany

In the more recent contributions to Organization Theory two related tendencies can be ascertained indicating an extension of research perspective:

1. Organizational subproblems are researched on the basis of approaches originating in different disciplines.

2. To a greater extent there is a discussion of basic methodological questions of an interdisciplinary organization theory to be generated via integration of singular theories, in line of which the concept of General System Theory is taken into consideration more and more.

On the one hand, the emerging reorientation calls for a critical résumé. On the other hand, it is necessary to discuss the possibilities and the limitations of a foundation of Organization Theory based on General System Theory.

I. UNIDISCIPLINARY APPROACHES TO ORGANIZATION THEORY

The following scheme used to classify and to evaluate the numerous research approaches to Organization Theory is oriented on epistemological criteria. According to the logical structure of scientific statements it can be distinguished between terminological, descriptive, empirico-cognitive, and praxeological scientific statements [1].

Terminological statements serve the laying down of conventions (definitions) for scientific terminology. *Descriptive* statements describe objects of the respective field of interest by linguistic expressions. *Empirico-cognitive* statements consist of sentences containing hypotheses about empirical regularities (laws or quasi-laws). They aim towards the explanation and prediction of empirical events. *Praxeological* statements aim towards purposive, structural action; they are characterized by an empirical, and by a logic-analytical component. The empirical aspect manifests itself in the dependence of a statement upon the underlying empirico-cognitive system about the suitableness of an action. Independent of this empirical problem, there is the necessity of a logical, decision-theoretic derivation of the consequences of alternative actions as well as the evaluation and selection of the respective course of design according to the criteria of the objective of that action [2].

Within the framework of this basic methodological concept a further classification seems to be suitable. It is oriented on the four following trends that can be distinguished in current organization-theoretic discussion:

(1) *Pragmatic approaches*. Under this line of research, Anglo-American management science literature and most of the organization theory, as it was developed in Germany, can be summarized.

(2) *Decision theoretic approaches*. In these approaches, which partly show strong relations to macro-economic questions, the classical unipersonal decision model is extended by the assumption that decisions take place in multi-personal decision units.

(3) *Behavioral approaches*. They are primarily represented by sociological, social-psychological, and psychological investigations.

(4) *Information- technological approaches*. With the greater use of servomechanisms and computers a growing discussion of the organizational problems of this tendency can be observed. Two aspects are of great interest: the effects of information-technological changes on organization structure, and the organizational structure of information processing system themselves.

1. *Terminological Statements*

Statements of the pragmatic research approaches have to be classified as primarily terminological. This field is characterized by two main lines of research showing significant similarities despite considerable developmental independence: Anglo-American management science, and Organization Theory in the German speaking area. The greatest part of management contributions - publications of Urwick [3], Koontz/O'Donnell [4], and Dale [5] can typically be mentioned - has the following characteristics: (1) Point of departure is a predetermined objective or task. (2) From the given objective subtasks can be derived. (3) The core of the organizational problem is structuralization, that is the attribution of subtasks to organization units. Questions of formation of positions (line, staff) are in the center of interest, strongly emphasizing the hierarchical aspect. (4) People performing the task are considered as performing abstract functions while neglecting individual properties and motivations.

Most contributions to German Organization Theory [6] can be distinguished from the management approach by a more extensive formalization and systematization as well as by a greater influence of scientific management viewpoints evident in process organization primarily. The theoretically best developed conception in this tendency is the system of Kosiol [7].

Terminological systems of the *decision theoretic* approach are mainly developed by the theory of games. Besides contributions of Shubik [8] and Helmer [9] the concept developed by Morgenstern [10[should be emphasized.

In *behavioral approaches* to organization theory several theoretical systems can be found. The organization-theoretic systems of Max Weber [11], Barnard [12], and Simon [13] are characterized by a distinct terminological conception besides their empirico-cognitive set of statements. In one study, Bakke [14] has developed a terminological system for a behavior-oriented organization theory.

Parsons, in particular, pointed out the significance of the terminological aspect for the development of sociological

theories. The terminological system developed by him is related to a theoretical frame of reference whose validity is
postulated for all social subsystems. The central idea of
this concept, which can be described as a "system theoretic"
approach, is the model of a self-regulating system [15].

2. *Descriptive Statements*

Descriptive systems are mainly to be found under the behavioral approaches to Organization Theory. But also by the
pragmatic line of research single descriptive studies were
done.

A typical example is the study of Carlson [16] about
different activities in the task procedure of a manager. A
great deal of these studies go beyond descriptive statements;
the descriptive part serves the formulation of hypotheses
about generally valid laws. In this context it can be ascertained that at the beginning of researching a phenomenon the
part of descriptive statements is relatively great. It is
the task of single descriptive investigations to facilitate
the finding of meaningful hypotheses; hence, their statistical significance has to be proved by a series of investigations.

In recent approaches, i.e., the investigation of behavioral aspects of innovative decisions [17] descriptive
studies are predominant; in such "classical" fields of research like influence relations between superordinates and
subordinates the portion of descriptive statements is comparatively small [18].

3. *Empirico-Cognitive Statements*

Current state of Organization Theory does not allow
generally valid statements about laws on business systems.
To a great extent, the hypotheses used are not empirically
tested in a sufficient way. Empirico-cognitive approaches
can mainly be found in sociologically, social-psychological-
ly, and psychologically oriented Organization Theory.

An empirically oriented discussion of the problem of
organization started with the appearance of the paper "Wirtschaft und Gesellschaft" by Max Weber [19]. Point of departure of Weber's approach is the industrial large-scale

enterprise and the government agency as a bureaucratic form
of authority.   It was Weber's objective to analyze bureaucratic organizational form as rational means for the solution of industrial and administrative processes.   The idea
of bureaucratic organizations is dominated by the significance of the hierarchical principle, by the emphasis of general, unequivocal, and unpersonal regulations as well as by
the idea of rationality and technological efficiency.   This
ideal concept is viewed as "admixture of a conceptual scheme
and a set of hypotheses" [20] by Blau and Scott.   It might
be questionable, whether the hypotheses stated allow an empirical test, in so far as they can be formulated operation-
ally at all.   In later contributions to bureaucracy, however,
the empirico-cognitive question found a much stronger consideration [21].   In these approaches predominantly based on
field studies unpredicted "informal" aspects gain stronger
attention.

Besides Weber, mainly Barnard [22] has a lasting influence on the development of organization theory.   In its empirical core this organization theory which was carried on
by Simon [23] is a theory of motivation.   The theory analyzes
the conditions under which an organization is able to induce
members of the organization to a further membership which
means a guaranteed continuation of the organization.   The
terminological concept of Barnard and Simon might have been
of great importance as well; it is primarily concerned with
decisions and the organizational coordination of participa-
tory decision processes.   The extension of this approach is
concentrated on two problems: On one hand, psychological
aspects of individual cognitive and decision processes are
researched [24], on the other hand, sociological variables
are interrelated with economic variables in order to generate
statements about the behavior of the operating organization
[25].   Both tendencies use computer simulation as a research
tool.   By this technique it is possible to combine hypotheses
about partial relationships to a model of the overall organization with a high explanatory value [26].

Extensive empirical studies were done in order to research sociological relationships in small groups [27].   By
far the greatest part is concerned with the interdependencies
between the following variables: distribution of power
within a group, leadership behavior, decision mode

(participation of single members in the decision), group cohesion, consensus about norms and group efficiency. In the single experiments mostly two or three variables were singled out; the influence of other variables on group behavior is mostly neglected. This partly explains the high percentage of contradictive results. The overall models of small group behavior developed by Collins and Guetzkow [28], and by Golembiewski [29] do show, however, that some general tendencies can be derived from those studies. Laboratory experiments, in which the dependence of group efficiency on communication structure is researched, are of particular interest [30]. According to these studies different types of communication structure could be placed in a relatively unequivocal rank order according to their positive influence on group efficiency.

There are two possibilities to utilize the results of small group studies for a comprehensive organization theory: either one uses them as analogies for the explanation of behavior of organizations, or one tries to integrate the microsystem of the small group into the macro-system of the organization. Whereas the first procedure generates hypotheses requiring an empirical test in the context of the organization, the second method really is equivalent to theory construction. So far, there is only one attempt by Golembiewski aiming in this direction [31].

4. *Praxeological Statements*

Praxeological statements have relatively seldom been developed in organization theoretic literature. From the decision theoretic tendency the theory of teams and transfer pricing can be mentioned. While these two directions of research are characterized by a logic-analytical type of approach, the empirical component is considered more in the information-technological approaches. The human relations movement represents a comprehensive praxeological approach with a stronger empirical orientation.

The starting point of the *decision-theoretic approaches* in organization theory is the traditional unipersonal decision model of macro-economic theory. It is characterized by a preference (objective) function, as well as by assumptions about states of the world and courses of action of the decision unit which, both, cannot be influenced. The problem

is to determine the courses of action allowing an optimiza-
tion of the objective function. In the theory of teams [32]
this logic of decision is primarily extended by the following
aspects, abstracting from all psychological and sociological
constants of the decision makers: (1) By considering more
than one decision maker the analysis is extended to a group
problem: a majority of decision makers strives for optimiza-
tion of a given group-preference function with their actions
or their decisions respectively. (2) The assumption of full
information of the decision makers is dissolved. The respective state of information can be influenced by the team members through acts of information acquirement. (3) The state
of information can be changed by acts of communication between single team members. (4) Cost of information acquirement and communication are considered explicitely.

Transfer pricing or the theory of "Lenkpreise" respectively has certain similarities with the theory of teams. The
basic idea is to steer single decisions of the organization
units in such a manner that an overall optimum is reached.
One of the oldest approaches goes back to Schmalenbach [33].
In his "pretiale Lenkung" the steering function is exercised
by the "optimale Geltungszahl" or the "Betriebswert", respectively. There is an obvious analogy between macro-economic
market processes and operational procedures: both problems
have the same formal structure. The lines between the macro-
economic approach and the organizational micro-approach are
fluent.

The development of mathematical methods like linear and
dynamic programming caused a new boom in the discussion on
the steering function of prices in organizations. The current state of research is characterized by two central problems: (1) the prerequisite for an unequivocally determined
allowance of transfer prices is the solution of the allocation problem; for this reason, transfer prices would not have
an independent organizational meaning. Therefore, the discussion is primarily concentrated on the interpersonal and
iterative calculation of transfer prices. (2) Still unsolved is the problem of considering individual motivation of
the members of the organization by inducements while fixing
the transfer prices.

Progress in *information technology*, as can be realized
by an increasing use of computers has caused an increasing
organization theoretic discussion of conditions of information technological structuralization and its influence on
the structure of organizational systems.

A great deal of papers on information technology is engaged in the optimal structuralization of machine systems
(hardware), and programming systems (software). The problem
of application oriented systems (*Anwendungssysteme*), however,
that is the structuralization of organizational information
systems while using automatic data processing units has found
a greater attention just in the last years [34]. The often
slogan-like use of terms like "management information system"
or "total management system" [35] easily smoothes over the
fact that the praxeological range of explanation is currently
very limited. Empirical investigations of the problem of
structuralization of information technological systems only
deal with subproblems so far. Since automatic data processing units are primarily used for the procession of those
tasks characterized by a high degree of procedural routine,
the focus of interest of most empirical studies is on the
effects in the task structure of middle management. Statements on the possibilities and consequences of information
technological structuralization on top management are seldom,
however. The current limitation of a use of computers on
this level lies in creative, not yet programmable decisions.

A further aspect of the structuralization problem has
been summed up in the literature in a rather simplifying manner under the alternative of a centralized or decentralized
structuralization of the computerized information system.
The opinions concerning this problem are not uniform. One
portion of the deviant opinions can without any doubt be reduced to terminological differences. A further reason can
be seen in the fact that many firms have not or only to a certain extent used the technologically possible degree of cen-
tralization for reasons not always rationally motivated.
vated.

In each developmental phase of organization theory there
are attempts to utilize theoretical insight for practical
purposes.

The first approach to a praxeological organization theory is the "Scientific Management" movement [36] that goes back to Taylor. It is primarily physiologically oriented. The "Human Relations" movement can be regarded as a counter-movement; the latter postulates an interdependency between organizational efficiency and satisfaction of its members [37]. The normative accentuation, in particular, and the doubtful empirical foundation of "Human Relations" ideas can be emphasized critically.

II. TRENDS ON AN INTERDISCIPLINARY ORGANIZATION THEORY

The previous overview over the most important contributions to organization theory discloses a multiplicity of approaches, which are different in their terminology as well as in their subject. This heterogenity can primarily be explained by the nature of the organization as research object. Organizational forms can evolve in three different versions: as man-systems, machine-systems, and man-machine-systems [38]. While man-systems are primarily the subject of sociological, psychological, and socio-psychological investigations, and while machine-systems are dealt with in engineering, the properties and behavioral patterns of complex man-machine-systems cannot be described and explained exclusively from the point of view of a special discipline because of their heterogeneous elements.

The treatment of organizational subproblems from a sociological, psychological, and technological point of view is necessary without any doubt because of the universality of the "organization" phenomenon. However, the partial results arrived at so far are by no means sufficient for the explanation of those problems resulting from the interdependencies between men and machines. In view of the specific organizational problem structure resulting from the interrelation of men and machine it ought to be examined whether a comprehensive system of scientific statements could be developed, which would be able to yield a uniform description, explanation, and prediction of behavioral patterns of complex man-machine-systems. Currently, two different methodological approaches towards a realization of this postulate are to be found. On one hand, a cooperation of various disciplines via an appropriate organization of research work, i.e.,

teamwork, interdisciplinary institutes, etc. is aspired. The
results of this procedure are scientific statements relating
singular hypotheses from various disciplines in order to explain certain phenomena. On the other hand, there is the attempt to develop a complete interdisciplinary systems theory
with a uniform terminological system and generally valid hypotheses.

The concept of General Systems Theory, in particular,
seems to be appropriate as a basis for developing a comprehensive interdisciplinary oriented organization theory. Whereas
system-theoretical questions have been discussed in various
disciplines in the Anglo-American area for several years,
origin, state of knowledge, and developmental tendencies of
General Systems Theory have rarely been discussed in the German literature, although several authors pointed out a possible importance of General Systems Theory for the treatment of
organizational problems [39]. Starting with a brief description of the content and the objectives of General Systems
Theory it will be investigated in subsequent chapters, whether
and to what extent the system theoretic approach can be significant for organizational theory construction, and for
the structuralization of organizational systems as well under
the special consideration of man-machine-systems.

1. *Foundations of Systems Theory*

In line with the development of the General Systems concept the way to think in terms of systems is so popular, primarily in the Anglo-American area, that it can be talked
about a "systems area" [40]. Within this system area two
tendencies can be distinguished at present: the theoretically oriented field of General Systems Theory and the practically oriented fields of "Systems Philosophy" or "Systems
Science", under which fields like "System Engineering", "Systems Design", "Systems Development", and "Systems Analysis"
can be subsumed.

Besides Bertalanffy, Ackoff [41[, Ashby [42], Boulding
[43], and Mesarovic [44] have contributed to General Systems
Theory. The mentioned authors as well as numerous other autho
[45] draw primarily from von Bertalanffy's concept; it can
therefore be considered as representative for content, range
of explanation, and aims of General Systems Theory, and it

will particularly be considered in the following discussion
[46].

1.1. *Historical and Scientific Background*

From historical point of view General Systems Theory originates in the thoughts of "Ganzheitslehre" and the organic
conception of biology. The idea of "Ganzheitslehre" [47] can
be traced back to the Antique; however, it gains a final
influence on scientific thinking since the beginning of the
20th Century [48]. Names like Driesch, Ehrenfels, Köhler,
and Spann are closely connected with this wholistic way of
thinking, which results in the surmounting of mechanistic-
summative explanation of reality. All attempts to conquer
the mechanistic way of thinking by a wholistic one have in
common that real objects are structured wholes. In this way
it should be taken into consideration that real phenomena
cannot be explained by an isolated investigation of properties and behavioral patterns of the parts. The following
statement is characteristic for this point of view: the whole
is more than the sum of its parts. With this statement, however, the feature of certain real objects is described only
qualitatively; the statement is unable to provide a theoretically based explanation for the terminologically conceived
"Ganzheitlichkeit" [49].

Especially in Biology, the contradiction between the
"mechanistic" and "wholistic" way of thinking was evident [50].
The mechanistic tendency in Biology tried to treat properties
and behavioral patterns of organic systems with physical methods, and to explain them by physical and chemical laws [51].
Teleological procedures, like adaptation, self-regulation,
and self-regeneration, however, could not exclusively be explained by physical and chemical principles, and they were
therefore considered as metaphysical procedures. The biologist and natural philosopher Driesch [52] tried to give the
experimental proof that physical and chemical principles are
not sufficient for the explanation of biological problems:
the organism was more than the sum of its material parts;
it represented a whole, and all occurrences in the organic
nature were dominated by a wholistic causality ("Ganzheits-
kausalitat"); the idea of the whole was inherent in the parts
already, and the soul-like factor of "entelechy" purposively
regulated and steered all procedures and processes in the
organism. Similar to Driesch, von Bertalanffy emphasizes

the wholistic character of organic systems [53]. Contrary
to Driesch, however, he rejects the "vitalistic" assumption
that the "factor of entelechy" determined this wholism, because it was metaphysic and therefore not scientific: the
wholistic concept was only suitable for a description of the
character of organic forms with regard to the contents, and
was unable to explain the properties and patterns of behavior
of these forms [54]. It was necessary, therefore, to investigate and explain the factual situation described by the
term "Ganzheit" in a scientifically exact way. For this purpose, von Bertalanffy substitutes the term "Ganzheit" by the
term "system"; the latter he defines as a complex of mutually effecting and dependent elements [55]. Departing from
this definitorial basis he conceives the organism as a dynamic system, whose characteristical properties and behavioral
patterns underlie certain systems laws. The finding and
formulation of those laws is a task of "organismic" biology
[56]. The postulated systems view of the organism is appro-
priated and extended by von Bertalanffy within the organismic biology culminating in the "open system" model [57].
This model is a suitable base for presenting and explaining
biological problems of organization like growth, adaptation,
regulation, and questions of equilibrium as well.

   Starting with the assumption that the structure of biological problems of organization, which can be described and
explained by the open systems model, often show a striking
isomorphy to problems treated in other disciplines, von
Bertalanffy generalizes and extends the biological systems
view and the open system model to a "General Systems Theory".
Accordingly, the basic idea of General Systems Theory is
that the properties and behavioral patterns of materially
different systems often can be explained by formally isomorph systems laws [58]. Accordingly, General Systems Theory
tries to disclose formal isomorphisms in the structure of
theories on materially different objects, to describe them
with a homogenous terminology, and to integrate them into
disciplinary generalized theoretical systems using a mathematical formulation.

1.2. *Terminological Foundations*

   The term "system" is used in different disciplines and
in different ways in characterizing different real and ideal

matters. Philosophically, "system" means a wholistically
organized set of things, procedures, and parts in which the
nature of the single units is determined by the superimposed
whole [59]. Wieser, for example, points out that each system represented an organized whole, in which the wholeness
results from the organization of communicating elements [60].
Similarly, von Bertalanffy reduces the wholeness of systems
to the interdependencies between elements forming the system [61]. Despite the multiple possibilities to use the term
"system" only two areas are addressed to. On one hand, it
is about real and material object systems, on the other hand
it is about scientific statements in the form of models and
theories on these object systems. Although the areas addressed to lie on different levels, the term "system" can
generally be defined as a number of elements with certain
properties, which are connected by certain relationships [62].

1.3. *Properties and Behavioral Patterns of Systems*

Qualitative differences in properties and behavioral patterns of real systems result from the properties of the elements forming the system, and from the features and the richness of the relations between these elements [63]. According
to how similar elements are connected in a system by interrelationships, or are going to be connected they can have
qualitatively different properties and behavioral patterns
within the system. To these different qualities of the system different degrees of complexity can be referred [64].

Beer [65], for example, attempts to characterize the differences in quality of real systems by the graduation of the
attributes "complexity"-simple, complex, very complex - and
"determinedness" - determined, probabilistic. Similarly,
Boulding [66] develops a nine-level hierarchy of complexity
of systems. In comparison to the typologies mentioned above
the categorization in "closed" and "open" systems [67] proposed by von Bertalanffy has a far greater relevance within
the framework of General Systems Theory. According to Bertalanffy, real object systems can exchange matter and/or
energy. Whereas open systems exchange matter as well as energy, there are exclusively energetic relationships between
closed systems and their environment [68]. Besides material
and energetic exchange processes between open systems and
environment, however, information inputs and outputs have to

be considered [69]. A system has to be called "open" accordingly, if it accepts matter and energy flows [70], and/or
information from the environment, proceeds it internally,
and if it returns them to the environment in a transformed
manner. Contrary to closed systems, there is a permanent
exchange of matter and energy, and/or information between
open systems and their environment [71]. During this exchange procedure, the elements forming the system are continuously decomposed and renewed, i.e., there is a continuous
flow and transformation of energy and matter, and/or information in those systems. This state of open systems in a continuous flow of matter, energy, and information, and a permanent change of the elements is called "steady state".
Closed systems, however, reach the final state of a static
equilibrium [72].

Attaining a steady state is not dependent upon the initial conditions of open systems, but depends upon the respective actual systems parameters underlying the behavior of
the system. Accordingly, an open system is able to attain a
steady state starting from different initial conditions, in
different ways and despite internal and external bias, and
in this sense the system behaves "equifinal" [73]. The teleological behavior of open systems requires balancing and coordination of actions and processes. The required regulative
means can take place according to the principle of "primary"
regulation as well as the principle of "secondary" regulation [74].

In open systems teleological behavior is often based on
the ability to go beyond the spread of a given standard, and
to react on bias by structural changes. Since processes of
adaptation of this kind are often connected with a change
of the steady state, one talks about "regulation based on
a steady state" or "primary regulation" in this context.
In contrast to that, adaptive procedures caused by functionally or structurally determined mechanisms can be called
"secondary regulation". If certain properties of elements
forming the system are permanently utilized in the same way -
for example, when one element always fulfills the same functions within the overall system - a specialization of this
element, and, at the same time, a regeneration of the unused
or only rarely used properties is the result. In the extreme
case this leads to a functional determination and a structural

torpidity of the system. On one hand, this advancing process of specialization and mechanization can lead to an increased efficiency of the system; on the other hand, the spread of the ability for structural adaptation, and therefore the ability of primary regulation is narrowed [75].

2. *Value of Explanation and Relevancy of General Systems Theory for Organization Theory*

General Systems Theory assumes that properties and behavioral patterns of different real systems can be explained in many cases by formal isomorph systems laws. Accordingly, it views its task in comparing, generalizing, and transferring scientific statements of different disciplines to other disciplines. This interdisciplinary process of theory building is facilitated by the development of a generally valid terminology not connected with certain disciplines, which will necessarily have a high degree of abstraction [76].

Whereas system theoretic terminology and models developed in General Systems Theory are utilized more and more for the description and explanation of biological [77], sociological [78], social-psychological [79], and psychological [80] problems [81], the relevancy of General Systems Theory for theoretical and instrumental treatment of operational and organization questions has comparatively seldom been investigated [82].

Since there are common footholds in General Systems Theory as well as in organization theory, contentwise and intentwise, it has to be proved, whether and to what extent General Systems Theory can facilitate the process of organizational theory building, and above that, whether it can offer footholds for the structuralization of operational systems.

2.1. *Organization Research Oriented on Systems Theory*

The relevancy of General Systems Theory for organizational theory building is first of all of a terminological nature. Organizational states of affairs being existent in different areas of reality can be described in a uniform way by the terminology of systems theory. The descriptive scientific statements generated that way represent the basis for a comparison of materially different systems, and they offer first clues for the determination of isomorphisms in problem structures of different disciplines.

Besides the terminological generalization and standardization of descriptive scientific statements, General Systems Theory further meets a heuristic function within the organization theoretic framework of discovery. The heuristic meaning of General Systems Theory lies in the fact that generalize theories can be called upon in order to explain those systems whose structures and functions are formally isomorph. Closely connected with these terminological and heuristic aspects is the further question concerning the possibilities and the forms of an interdisciplinary cooperation within organization research, which is system-theoretically oriented.

2.11. *The Terminological and Descriptive Function of General Systems Theory*

A comparison of operational man-machine-systems with other object systems, and the description and explanation of structure and function of operational systems with generalized, interdisciplinary system models is facilitated by describing operational states of affairs with the system-theoretic terminology mentioned above.

From a system-theoretic point of view the firm is represented by an artificial system created by man that is compose by the elements "man" and "machine" (Sachmittel). According to the circumstances how man and machine elements are arrange and interconnected, the "firm" as a system is able to attain given goals, and to fulfill the therefore necessary tasks. Prerequisite for the processes of goal attainment is a continuous exchange of energy, matter and information flows between the firm and its environment, as well as between the operational elements and the subsystems. The firm is represented, therefore, by an artificial open man-machine-system with a multiple goal structure. The firm in its entirety as well as the operational subsystems are able to react on short - or long-range bias. This adaptive behavior can be interpreted as a search process in order to adapt to changed states of the environment within the "economy" as a supersystem. In case of considering the internal system, however, interactions between the elements and adaptive behavior of the operational subsystems are well to the fore. Accordingly, the behavior of the subsystems can be understood as

a search process in order to accomplish operational sub-
goals with regard to the realization of the overall goal.
In order to be able to react to internal as well as external
short- and/or long-range bias the preservation of the operational dynamic order in a steady state is necessary. The
elementary prerequisite for this is a continuous supply of
matter, energy, and information from the environment.

On one hand, operational occurrences are characterized
by a continuous exchange of flows with the environment, on
the other hand, they are characterized by a transformation
of those items within the system. The regulation procedures
necessary for maintaining the steady state and for adaptation can proceed according to the primary regulation principle as well as to the secondary regulation principle. Since
the firm as an open system is able to attain internal as
well as external goals in different ways, starting from different initial conditions despite internal and external bias,
the system as a whole shows equifinality. This does not exclude that the behavior of subsystems can be determined because of progressive functional specialization and mechanization.

2.12. *Heuristic Function of General Systems Theory*

Besides the generalization of descriptive scientific
statements in order to identify similarities in problem structures of materially different organizational states of affairs
system-theoretic terminology is further able to facilitate
discovery of formal isomorphisms in the structures of empirico-
cognitive theories about materially different organizational
states of affairs. The function of system-theoretic terminology is only of an indirect nature in case of a terminological generalization of descriptive scientific statements
as well as in a generalization of the terms of empirico-
cognitive theories. In comparison to that, the identification of formal isomorphisms in the structures of empirico-
cognitive theories has a far greater and direct importance
in the framework of organizational discovery.

If there is a one-to one-correspondence between the formalized terms of two theories, that means if the terms of
the theories are in a reflexive, symmetric, and transitive
relation, both theories have the same logical structure [83].
In this case it can be talked about a formal isomorphism of

both theories, and each theory can alternatively be interpreted as a model for the other one [84]. In the framework
of organization research system-theoretically oriented the
process can be described like this: If there are empirico-
cognitive theories available, which proved true in different
disciplines for the explanation of materially different but
in the formal structure isomorph organizational problems,
these theories can terminologically be standardized by system-theoretic terminology. Starting from this basis the
terms of the theories have to be formalized, in order to find
out whether there is structural isomorphism between the theories. If such isomorphism can be identified, originally uni-
disciplinary theories can be combined to a general, interdisciplinary theory. This generalized theory can be utilized
in different disciplines as a model for the explanation of
respective organizational states of affairs [85]. For example, if there is a biological theory of adaptation T_{BA}, a
sociological theory of adaptation T_{SA}, and a respective psychological theory T_{PA} available, these theories can be combined to a problem-specific, general, and interdisciplinary
theory of adaptation T_A in the framework of General Systems
Theory, if the formal structure of the mentioned unidiscipli-
nary theories are isomorph [86]. If only descriptive statements on the specific organizational phenomenon of "adaptation" are in existence, T_A can be interpreted as a model for
T_{OA} under the assumption that there is a formal structural
isomorphism between the system-theoretically generalized
theory T_A and the organizational theory T_{OA} to be developed.
In this case system-theoretically generalized hypotheses [87]
which first will have a high degree of abstraction [88] about
the specific organizational state of affairs can be deduced
from the general model T_A. The system theoretically generalized theory set meets a heuristic function within the framework of organization research. The importance of this
heuristic function lies in the fact that hypotheses deduced
from the general theory set can contribute disclosing existing gaps of research, and about that pointing out possible
ways of their removal. Whether and to what extent the hypotheses deduced from a system-theoretically generalized system of theories are suitable for the explanation of the
respective organizational problem at hand cannot be judged
in the context of discovery already. For this task, opera-
tionalization and empirical test of hypotheses in the framework of argumentation is necessary. The efficiency of the

described heuristic procedure will among other things be
dependent upon the size of the set of generalized theories
within General Systems Theory, which can be interpreted as
models of the interdisciplinary problems to be explained.
The greater the number of general systems models that seem
to be isomorph to the respective problems at hand, the
greater might be the probability that the phenomena which
have to be explained can be conceived with the hypotheses
deducable from general systems models.

2.2. *Systems-Theoretically Oriented Structuralization of Man-Machine-Systems*

In the previous discussion, the importance of the system-
theoretic approach for the development of theories about
organizational states of affairs was the center of interest.
In the last years a stronger discussion of system-theoretic
questions for a scientific foundation of the structuralization of organizational systems is observed. It is primarily
about the already mentioned tendencies of "Systems Engineering" and "Systems Analysis", which follow the concept of systems theory as the names may easily show. As a close analysis
of these approaches shows most of them depart from the systems idea characteristic to General Systems Theory [89].
Systems Engineering emphasizes, for example, that organizational structuralization of operational subunits - in the
technological field in particular - is not a subproblem that
could be solved in isolation [90]. A similar approach is
chosen by Systems Analysis that has gained a special importance besides Systems Engineering in the framework of structural approaches oriented on systems ideas. From the statement that a change of one element necessarily leads to
changes of those elements interdependent with the former one,
a postulate is deduced that in the analysis of systems not
only the elements forming the system should be considered,
but at the same time the interdependencies between them, too.
Systems Analysis represents a method, therefore, by which
already during the analysis preceeding every structuralization
of systems the interdependencies between the elements of the
system to be created should be conceived. It is the objective
of this procedure to be able to tell in a preliminary structuralization concept already, what the influence of structural and functional changes of elements and subsystems will
possibly be on the structure and functioning of the inter-

related elements and subsystems, and on the whole system.
For this purpose one intentionally aims towards a cooperation of representatives of different disciplines in the process of structuralization of man-machine-systems, in order
to be able to deal with various sociological, social-psychological, and technological aspects of the respective area of
structuralization. On the whole, it can be stated that statements of General Systems Theory are considered only to a
limited extent in these two most important forms of system-
theoretically oriented structuralization of complex man-
machine-systems. Apart from some terms developed by systems
theory only relatively general systems phenomena are usually
referred to.

The Systems Engineering and Systems Analysis approaches
outlined emphasize the procedural and methodological aspects
of structuralization [91]. Their objective is to develop
efficient strategies of structuralization that are valid in
a general form for materially different systems. The statements formulated are not only based on hypotheses about behavior of systems, therefore, but also on hypotheses about
the efficient strategy of structuralization processes. The
current focal point of General Systems Theory is the identification of generally valid laws concerning the behavior of
materially different systems. Their value of evidence for
procedurally oriented concepts of structuralization is rather
limited at the current time. It will be the task of future
research to integrate system-theoretic knowledge in concepts
of structuralization, and to attempt to develop generalized
strategies of structuralization. The framework has been
pointed out, within which the scientific discussion of systems-theoretic and organization-theoretic questions will
center in the future.

REFERENCES

1.   See ZETTERBERG, H.L., "Theorie, Forschung und Praxis in
     der Soziologie", In: *Handbuch der empirischen Sozial-
     forschung, 1*, 65, 2nd ed., KÖNIG, R. (ed.), Stuttgart,
     1967.
     ALBERT, H., "Probleme der Theoriebildung. Entwicklung,
     Struktur und Anwendung sozialwissenschaftlicher Theorien"
     In: *Theorie und Realität*. "Ausgewählte Aufsätze zur

Wissenschaftslehre in den Sozialwissenschaften", 3-70,
ALBERT, H. (ed.), Tübingen 1964.
WILD, J.,"Organisatorische Theorien, Aufbau und Aussage-
gehalt". In: *Handwörterbuch der Organization*, columns
1265-1280, GROCHLA, E. (ed.), Stuttgart, 1969.

2. For this problem see FRESE, E.,"Wirtschaftlichkeit und
    Organisation". In: *Handwörterbuch der Organisation*,
    columns 1787-1802, GROCHLA, E. (ed.), Stuttgart, 1969.

3. URWICK, L., *The Elements of Administration*.   New York-
    London, 1943.

4. KOONTZ, H. and O'DONNELL, C., *Principles of Management*,
    3rd ed., New York, 1964.

5. DALE, E., *Management Theory and Practice*. New York-
    St. Louis and others, 1965.

6. See LEHMANN, H.,"Organisationslehre (I),   Entwicklung
    im deutschsprachigen Raum". In: *Handwörterbuch der
    Organisation*, column 1150, GROCHLA, E. (ed.), Stuttgart,
    1969.

7. KOSIOL, E., *Organisation der Unternehmung*, Wiesbaden,
    1962.

8. SHUBIK, M.,"Games Decisions and Industrial Organizations",
    Management Science, *6*, 455-474, 1960.

9. HELMER, O.,"The Prospects of a Unified Theory of Organi-
    zations"; *Management Science*, *4*, 172-176, 1958.

10. MORGENSTERN, O.,"Prolegomena to a Theory of Organization".
    The Rand Corporation Research Memorandum 734. Santa
    Monica, 1951.

11. WEBER, M., *Wirtschaft und Gesellschaft*, *2*, 4th ed.,
    Tübingen, 1956.

12. BARNARD, C.I., *The Functions of the Executive*. Cam-
    bridge, Mass., 1938.

13. SIMON, H.A., *Administrative Behavior. A Study of Decision-Making Processes in Administrative Organization*, 2nd ed., New York, 1957.

14. BAKKE, W.E.,"Concept of the Social Organization". In: *Modern Organization Theory*, 16-75, HAIRE, M. (ed.), New York-London, 1959.

15. See PARSONS, T.,"Systematische Theorie der Soziologie". In: PARSONS, T., *Beiträge zur soziologischen Theorie*, 38, RUSCHEMEYER, D. (ed.), Neuwied-Berlin, 1964.

16. CARLSON, S., *Executive Behaviour*. Stockholm, 1951.

17. See, e.g., CYERT, R.M., SIMON, H.A., TROW, D.B.,"Observation of a Business Decision", *Journal of Business, 29*, 237-248, 1956; BURNS, T., *Stalker, G.M., The Management of Innovation*. London, 1961.

18. See, e.g., LIKERT, R., *New Patterns of Management*. New York-Toronto-London, 1961.

19. WEBER, M., *Wirtschaft und Gesellschaft*, op. cit.

20. BLAU, P.M., SCOTT, W.R., *Formal Organizations*, 33, San Francisco, 1962.

21. See especially the papers of MERTON, R.K., *Social Theory and Social Structure*, 2nd ed., Glencoe, Ill., 1957; GOULDNER, A.W., *Patterns of Industrial Bureaucracy*, Glencoe, Ill., 1954; SELZNICK, P., *Leadership in Administration*, Evanston, Ill., 1957.

22. BARNARD, C.I., *The Functions of the Executive...*, op. cit.

23. SIMON, H.A., *Administrative Behavior...*, op. cit.

24. See REITMAN, W., *Cognition and Thought*. New York-London-Sydney, 1965; SIMON, H.A., *The Shape of Automation for Men and Management*, New York-Evanston-London, 1965.

25. See CYERT, R.M.; MARCH, J.G., *A Behavioral Theory of the Firm*, Englewood Cliffs, N.J., 1963.

26. For the different models see CYERT, R.M.; MARCH, J.G., *A Behavioral Theory of the Firm*, op. cit., 128. For the explanation of growth of the firm the behavioral approach and computer simulation is used in KIESER, Alfred, *Unternehmungswachstum und Produktinnovation*, Ph.D. Thesis, Köln, 1968.

27. A summary of different empirical investigations on small groups can be found in HARE, A.P., BORGATTA, E.F., BALES, R.F., *Small Groups*, 2nd ed., New York, 1966.

28. COLLINS, B.E., GUETZKOW, H., *A Social Psychology of Group Processes for Decision-Making*, 69, New York-London-Sydney, 1964.

29. GOLEMBIEWSKI, R.T.,"Small Groups and Large Organizations". In: *Handbook of Organizations*, 87, MARCH, J.G. (ed.), Chicago, 1965.

30. For a summary of these experiments see COLLINS, B.E., GUETZKOW, H., *A Social Psychology of Group Processes...*, 63, op. cit.

31. GOLEMBIEWSKI, R.T., *Small Groups and Large Organizations*, 101, op. cit.

32. See MARSCHAK, J., "Towards an Economic Theory of Organization and Information". In: *Decision Processes*, 187-220, THRALL, R.M., COOMBS, C.H., AND DAVIS, R.L. (eds.), New York, 1954; MARSCHAK, J.,"Problems in Information Economics". In: *Management Controls*, 38-74, BONINI, Ch.P., JAEDECKE, R.J., and WAGNER, H.M. (eds.), New York, 1964.

33. SCHMALENBACH, E.,"Pretiale Wirtschaftslenkung", *Die Optimale Geltungszahl, 1,* Bremen-Horn, 1947.

34. The research done at the "Betriebswirtschaftliches Institut für Organisation und Automation" at the University of Cologne should be pointed out at this point.

35. i.e., BECKET, J.A.,"The Total Systems Concept: Its Implication for Management". In: *The Impact of Computers on Management*, 204-235, MYERS, Ch. A. (ed.), Cambridge, Mass.-London, 1967.

36. See TAYLOR, F.M., *Die Betriebsleitung insbesondere der Werkstätten*, 3rd ed., Berlin, 1914.

37. See MAYO, E., *Probleme industrieller Arbeitsbedingungen*. Frankfurt/M, 1949.

38. See GROCHLA, E., *Automation und Organisation. Die technische Entwicklung und ihre betriebswirtschaftlich-organisatorischen Konsequenzen*. Wiesbaden, 1966.

39. For example in the works of the following authors: MAYNTZ, R., *Soziologie der Organisation*, 34. Reinbek b. Hamburg, 1963; KOSIOL, E., SZYPERSKI, N., CHMIELEWICZ, K., "Zum Standort der Systemforschung im Rahmen der Wissenschaften", *Zeitschrift für betriebswirtschaftliche Forschung*, *17*, 337, 1965; GROCHLA, E., *Automation und Organisation*, 121, op. cit.; ULRICH, H., *Die Unternehmung als produktives soziales System*, Bern-Stuttgart, 1968; IRLE, M., "Soziale Systeme". In: *Handwörterbuch der Organisation*, columns 1505-1509, GROCHLA, Erwin (ed.), Stuttgart, 1969; MAYNTZ, R., ZIEGLER, R., "Soziologie der Organisation". In: *Handbuch der empirischen Sozialforschung*, *2*, 451, KONIG, Rene (ed.), Stuttgart, 1969.

40. For this phenomenon, see CHURCHMAN, C.W., *The Systems Approach*. New York, 1968.

41. ACKOFF, R.L., "Systems, Organizations and Interdisciplinary Research". *General Systems*, *5*, 1-8, 1960.

42. ASHBY, W.R., "General Systems Theory as a New Discipline", *General Systems*, *3*, 1-6, 1958.

43. BOULDING, K., "General Systems Theory - The Skeleton of Science", *General Systems*, *1*, 11-17, 1956.

44. MESAROVIC, M.D., "Foundations for a General Systems Theory" In: *Views on General Systems Theory. Proceedings of the Second Systems Symposium at Case Institute of Technology*, 1-24, MESAROVIC, Mihajlo D. (ed.), New York-London-Sydney 1964.

45. See especially the numerous contributions in: *General Systems. Yearbook of the Society for General Systems Research.* Further contributions to General Systems Theory can be found in: *Systems: Research and Design. Proceedings of the First Systems Symposium at Case Institute of Technology,* ECKMAN, D.P. (ed.), New York-London, 1961; *Views on General Systems Theory. Proceedings of the Second Systems Symposium at Case Institute of Technology,* MESAROVIC, M.D. (ed.), New York-London, 1964; *Systems Thinking. Selected Readings,* EMERY, F.E. (ed.), Harmondsworth-Baltimore-Victoria, 1969.

46. The presentation of von Bertalanffy's systems concept is among other things based on a Master's Thesis by my scholar and assistant, GAGSCH, S., titled: *Der Beitrag Bertalanffy's zur Allgemeinen Systemtheorie. Eine ergänzende Analyse.* Köln, 1967/68.

47. For the relevance of "Ganzheitslehre" for the development of science see for example HEIMSOETH, H.: "Die Philosophie im zwanzigsten Jahrhundert". In: WINDELBAND, W., *Lehrbuch der Geschichte der Philosophie,* 596 and 599, 15th ed., HEIMSOETH, Heinz (ed.), Tübingen, 1957; ASTER, E.V., *Geschichte der Philosophie,* 422, 11th ed., Stuttgart, 1956.

48. See for example the papers in : *Die Ganzheit in Philosophie und Wissenschaft. Othmar Spann zum 70. Geburtstag,* HEINRICH, W. (ed.), Wien, 1950.

49. For a critique of the "Ganzheitslehre" see for example NAGEL, E., Uber die Aussage: "Das Ganze ist mehr als die Summe seiner Teile". In: *Logik der Sozialwissenschaften,* 225-235, TOPITSCH, Ernst (ed.), Köln-Berlin, 1965; SCHLICK, M.,"Uber den Begriff der Ganzheit". In: *Logik der Sozialwissenschaften,* 213-224, op. cit.; LEINFELLNER, W., *Struktur und Aufbau wissenschaftlicher Theorien. Eine wissenschaftstheoretisch-philosophische Untersuchung,* 219, Wien-Würzburg, 1965.

50. For the different standpoints advocated in biology in order to explain life see for example UNGERER, E., *Die Wissenschaft vom Leben. Eine Geschichte der Biologie, 3,*

Der Wandel der Probleme der Biologie in den letzten Jahrzehnten, 17, Freiburg-München, 1966.

51. For this and the following see VORLANDER, K., *Geschichte der Philosophie, 2: Die Philosophie der Neuzeit*, 95, 130, 9th ed., Hamburg, 1955; ASTER, E.V.: *Geschichte der Philosophie*, 249, op. cit.

52. DRIESCH, H., *Philosophie des Organischen. Gifford-Vorlesungen, gehalten and der Universität Aberdeen in den Jahre 1907-1908, 1 und 2*, Leipzig, 1909.

53. See von BERTALANFFY, L., *Theoretische Biologie, 1: Allgemeine Theorie, Physikochemie, Aufbau und Entwicklung des Organismus*, 80, Berlin, 1932.

54. For this and the following see von BERTALANFFY, L., *Theoretische Biologie, 1*, 80, op. cit.; BENDMANN, A., *L. von Bertalanffys organische Auffassung des Lebens in ihren philosophischen Konsequenzen*, 20, Jena, 1967.

55. See von BERTALANFFY, L., *Das biologische Weltbild. Bd.1: Die Stellung des Lebens in Natur und Wissenschaft*, 24, Bern, 1949.

56. von BERTALANFFY, L., *Das biologische Weltbild, 1*, 31, op. cit.

57. For the systems view of the organism, as well as for the open systems model used see in detail von BERTALANFFY, L., *Das Biologische Weltbild, 1*, 127, op. cit.

58. See von BERTALANFFY, L.,"Zu einer allgemeine Systemlehre". In: *Biologia Generalis, 19*, 114, Heft 1, Wien, 1949.

59. See EISLER, R., *Wörterbuch der philosophischen Begriffe*, 3, 204, 4th ed., Berlin, 1930.

60. See WIESNER, W., *Organismen, Strukturen, Maschinen. Zu einer Lehre vom Organismus*, 12pp., Frankfurt am Main, 1959.

61. See von BERTALANFFY, L., *Das biologische Weltbild*, *1*, 140, op. cit.; von BERTALANFFY, L., *Zu einer allgemeinen Systemlehre*, 115, op. cit.

62. See HALL, A.D., FAGEN, R.E., Definition of System; *General Systems*, *1*, 18, 1956.

63. See FUCHS, H., "Systemtheorie". In: *Handwörterbuch der Organisation*, column 1621, GROCHLA, E. (ed.), Stuttgart, 1969; LEHMANN, H., "Integration". In: *Handwörterbuch der Organisation*, column 770, GROCHLA, E. (ed.), Stuttgart, 1969; according to Wiesner the complexity of a system is primarily due to the richness of interdependencies. See WIESNER, W., *Organismen, Strukturen, Maschinen*, 26, op. cit.

64. See WIESNER, W., *Organismen, Strukturen, Maschinen*, 26. op. cit.

65. BEER, S., *Kybernetik und Management*, 27-34, Frankfurt/M., 1962.

66. BOULDING, K., *General Systems Theory - The Skeleton of Science*, 14, op. cit.

67. Among other numerous authors see von BERTALANFFY, L., *Biophysik des Fliessgleichgewichts. Einführung in die Physik offener Systeme und ihre Anwendung in der Biologie*, 1, Braunschweig, 1953; KAMARYT, J., "Die Bedeutung der Theorie des offenen Systems in der gegenwärtigen Biologie. (Zur Kritik der Philosophie des Organischen bei Bertalanffy)". In: *Deutsche Zeitschrift für Philosophie*, *9*, 1244, 1961.

68. See von BERTALANFFY, L., *Biophysik des Fliessgleichgewichts*, 11, op. cit.

69. See HALL, A.D., FAGEN, R.E., *Definition of System*, 23, op. cit.

70. For this definition see FUCHS, H., *Systemtheorie*, column 1620, op. cit.; LEHMANN, H., *Integration*, column 772, op. cit.

71. For the properties and behavioral patterns of open sys-
    tems see von BERTALANFFY, L.,"The Theory of Open Systems
    in Physics and Biology", *Science, 111*, 23, 1950;
    von BERTALANFFY, L., *Biophysik des Fliessgleichgewichts,*
    12, op. cit.; von BERTALANFFY, L., *Zu einer allgemeinen
    Systemlehre,* 121, op. cit.; von BERTALANFFY,"An Outline
    of General System Theory", *The British Journal for
    the Philosophy of Science, 1,* 155, 1950; KAMARYT, J.,
    *Die Bedeutung der Theorie des offenen Systems in der
    gegenwärtigen Biologie,* 1244, op. cit.

72. For the problem of demarcation between "open" and "closed"
    systems, and the related questions of equilibrium see in
    detail FUCHS, H., *Systemtheorie,* column 1623, op. cit.

73. See von BERTALANFFY, L., *Zu einer allgemeinen Systemlehre,*
    123 and 125, op. cit.; also MILLER, J.G., Living Systems:
    Basic Concepts; *Behavioral Science, 10*, 233, 1965.

74. For this and the following see von BERTALANFFY, L.,"A
    New Approach to Unity of Science".6. "Towards a Physical
    Theory of Organic Teleology, Feedback, and Dynamics".
    In: *Human Biology, 23,* 354, especially 360, 1951; von
    BERTALANFFY, L., *Biophysik des Fliessgleichgewichts,*
    11 and 37, op. cit.

75. See von BERTALANFFY, L., *Biophysik des Fliessgleichge-
    wichts,* 39, op. cit.

76. See MILLER, J.G., *Living Systems: Basic Concepts,* 215,
    op. cit.; BOULDING, K., *General Systems Theory - The
    Skeleton of Science,* 11, op. cit.

77. See *Systems Theory and Biology, Proceedings of the Third
    Systems Symposium at Case Institute of Technology,* Berlin-
    Heidelberg-New York, 1968.

78. See BUCKLEY, W., *Sociology and Modern Systems Theory.*
    Englewood Cliffs, N.J., 1967.

79. See KATZ, D., KAHN, R.L., *The Social Psychology of Orga-
    nizations.* New York-London-Sydney, 1966.

80. See the papers in: *General Systems Theory and Psychiatry,*
GRAY, W., DUHL, F.J. AND RIZZO, N.D. (eds.), Boston, 1969.

81. See the presentation and analysis of systems-theoretic
approaches in different disciplines in YOUNG, O.R.,"A
Survey of General Systems Theory". *General Systems,*
9, 61-80, 1964; see also von BERTALANFFY, L., *General*
System Theory Foundations, Development, Applications,
192, New York, 1968.

82. First approaches in this direction are the following
papers, for example: JOHNSON, R.A., KAST, F.E., and
ROSENZWEIG, J.E.: *The Theory and Management of Systems.*
London, 1963; MESAROVIC, M.D., SANDERS, J.L., and
SPRAGUE, C.F.,"An Axiomatic Approach to Organizations
from a General Systems Viewpoint". In: *New Perspectives*
in Organization Research, 493-512, COOPER, W.W., LEAVITT,
H.J. and SHELLY II, N.M. (eds.), New York-London-Sydney,
1964; GROCHLA, E., *Automation und Organisation,* 73,
op. cit.

83. See ALBERT, H., *Probleme der Theoriebildung,* 28, op. cit.

84. See BRODBECK, M.,"Models, Meaning, and Theories". In:
Symposium on Sociological Theory, 379, GROSS, Llewellyn,
Evanston-New York, 1959.

85. For the implementation of this process see SPINNER, H.F.,
"Modelle und Experimente". In: *Handwörterbuch der Organi-*
sation, columns 1003, GROCHLA, Erwin (ed.), Stuttgart,
1969; see also MILLER, J.G., *Living Systems: Basic*
Concepts, 215, op. cit.

86. For an attempt to transform a theory T_i directly into
a theory T_j without any reference to a general theory
T_A see HAIRE, M.,"Biological Models and Empirical
Histories of the Growth of Organizations". In: *Modern*
Organization Theory, 272, HAIRE, M. (ed.), New York, 1959.

87. A summary of generalized hypotheses on properties and
behavioral patterns of systems can be found in MILLER,
J.G., Living Systems: "Cross-Level Hypotheses".
Behavioral Science, 10, 380-411, 1956.

88. This fact has often been the reason for critical objections to general systems theory. See, for example,
HEMPEL, C.G.,"General Systems Theory: A New Approach
to Unity of Science".2."General System Theory and the
Unity of Science"; *Human Biology, 23*, 313-322, 1951;
von BERTALANFFY, L., *General System Theory — A Critical
Review, 8*, op. cit. A revision of this originally
rather sceptical view can be found in Simon. See SIMON,
H.A., The Architecture of Complexity, *General Systems,
10*, 63, 1965.

89. See GIBSON, R.E.,"The Recognition of Systems Engineering".
In: *Operations Research and Systems Engineering, 58*,
FLAGLE, Ch.D, HUGGINS, W.H., and ROY, R.H. (eds.), Baltimore, 1960; WEGNER, G., *Systemanalyse und Sachmittelein-
satz in der Betriebsorganisation, 68*, Wiesbaden, 1969.

90. See KERSCHNER, R.B.,"A Survey of Systems Engineering Tool
and Techniques" In: *Operations Research and Systems
Engineering, 140*, FLAGLE, Ch. D, HUGGINS, W.H., and ROY,
R.H. (eds.), Baltimore, 1960.

91. In the process of structuralization of complex organizational systems two different aspects have to be considered: on one hand, rational structuralization requires
empirical information on quasi-laws of the system to be
structured; on the other hand, considering the procedural problem the process (not the result) of structutal-
ization is regarded as the problem. See FRESE, E.,"Ein-
flussgrössen organisatorischer Umstrukturierungsprozesse",
Zeitschrift fur Organisation, 38, 134-141.

PRAGMATIC STRATEGIES IN THE FORMATION
OF SOCIOLOGICAL THEORIES

LLEWELLYN GROSS

Department of Sociology, State University of New York at Buffalo, N.Y., U.S.A.

RONALD JONES

Faculty of Education, University of British Columbia, Vancouver, B.C., Canada

> Every one is at liberty to define 'science' as he pleases. But the least requirement which can be expected of a definition is that it does not fly too much in the fact of the actual state of affairs. But this is precisely what is done by a definition of science which makes it equivalent to mathematical physics. According to this definition not only are the 'mental sciences' — psychology, sociology, history, etc. — not sciences, and never can be such, but the same will be true of large branches of natural science as well.
>
> Ludwig von Bertalanffy
> *Modern Theories of Development*

The principal assumption of this essay is that sociological methods of inquiry must be geared to current levels of attainment in sociology, and not to those standards of the "exact" sciences which are presently beyond realization [1]. Confronted with the need for an imaginative balance between clarify of conception and economy of procedure it upholds the thesis that logical rigor cannot be the most essential requisite for all sociological theory. That the most rigorous methods are themselves open to continuous inquiry is evidenced by the observation that logicians differ in their viewpoints on logical usage. A brief examination of certain of these viewpoints will orient the reader to the strategies which follow from the thesis.

SOME VIEWPOINTS ON THE USE OF LOGIC

Textbook proponents of traditional logic often view logical reasoning as consisting of the formal transformation of propositions possessing identical meanings. An antecedent proposition is said to *entail* a consequent proposition by virtue of the condition that both contain identical meanings. Since the consequent is a kind of analytic definition of the antecedent, the former follows of necessity from the latter; to deny this necessity is tantamount to violating the law of non-contradiction, without which thinking would be impossible. From this point of view the meaning and validity of a sequence of logical expressions is dependent upon the chain of connections that constitute their propositional form. Devoid of content the laws of logic are neither empirical nor synthetic [2].

The proponents of *pragmatism* have qualified this interpretation of *logical entailment*. They contend that the identical meanings expressed in any logical relationship are ultimately subject to validation through application to empirical instances. This viewpoint assumes that what is true of every hypothetical member of a universal logical category (class, propositional function) must be true of every existential member of that category. So interpreted, logical entailment functions in the same way as universal laws of nature. Other pragmatists contend that the connection between logical propositions rests on empirical tests of the uniformity of nature assumption and not on the kind of necessity found in the "definitional interrelation of meanings" connoted by entailment. On this interpretation, *logical implication* depends upon standards of confirmation which apply to scientific hypotheses.

The proponents of *material implication* as a form of logical reasoning contend that it holds between any two propositions regardless of what they mean (exemplify or denote) and regardless of their truth and falsity, providing that the consequent is not factually false when the antecedent is factually true. Thus, each of the propositions, (a) "Criminal behavior is learned" and (b) "Criminal behavior is not learned", would materially imply the proposition "Yosemite is a national park". In turn, if the latter proposition materially implied (a), then it would not materially imply (b).

The proponents of *strict implication* add a further restriction to the notion of material implication, viz., that of negative consistency. One proposition (the antecedent) implies another (the consequent) when it is impossible for the antecedent to be true and the consequent false. Since the falsity of the proposition "Yosemite is a national park" would not be inconsistent with the truth of the proposition "Criminal behavior is learned", the latter does not strictly imply the former. It is only when the affirmation of the antecedent and the denial of the consequent are mutually contradictory that strict implication holds. Thus, the preceding proposition, "Criminal behavior is learned", strictly implies the proposition "Criminal behavior is acquired", since to deny the latter is to contradict the former.

That certain limitations accompany all forms of logical reasoning has been demonstrated by critical logicians. To review the paradoxes that follow from the assumption that any proposition is implied by a false or impossible proposition (as in material and strict implication, for example) would take us beyond the purpose of this paper. Perhaps the reader will agree that connections between terms in traditional logic are overly necessary and compelling, in material and strict implication insufficiently necessary and compelling, to provide a suitable analytic framework for defining sociological relationships [3]. The fact that matrix calculi are proving to be of considerable use may be noted but need not be discussed.

LIMITATIONS OF TRADITIONAL LOGIC

By focusing upon the formal transformation of identities, the traditional view of entailment seriously restricts
the utilization of equivalent *empirical* meanings in theory
construction. Perfect consistency requires that we proceed
from one formally true proposition to another with no propositions containing vague or ambiguous expressions that are
in any respects logically false. Quite obviously, this
requirement is tantamount to sacrificing varying shades of
empirical meaning for tautological consistency. Unfortunately, however, empirically grounded meanings cannot be so
neatly isolated that it can be said of every phenomenal
event that it is either one thing or another, that it must
be what it is and cannot be changed in the slightest by the
context of conditions in which it is placed.

If the truths of logic are purely formal and the most
highly formalized sociological truths contain some degree
of empirical meaning, then there can be no decisive merging
of logic with sociology, no incorrigible methodology in
the latter area [4]. The present choice is to accept logic
as traditionally conceived or to interpret logical usage in
ways which will best implement the aims of sociology. The
latter alternative means that we must accept the possibility of partial consistency, that statements possessing some
measure of self-contradiction may yet yield new truths. It
means that we must accept the possibility that sociological
problems can be satisfactorily resolved even though their
empirical foundations cannot be completely stated in terms
of explicitly defined syntactic and semantic rules.

So irreverent a viewpoint may be of utmost practical
value. Few researchers, it seems can afford to doubt that
useful results may follow from a train of thought that is
formally invalid, or that formally valid thought may produce results of little scientific value. How else can one
explain the scientific use of procedures founded upon extra-
logical assumptions which are formally invalid or non-valid
[5]? If this general viewpoint is accepted, then logic,
traditionally conceived, becomes a means of validating but
not of invalidating a theory, whereas logic, pragmatically
conceived, becomes a means for testing both the validity
and the invalidity of a theory.

THE CASE FOR EMPIRICAL LOGIC

We have suggested that all sociologically useful forms
of logic are conditioned *at some point* by empirical results.
This means that the consistency of logical forms is not
independent of their empirical interpretations[6]. So con-
strued, p may be held to factually imply q only when there
is a highly confirmed empirical generalization underlying
the linkage of p with q. That consistency here is a matter
of empirical test can be seen by interpreting the formal
proposition, "all p is q", in concrete terms. This proposition asserts that all members of the subject term possess
qualities contained in the predicate term. Now if the concrete term for p is "criminal" and the concrete term for q
is "lawabiding", the proposition is only probably false
since it could, under certain conditions, be true. Briefly,
then, identities and ambiguities of meaning shade into one
another, and there is no *a priori* logical method for guar-
anteeing scientific truth. Risk and uncertainty, failure
and confusion, surprise and discovery are part and parcel
of the scientific endeavor.

For sociology, the principal advantage of logical formulas stems from the provision of a clear and rapid grasp
of the systematic connections which obtain within phenomena.
To the kind of scientific understanding which consists of
the abstract comprehension of interchangeable forms, logic
has much to offer. But logic as a tool may be used to de-
feat the purposes of sociological understanding. This is
apt to occur when the social researcher, turned logical
enthusiast, becomes so enamoured with the multiplication of
propositions that the thread of general principles, upon
which his analysis proceeds, is lost from sight. Paradoxi-
cal as it may seem, experienced scientists have discovered
that when inferential routes are not too lengthy or complicated, new hypotheses may be more easily constructed. Under conditions of precise analytical simplicity, perceptual
sensitivity to empirical phenomena of crucial significance
may be heightened and major steps taken toward the confirmation of new theory.

Even though the sociologist must strive for some sort
of formal explication of his thinking, this should not be

done by foregoing a firm grasp of the palpable problems
upon which his thinking hinges. Perhaps he would then do
well to accede to the principle that "No proposition is
wholly true, since there is invariably some qualification
which would make it false; and no proposition is wholly
false, since there is invariably some qualification which
would make it true". The universality of this principle
permits of countless illustrations. Thus, the proposition
"White collar criminals are people of high social status
who commit acts in violation of law" is true as long as
we grant that it applies to adults and not juveniles, includes penal sanctions irrespective of custom or convention,
and refers to the violation of criminal rather than civil
laws. Moreover, the proposition is false if we assume that
it applies to offenses against tribal laws in some remote
part of the world or to laws concerning murder, rape, tor-
ture, and similar forms of violence.

The human condition, that every sociological analysis
will, for our era, display a *mixture* of statements, some of
which are related by implication while others are descriptive of portions of data related through empirical association, is one of those irreconcilable circumstances which
must be accepted for better or worse. The fitting of logical form to empirical content (or vice versa) is dependent
upon a two-directional process in which either form or content may outdistance the other in development. The resulting unevenness in conceptual expression is bound to leave
the serious scholar with a persistent sense of irresolution.

PRAGMATIC STRATEGIES

If the conception of logic developed in the preceding
paragraphs is justified, then most problems in the methodology of theory construction can be approached in the pragmatic manner in which sociologists often approach problems
in empirical research. A "pragmatic strategy" is any procedural or attitudinal contrivance which can serve as a
workable substitute for the more rigorous techniques of
mathematics and physical science. It is a quasi-scientific,
quasi-artistic style for selecting relevant data and ordering
a wide gamut of conceptual possibilities. To be sure,

serious compromises may follow from its use, but if the
sociological theorist is willing to console himself with
attainable outcomes he may leave a legacy for future generations that will, in the long view, hasten the creation of
a science of society.

The methodological problems discussed below are designed
to describe the more prominent obstacles confronting the
sociological theorist. For every problem a correlative
strategy is proposed [7]. Each strategy is, of course,
exploratory and programmatic rather than definitive.

OBSERVATION SENTENCES

Interpretation: It is uncommon in sociology to read
eye-witness accounts of behavioral events descriptive of the
moment-to-moment observations of one who has been "on the
spot" to record them in their full immediacy. Demands for
economy of space seem to mean that partially generalized
empirical sentences must represent the lowest levels of
abstraction admitted as data.

Strategy: When using primary sources, record all tangible data which arrest the flight of attention and tend to
restrain uncontrolled speculation. Prefer any datum that
has an indivisible (irreducible) toughness about it; that
possesses the degree of stability required to maintain a
kind of existential independence despite distortions of
context — empirical or analytical.

When using secondary sources attempt to isolate the
more trenchant observational sentences, setting them apart
from the running commentary constituting the main body of
notes or text. Then group sentences into categories of
descriptively similar kinds, labeling some "generalizations"
and others "evidence". When possible, translate all sentences into words which can be: (1) safely left undefined,
or (2) defined unambiguously by brief, precise phrases.
Certain vague terms (those devoid of exact quantitative
meaning) can be made more definite by adding quantifying
adjectives, denoting rough estimates of their amounts.
After doing this, strive for closeness of logical connection
and sequence in ideas. In these ways, excess verbiage may

be reduced and vague words clarified by placing them in
precise contexts. One must, of course, make sure that a
particular context does not provide a different meaning
from what one wishes to designate by a given sentence.
As a final recourse, examples may be given, though they
have the limitations of selective perception.

By using structural devices such as these, more space
will be available for recording observation sentences which
are individually representative and collectively sufficient
for the purposes at hand.

PROBLEMATIC FOCI

Interpretation: The problems sociologists usually
study have multiple lines of reference, which is to say,
shifting and indeterminate boundaries. When a sociological
problem is lacking in focus, precise questions cannot be
put to it nor can precise hypotheses for answering these
questions be formulated. On the other hand, when the focus
of a problem is reasonably stable and clear, the questions
which it suggests are apt to be more precise and the hypotheses offered to account for the problem will be fewer in
number.

Strategy: Begin by accepting the procedural viewpoint
that data are "taken" out of concern for the resolution of
a problematic situation. If the conventional focus of a
particular problem is unclear, choose one or more foci appropriate to one's scientific goals and define them by several imaginatively fresh statements. Risk the hazards
which normally ensue from the deliberate restructuring of
familiar statements (through hunch, analogy, the addition
of novel elements, etc.) to bring them in line with the
prevision of specific questions to which testable answers
(hypotheses) can be foreseen.

Direct specific questions toward the subsumption of
narrowly bounded regions of phenomena. Within each region
attempt to locate a few palpable impressions — perceptible
points of reference — time, place, position, or any discernible qualitative or quantitative difference to which

familiar labels can be attached. Report observations in the
form of simple descriptive phrases. When descriptive phrases
are not readily suggested, concepts may be introduced from
the "outside" and provisionally imposed, as it were, in
much the same way that a searchlight is used to illuminate
obscure areas. Concepts of nearly universal applicability
like "before and after", "near and far", "part and whole",
"smaller and larger", "higher and lower", "similar and dissimilar", "stable and unstable" may serve to expose aspects
of phenomena which would otherwise escape attention.

When possible, test concepts by physical operations
designed to alter the observed course of events. With increasing clarification of the region under surveillance a
delimitation of the more prominent ingredients may emerge,
expressible, perhaps, by concepts of greater discriminatory
capacity: "conditions and consequences", "operations and
results", "structures and functions", "attributes and variables". Aided by these "second order" concepts the region
under examination may then be represented by analytical
statements possessing still greater clarity and discriminatory power. These statements may, in their turn, be encompassed by third or fourth order concepts of sufficient
exactness to resolve explanatory issues. By shuttling back
and forth between analytical statements and observational
sentences, each of which is utilized to achieve successive
degrees of mutual approximation, salient distinctions within
and among problematic foci may be securely grounded.

LEVELS OF ABSTRACTION

Interpretation: In the typical sociological product
it is difficult to place a particular passage within an
identifiable level of abstraction. When the superimposed
"floors" of a scheme of crucial statements are not expli-
cated, it is often impossible to maintain conceptual integrity. "How then, may the theorist ferret out the more
persistent or pervasive dimensions of theoretical organization, those which seek to explain the unique and idioma-
tic?" The resolution of this question is equivalent to
uncovering invariant lines of analysis, symbolic expressions
which exhibit constancy of form through changing social
events.

Strategy: Separate sentences into groups of wide and narrow scope. If those of narrow scope seem to refer to data of higher visibility and to be contained within those of wider scope, then there are at least psychological grounds for assuming that the former are more empirical. If the ratio of characteristics to things, of the number of connotations (attribute terms) to the number of denotations (noun terms) is high, the statement in question approaches the more abstract levels; if low, the more empirical levels. But one must take special care that this separation is not confounded by terms which are meant to carry private associations in addition to denoting particular objects and events. The confusion fostered by mixing attributes with objects increases the burden of distinguishing explanatory sentences from descriptive sentences.

For a more thoroughgoing analysis assume that "higher-level" phenomena stand in the relation of structure to content, whole to part, container to contained, necessary to sufficient conditions, with reference to "lower-level" phenomema. Assume, too, that events which tend to be atomistic, fluctuating and peripheral, distinctly short run, concretely instrumental, or finitely structured, are of lower level occurrence. The following rule will encompass most of these distinctions: "Of any two sets of statements that set is 'higher' in pattern of organization which has the smallest number of its terms reducible to the other, whose designated events can be most readily taken as conditional for the events embraced by the other; and whose predictions will permit of smaller errors when the events of the one are taken as prognostic of the other"

However, care must be taken against pressing criteria too far or adhering too strictly to any rule. There is no sure way of determining in advance whether a given level possesses features which are operative on other levels. Initial discontinuities between levels may be eliminated by changing problematic foci or choice of conceptual tools. In the beginning, intuitive inference, plausibility, or mere expectation of continuity may have to suffice as substitutes for rational inference and rigorous implication. The extent to which levels possess unique or derivative elements, are conjoined with or isolated from one another, are united by intersecting or parallel patterns of order,

must be established by systematic analysis. Remember that
valid inferences are sometimes drawn from unconsciously
observed events which are, perforce, inadequately
conceptualized.

GENERALIZATIONS

   Interpretation: Admitting the desirability of cate-
gorizing one group of sentences as premises or hypotheses
and another group of sentences as their evidential consequences, how is one to justify the particular linkages one
chooses to make between these groups when the necessary
supporting generalizations are either not provided by the
sociologist or are deeply buried in his writings? According
to pragmatic rules of logic, it is not possible to deduce
evidential consequences from hypotheses without the support
of highly confirmed generalizations covering the respective
categories of instances described by both hypotheses and
consequences.

   Strategy: In most situations the best that can be
done, short of painstaking efforts to establish appropriate
generalizations, is to impute or invent the kinds of generalizations which seem most warranted by the author's analysis. By asserting those generalizations which *would* have
to be true if certain hypotheses *were* confirmed, one both
enlarges and limits the area of search for relevant empirical instances. Generalizations obtained in this manner
may be classified into categories representative of both
actual and hypothetical types of data. Insofar as actual
data are available within the scope of a written work, or
can be derived from converging research, some estimate of
the probable confirmation of a generalization can be made.
Insofar as hypothetical data may be inferred from analogi-
cal parallels in allied fields, reasonable conjectures about
the significance of a generalization may be drawn. When
these procedures are not feasible, one may select certain
key terms in both hypotheses and consequences and translate
them into the wider terms equivalent to the larger classes
of which each are assumed to be members. If these classes
point to the derivation of new categories of confirmable
data, one may accept the provisional advantage offered by
them.

POSTULATES

Interpretation: The theoretical postualtes underlying
the most notable analyses in sociology are rarely made explicit, and when they are they are seldom collected together
and set apart from other kinds of statements for all to
see and judge. Though it may be contended by some sociologists that the logical ideal of a complete set of postulates,
each of which is necessary and independent of the others,
is too remote to be taken seriously, the practical question
of choosing reasonable procedures for achieving the sem-
blance of a postulate model must be faced.

Strategy: Select a number of "workable" statements
and put them on trial as postulates by ordering them in
different patterns and placing them in close proximity with
statements which can be scaled in degrees of observability.
Perhaps the simplest way to begin is to coordinate trial
postulates by use of the conjunction *and* on the assumption
that each statement has equivalent logical power. This
assumption can then be modified for all statements which
subsume a distinguishing type of generalization. By arranging statements in a variety of patterns one should be able
to discover some kind of coherence in them. At least one
should be able to shift them about and couple them in such
a way as to give them the likeness of a postulate system.
Through piecemeal efforts — beginning with the nearly singular solution of each structural problem — one may be able
to uncover the most apparent contradictions and approach
the lower limits of the logical ideal of consistency. In
place of the formal requirement that statements are either
consistent or inconsistent, one may have to substitute the
psychological requirement of degrees of confidence, much as
the statistician does in judging the significance of sample
differences for estimating the probabilities of parameters.

By shortening the inferential gap between postulates
and observational sentences, standing in the relation of
evidence to them, the stage is set for the free play of
imaginative insight — the process of "illumination". Short
of well ordered rules of inference, the best the sociologist can hope for are statements of viable meaning abstract
enough to represent types of universal forms pervading a

wide variety of social events. Though phenomenally different, hypothetically similar things may be unified through
the postulates which serve to define their theoretical
meaning.

NOTES

1.   We dedicate this essay to von Bertalanffy in acknow-
      ledgement of his scientific cosmopolitanism. Trained
      in positivism (Vienna Circle), he sought its limita-
      tions and went on to explore the significance of causal,
      organismic, and historical connections in biological
      research. See especially his *Modern Theories of De-
      velopment,* Harper, 1962, and his article on "The Rela-
      tivity of Categories" in *Philosophy of Science* (Oct.,
      1955).

2.   So brief a statement cannot do justice to those who
      support this position. We have simplified their per-
      spective that it might serve as an opening from which
      the arguments of the present paper could be developed.

3.   It might be said that this essay examines the case for
      "subjective rigor" or "objective leniency" insofar
      as these concepts are meaningful vis-a-vis the extremes
      of either "objective rigor" or "subjective leniency".

4.   We do not deny that the formal terms and relations of
      axiomatic systems are often "interpreted" as having
      concrete empirical meanings, as applying to actual
      events. We merely raise the question of whether such
      terms and relations are ever purely formal, ever com-
      pletely detached from the "content" of experience.

5.   To list a few examples: (1) The assumption (generali-
      zation) that all A's are B's when inferred from the
      premise that all observed A's have been found to be
      B's. (2) The assumption that a hypothesis is true
      because one or more of the consequences deduced from
      it have been found to be true. (3) The assumption
      that one or more consequences are false because the
      hypothesis from which they were deduced has been found

to be false.   (4) The assumption that finite probabilities can be assigned to a scientific conclusion
(inference) without first estimating the temporal "influence" of every relevant condition.   (5) The assumption that certain psychological criteria, fecundity,
brevity, simplicity, convenience, elegance or symmetry,
are pertinent in the selection and formulation of hypotheses and postulate models.

6.   In addition to the limitations imposed by the meaning
of certain logical variables which delimit a range of
possible interpretations and are customarily defined
in the metalanguage of a system, one must, of course,
presuppose an acquaintance with the meaning of the
logical constants "not", "and", "or", "if", "then",
etc.

7.   We will not attempt to provide illustrations of these
strategies.   The fact is all too obvious that most accounts of a writer's techniques fail to describe the
kinds of improvisions resorted to in producing the
finished product.   In the absence of detailed records,
pertinent illustrations are hard to adduce.   Even so,
the strategies depicted are so broad in their implications that almost any selection of illustrations
would fall short of representing their full range of
application.

OSTENSIVE INSTANCES AND ENTITATIVITY IN LANGUAGE LEARNING

DONALD T. CAMPBELL

Dept. of Psychology, Northwestern University, Evanston, Illinois 60201, U.S.A.

This paper pays homage most directly to Ludwig von Bertalanffy's seminal "Essay on the Relativity of Categories" (1955). As in that analysis, there is here an effort to avoid the extremes of naive realism and of utter skepticism, to recognize that linguistic categories and science are indeed man-made conventions, and yet at the same time to acknowledge the ways in which they can also reflect an external reality. More generally, this essay is also Bertalanffyian in its underlying evolutionary grounding, and in its preoccupation with systems which come to fit, or adapt to, or map, or know, other systems.

Like the "Essay on the Relativity of Categories", this essay acknowledges the role of language in focussing attention on limited perspectives of reality. It extends a complementary emphasis of that essay in the direction of explicating how the structure of the physical world limits and edits the word meanings that can be taught and that can thus become parts of a working language. Without denying

* An earlier version of this paper was presented to a Seminar on Linguistics at the Center for Advanced Study in the Behavioral Sciences of February 15, 1966. The writer's year at the Center was supported by USPHS Special Fellowship 1-F3-MH-30, 416-01, 1965-66. Rommetveit (1968) briefly, and MacCormac (1971) in great detail, have reacted to the earlier version.

relativity in human categories of knowing, without denying the role of language in shaping our view of the world, this essay points to the complementary role of the world in shaping language.

While there is agreement with von Bertalanffy on these points, there is a tension between our views regarding the role of natural selection in evolution and its analogues in other processes of adaptation. Unlike von Bertalanffy in his recent writings, the present writer finds a blind variation and selective retention process an essential part of every increase in the fit of one system to another, in all forms of knowing as well as in all forms of adaptation such as organic evolution (Campbell, 1956; 1959; 1960; 1971). By recognizing vicarious and covert search processes, the crudity and distinctiveness of this austere perspective are reduced, and the difference perhaps made negligible. In what follows, readers, including the one we honor, are invited to substitute their own preferred mediational explanation at those few points of clash. In the history of biology and psychology, reductionists have tended to deny the obvious teleological facts of growth, regeneration, and purpose which they could not explain with the crude mechanisms then available. Von Uexküll is honored by von Bertalanffy, and Konrad Lorenz (and I), for the purposive and teleological facts which he correctly insisted upon, not for the vitalistic and teleological explanations he offered for them. Analogously, I honor von Bertalanffy for the truths of system, equifinality, emergent levels, wholes which shape parts, etc., which he insists any adequate biology and psychology must take account of. As a confirmed Weismannian-Darwinian, I must accept the theoretical challenge of explaining these facts in terms of the natural selection model.

Modern philosophies of science, including that of von Bertalanffy, reject the model of passive induction of Bacon and Mill. Inference, discovery, expansion of knowledge are instead seen as a much more active, indirect, and presumptive process. One of the major emphases of this paper is that language learning too, as another instance of fit, must partake of this profoundly presumptive indirection.

We cannot learn anything "directly", in its "own terms": all we can do is to choose among two or more of our own conceptions the one which fits better. The questions we ask of nature are expressed in our language, not nature's; the answers we get, or even the surprises, are left in our language of inquiry. The objectivity of science, or of blind maze learning, comes through the editing of our guesses. This is as true of the rat in the maze as it is for the scientist. That 100 rats end up with the same maze-running pattern testifies to the objectivity of the process, given the wide-ranging exploration of each rat. Starting from a heterogeneity of first run patterns, a final consensus is approached by the selection from within each rat's repertoire of those most appropriate. Experimentation in science has a similar function. Likewise, it can only choose among those theories that have been formulated.

Such is the recent revision of the passive inductivism which once dominated our model of science and of animal learning. In philosophy of science, Karl Popper (1959, 1963) has been particularly clear on this, although other developments have likewise presaged it, such as the concept of "posit" and the distinction between the context of discovery and the context of verification in Reichenbach (1938). Not only falsificationism, but also verificationism and the emphasis on mathematico-deductive theory point this way, in that we cannot verify an unformulated theory, as is essentially called for in Baconian induction. Toulmin (1953, 1961), Hanson (1958), and Kuhn (1962) are among others who have made the point, generally with a more subjectivist emphasis.

The revision is also present, if less clearly announced, within learning theory. Cognitive and Gestalt criticisms of pure frequency theories and emphasis on discontinuity represent moves in this direction. But from within behaviorism itself has come the clearest shift, to be found in the advocacy of all-or-none learning models in mathematical learning theory. The pure frequency behaviorisms might be parodied as "passive-omniscient", as assuming that the animal has a separate frequency cumulator for every stimulus feature in each momentary environment and each response possibility in his repertoire, cumulating reinforcement contingencies and response associations for each fragment of this manifold in a passive-inductive way. The one-trial-learning view more nearly describes an animal which notices only a few of the many stimulus features, and in a trial-and-error way tries out response attachments to these, moving from no association to total association in a single leap, making a "hypothesis" which may later be discarded for another. This model predicts better than the passive-omniscient model when they differ, although both predict a gradual learning curve in complex situations (Atkinson and Crothers, 1964).

Too long we made language learning on the part of the child unproblematic. Too long we assumed a passive, blotter-like absorption of words and meanings. Revisions of this orientation are currently being made, particularly in work on grammar. The purpose of the present paper is to make explicit such a revision for word meanings, with a resultant emphasis on the role of "objective" reality in their development and the limitations to ostensive definition. Linguistic relativism will be discussed in terms of the resulting orientation.

OSTENSIVE INSTANCE SETS

The concept of an ostensive definition partakes of the passive-absorptive model: the word is uttered, the mentor points, and the mentor's meaning of the word is trans-fused into the pupil's mind. But we now see that this cannot be done. All that can happen in one ostensive instance is that the word be associated with a meaning generated or evoked by the pupil. This meaning may or may not conform to that of the mentor. If it does not, then the pupil may occasionally misuse the term in the mentor's presence, or may hear the word used by others in ways that are incomprehensible to him, and thus come to recognize that his meaning is wrong, starting a trial-and-error process of successive conceptualizations, to be tested out in further ostensive instances. The learning of the meaning is thus one of selecting from among the learner's conceptualizations. At the ostensive level, all the tutor can do is choose among the tutee's meanings insofar as these manifest themselves

in word usage including ostensive questioning ("Show me a
_____".; "What is that?"). Of course, when words can
be defined in terms of other words, the situation is different — but that is only possible because of an established
ostensive vocabulary. What we have then in the learning of
word meanings is not an occasion of ostensive definition,
but rather an iterative sequence of ostensive instances.

For the early stages of language learning, at least,
no single ostensive instance is unequivocal, as many have
noted (e.g., Wittgenstein, 1953; Brown, 1958; Quine, 1960).
The word could stand for object color, act of pointing,
direction, specific object as proper noun, species, genus,
phylum, etc. Nor is any finite series apt to be entirely
unequivocal. For many words, such as in the personality
domain, the average person's set of ostensive instances
is too short to bring all users within a language community
to a common conceptualization. The heterogeneity or few-
ness of the alternative conceptualizations which a given
ostensive instance can elicit obviously conditions the degree of consensus developed. (This point will be further
developed.) The general validity of this orientation is
amply testified to by observations on the systematic nature
and even logical character of the errors in word usage by
children (e.g., Church, 1961).

YOU CAN'T TEACH A LANGUAGE BY TELEPHONE

Many expositions of language learning, particularly
those influenced by linguistic and cultural relativists,
emphasize the role of language in structuring the perception
of the environment. This is often presented so extremely
as to imply that no conceptualization or structuring of
the environment takes place prior to language learning. On
the contrary, structurings of the environment into entities
and conceptualizations are prerequisites to language learning. It is the child's already available entifications
of the physical environment which provide his trial meanings.

Language learning is sometimes portrayed as though it
takes place in a purely linguistic environment and is achieved prior to the child's perception and manipulation of

his object world. It is sometimes portrayed as though one
could teach a language by telephone. Instead, this is impossible. In addition to mentor and pupil there must be
present the third party of objects talked about. This is
necessary to provide the ostensive instances that instigate
and edit the pupil's trial and error of meanings.

Quine (1969) has recently made this point. "The word
refers, in the paradigm case, to some visible object. The
learner has now not only to learn the word phonetically,
but also has to see the object; and in addition to this,
in order to capture the relevance of the object to the word,
he has to see that the speaker also sees the object"
(1969, p. 28). "A child learns his first words and sentences by hearing and using them in the presence of appropriate
stimuli. These must be external stimuli, for they must
act both on the child and on the speaker from whom he is
learning" (1969, p. 81). A word on the more general relation of Quine's orientation to the one here advocated is
needed. Quine in many passages espouses a passive-omniscient version of conditioning theroy of the kind rejected
here. But this is not essential to his general views. He
would regard a "trial and error of meanings" such as advocated here as a mentalism to be rejected. Yet he comes to
this point of view in but slightly different words. "Such
is the quandary over 'gavagai'; where one 'gavagai' leaves
off and another begins... The only difference is how you
slice it. And how to slice it is what ostension or simple
conditioning, however persistently repeated, cannot teach."
(Quine, 1969, pp. 31-32) But an active trial-and-error of
conceptual slicings, and a series of ostensive instances,
can often lead to the learner's making the appropriate discovery, albeit without entailment. "Insofar as the native
sentences and the thus associated English ones seem to match
up in respect of appropriate occasions of use, the linguist
feels confirmed in these hypotheses of translation — what I
call *analytic hypotheses*". (Quine, 1969, p. 33) Not only
the linguist, but also the child, must learn word meanings,
as well as grammar, by a trial-and-error of such analytic
hypotheses, and with no guarantees of certainty or perfection. Such a trial and error of slicings and hypotheses
will, in spite of Quine, partake of a mentalism. No one
utterance, or response to an utterance, will specify such a

slicing hypothesis. Quine should give up saying "meaning
is a property of behavior" (Quine, 1969, p. 27) and say
instead, "behavior is a symptom of meaning, albeit an equivocal symptom for any finite sample of behavior.".

ENTITATIVITY AND WORD MEANING

The number of potential conceptualizations in any given
ostensive instance is nearly infinite. The number of
ostensive instances in any word-learning sequence is finite
and small*. Each conceptualization tends to be adhered to,
minor discrepancies do not invalidate it. Such being the
case, it is not surprising that for some words most native
speakers have idiosyncratic conceptualizations. More surprising is it that any words can become useful common coinage, i.e., that language is possible. More surprising too
is it that for that intermediate stage of language learning
during which the child actively seeks out the names of things,
a correct meaning is frequently achieved in a single ostensive instance. Such achievement of common meanings for
words is made possible by common tendencies of conceptualization which are related in turn to "real" features of the
environment.

Learning and perception have evolved in a world in
which they were useful — such utility implies stability
within diversity, reidentifiability of sites or entities
such that the reidentification provides improved predictive
accuracy as to outcomes. An important aspect of that stability was built up around entifiable aspects of the

----

* Relevant here is Bruner, Goodenough, and Austin's (1956)
distinctions among problem-solving strategies and memory
requirements. If all prior instances are retained and used
to invalidate any inconsistent conceptualization, then the
number of conceptualizations consistent with the whole set
of ostensive instances might be very small. But this requires that the pupil have noted all possible conceptualization bases, or a return to an objectionable part of the
Baconian model. Undoubtedly there is memory for more features of recent ostensive instances than the ones rejected
or the ones newly posited, but this is far from eliminating
in practice all conceptualizations logically excluded by the
total set of ostensive instances already experienced.

environment, a useful sameness of particulates irrespective
of environmental context, distance viewed, etc. Whether of
seed grains or insects or flowers or rabbits or wolves or
conspecifics, such entifiable aspects of the environment
were among the very most usefully diagnosed aspects for
both predator and prey, carnivore and herbivore. Inevitably
the equipment of perception and learning evolved to optimize
the diagnosis of entifiable aspects, even at the cost of
loss of efficiency for the unique stationary aspects, were
this necessary. For animals such as protoman, where manipulation and tool using are important, the focus on entity
diagnosis must become still more dominant, and must be one
of the factors favoring overlapping visual fields for the
right and left eye at the expense of a narrowed visual scope.
Human vision shows a strong bias in the direction of perceiving three-dimensional objects rather than two-dimension-
al surfaces, in the direction of perceiving objects as turning rather than as deforming, and in general of maximizing
the stable thinghood of the perceived world (Johansson, 1965).
This strong predilection toward the diagnosis of "real"
"entities" must be expected to dominate the first trial-and-
error of conceptualizations both in proto-human language
development and in childhood language learning efforts.
This shared base of expectancies and conceptualizations
(within the domain of entities as referents) makes possible
an almost perfect achievement of intersubjective equivalence
(Quine, 1959, pp. 34, 114-139).

The role of entitativity in guiding the boundaries of
conceptualizations and words can be seen through examples
of the kinds of designations that do not become words.
Take words about fragments of trees, for example: A word
for a tree-fragment including leaf may or may not be present
in a given language. If it is present, it will divide leaf
from tree at that point where leaves typically separate
from tree-limbs. There won't be a word for the extreme
three centimeters of leaf, nor a word for the whole leaf
plus the adjacent three centimeters of branch. If there
is a tree division in this region, the language will follow
Plato's advice and "cut nature at her joints". Likewise,
there will be no word for a teacup plus the immediately
adjacent thickness of saucer. Cupandsaucer may be designated by one word without division, or subdivided into two,

and if the latter, subdivision will take place at that dis-
juncture commonly used in washing dishes.

Language evolves in a speech community. We can imagine
there being a continual mutation of new conceptualizations
and namings. Only a few of these become part of the common
coinage. The selection pressure of the learner's guesses
reduces word meaning to those discriminanda identifiable by
others in the language community. Words unattached to de-
pendable discriminanda are lost from the start. Words utilizing subtle discriminanda where adjacent striking discriminanda go undesignated are rapidly vulgarized so that through
the multiple confusions of common usage, the meaning drifts
to the striking discriminanda.

Thus, through providing the referents utilized in the
editing of trial meanings, and through providing the basis
for the conspicuous and popular hypotheses as to word meanings, the common objects of the "real", non-linguistic
world to some extent edit any language. For the basic vocabulary that makes language learnable, language is limited
to the talkable-about. A common preverbal evolutionary
background strongly biases human beings in the direction of
finding "stable" "entities" highly talkable-about.

DEGREES OF ENTITATIVITY

We have already utilized considerations of degrees of
entitativity: the cup and saucer fragment had less entitativity than cup alone. We would readily agree that cupandsaucer has some entitativity greater than the cup and saucer-
fragment, less than cup alone, greater than cupandstewpan
were this juncture to be designated as a noun.

But so preponderant is entitativity in our thinking
about possible nouns that even our hypothetical examples of
words that would never become common coinage were very high
on entitativity in any absolute sense. Both leafplus and
cupplus designated spatially contiguous entity parts of
considerable stability. Were we to have tried to use as an
illustration a noun designating a specific congeries of
non-adjacent, dissimilar sensory or substance fragments,

the effort would have been so implausible, tedious, and incomprehensible as to have failed our illustrative purpose. Nor would it have been the kind of word meaning communicable by any set of ostensive instances.

Degrees of entitativity are potentially quantifiable (Campbell, 1958). At one extreme would be a ball of adamant — unbreakable, immutable, homogeneous as to substance and color. A crumbling clod of dirt and pebbles has less entitativity. The Gestalt psychologists in diagnosing the clues for perception of thinghood under conditions of very weak thinghood, specified these symptoms of entitativity: common fate, similarity, proximity, good figure, and boundary completeness. Imagine that we could tag the parts of potential entities and environs, and compute between each pair of particles a common-fate coefficient representing colocation as on spatial coordinates. Clusters of high mutual common-fate coefficients are our entities. The boundaries are the cracks across which the common fate coefficients are low, where "things" can be pulled apart, discretely manipulate

Once degrees of entitativity are recognized, with boundaries of greater or less sharpness, it can be noted that there are many more such boundaries than any one language uses. Nonetheless, the referent for any word that can become a part of the working language must embody one of these "objective", even if fuzzy, boundaries.

DEGRESS OF ENTITATIVITY AND ORDER OF LANGUAGE LEARNING IN CHILDHOOD

The early language learning of the child will occur from within those words whose referents have greatest entitativity. Words of lesser entitativity will be learned later on with greater difficulty, or by linguistic definition rather than by ostensive instance sets.

Consider the immediate environs of the child: "chair" and "bed" have greater entitativity than "floor" or "wall". "Chair" has greater entitativity than "table" if chairs are moved around more (note that the identical multiples for chair may create special effects over the one-of-a-kind

items). If one controlled for the order of learning expected from frequency of parental use in the environs of the
child, one would probably find that the more entitative
the referent the more readily it entered the child's vocabulary. Such an empirical study seems worth undertaking.

ENTITATIVITY IN VERBS

We have been talking so far solely about nouns referring to physical objects. The present discussion will not
get far beyond this, but some comment on verbs seems in
order. Were behavior to flow in a continuous stream, any
nominal unitizing would be both arbitrary and uncommunic-
able. According to our analysis, without reidentifiable
boundaries to the behavior being referred to, shared linguistic reference is not possible. Modern behaviorisms,
especially as infused with cybernetics, describe the consistency of consistent response tendencies in terms of effects achieved rather than muscles used (Campbell, 1956,
1963). A language of servosystem control settings, of feedback comparators, or of purposes, provides designata which
can be identified with the older analyses of intentions.
Such analysis provides "real" nodes of behavioral organization available for the ostensive instance sets. The prelinguistic survival-relevance of manipulating and acting
upon objects provides an entifying foundation for verbs
analogous to the evolutionary basis argued for nouns.

Nonetheless, it seems likely that verbs are lower in
entitativity than nouns, and that other parts of speech
are still lower, if indeed the concept has any relevance to
them at all.

ENTITATIVITY AND AMBIGUITY WITHIN THE LINGUISTIC COMMUNITY

Our orientation provides a basis for an *a priori* classification of terms as to the ambiguity of meanings, the
degree of idiosyncracy of usage within a single speech community. The two most relevant factors are entitativity and
frequency of usage. The more entitative the referent, the
less ambiguity. The more frequent the word usage, that is,

the longer the typical sets of ostensive instances, the
less the ambiguity.

ENTITATIVITY AND WORD-FOR-WORD TRANSLATION

As has been occasionally noted by comparative lingu-
ists, it is only in linguistic fields of high entitativity
(and of common importance) that we can expect word-for-word
synonyms in differing languages. The selection of the basic
100 words of glotto-chronology shows it. These terms all
turn out to have high entitativity of referents, as well as
high frequency, in comparison with any random sample of
words from the languages in question.

Esaïas Tegner in 1874 made the point: "each language
divides this field in its own way". "According to Tegner
it is only in semantic domains in which nature itself has
drawn the borderlines that the fields of various languages
correspond exactly". (Öhman, 1953, p. 130; Mounin, 1963,
p. 198)

LINGUISTIC RELATIVISM AND LINGUISTIC SOLIPSISM

In extreme form, linguistic relativism argues that
the language of childhood determines the perceptual and
thought categories of adult life, and that each language
does this uniquely. There results a kind of cultural-
linguistic solipsism in which one can never come to see
the world as it is seen by a person from a differing original language group, and that one can never truly speak
his language. The present analysis of language learning
supports a moderate version of this view, but not the extreme.

The cultural-linguistic solipsism is blunted by the
recognition of a parallel individual solipsism within the
language community. For words of low entitativity, it is
doubtful if any two speakers speak "the same" language.
The problem of the foreigner is but an intensified version
of this internal problem.

More importantly, the designata and discriminanda requisite for the establishment of any common meaning within a language community are "physical" or "public" and are available for the stranger as for the child. However, for the stranger the ostensive instance sets are shorter, and the predilections for the "erroneous" conceptualizations corresponding to those of his original language are much stronger. Particularly where the referents have both low entitativity and partial overlap, the stranger is apt to persist in systematic misunderstandings. Just as in pronunciation, his first phonemic system produces a bias which leads him to persist in speaking with a foreign accent, so too his first language category system may provide a "semantic accent" which persists unnoticed through years of second language usage. Note that this is more to be expected for almost identical semantic field cleavages than for clearly different ones.

IN SUMMARY

In accordance with von Bertalanffy's *perspectivism*, it is recognized that each language represents at best a limited aspect of reality, and different languages different aspects. To this extent at least, language can be said to shape the world view of its speakers. In a complementary fashion, for the primary ostensive vocabulary upon which language learning is based, the nature of the world shapes language, editing and setting limits on the word meanings that can be taught. Learning word meanings, like adapting and knowing, is unavoidably a very indirect process, and succeeds to the extent it does only through a trial-and-error of hypotheses as to word meanings. Ostension is equivocal. Extended series of ostensive instances weed out some wrong hypotheses. A prelinguistic perceptual predilection for diagnosing highly entitative things provides a person-to-person similarity in hypotheses which makes the process workable in the acquisition of the primary ostensive vocabulary.

REFERENCES

ATKINSON, R.C. and CROTHERS, E.J.,"A Comparison of Paired-Associate Learning Models Having Different Acquisition and Retention Axioms", *J. Math. Psychol.*, 285-312, 1964.

von BERTALANFFY, L., "An Essay on the Relativity of Categories", *Philosophy of Science*, *22*, 243-263, 1955.

BROWN, R., *Words and Things*. Glencoe, Ill: The Free Press, 1958.

BRUNER, J.S., GOODNOW, J.J. and AUSTIN, G.A., *A Study of Thinking*. New York: Wiley, 1956.

CAMPBELL, D.T., "Perception as Substitute Trial and Error", *Psychological Review*. *63*, 330-342, 1956.

CAMPBELL, D.T., "Common Fate, Similarity, and Other Indices of the Status of Aggragates of Persons as Social Entities", *Behavioral Science*. *3*, 14-25, 1958.

CAMPBELL, D.T., "Methodological Suggestions from a Comparative Psychology of Knowledge Processes", *Inquiry*, *2*, 152-182, 1959.

CAMPBELL, D.T., "Blind Variation and Selective Retention in Creative Thought as in Other Knowledge Processes", *Psychological Review*. *67*, 6, 380-400, 1960.

CAMPBELL, D.T., "Social attitudes and other acquired behavioral dispositions". In S. Koch (ed.), *Psychology: a study of a science*, *6*, *Investigations of man as socius*. New York: McGraw Hill, 94-172, 1963.

CAMPBELL, D.T., "Evolutionary Epistemology", *The Philosophy of Karl R. Popper*. (In: *The Library of Living Philosophers* series) SCHILPP, P.A., (ed.), La Salle, Illinois: The Open Court Publishing Co., 1973 (in press).

CHURCH, J. *Language and the Discovery of Reality*. New York: Random House, 1961.

HANSON, N.R., *Patterns of Discovery*. London: Cambridge, 1958.

JOHANSSON, G., "The Perception of Motion and Changing Form", *Scandinavian Journal of Psychology*. *5*, 181-208, 1964.

KUHN, T., *The Structure of Scientific Revolutions*. Chicago: Univ. Chicago Press, 1962.

MAC CORMAC, E.R., "Ostensive Instances in Language Learning", *Foundations of Language*. 1971, 7, 199-210.

MARCUS, H., *Die Fundamente der Wirklichkeit als Regulatoren der Sprache*. Bonn: H. Bouvier, 1960.

MOUNIN, Georges, *Les problèms théoriques de la traduction*. Paris: Gallimard, 1963.

ÖHMAN, S., "Theories of Linguistic Field", *Word*. *9*, 123-134, 1953.

POPPER, K., *The Logic of Scientific Discovery*. New York: Basic Books, 1959.

POPPER, K., *Conjectures and Refutations*. New York: Basic Books, 1963.

QUINE, W.V., *Word and Object*. New York: Wiley, 1960.

QUINE, W.V., *Ontological Relativity and Other Essays*. New York: Columbia University Press, 1969.

REICHENBACH, H., *Experience and Prediction*. Chicago: University of Chicago Press, 1938.

ROMMETVEIT, R., *Words, Meanings and Messages*. New York: Academic Press, 1968.

TOULMIN, S.E., *The Philosophy of Science*. London: Hutchinsons, 1953.

TOULMIN, S.E., *Foresight and Understanding: A Inquiry into the Aims of Science*. Bloomington, Indiana: Indiana University Press, 1961.

WITTGENSTEIN, L., *Philosophical Investigations*. New York: Macmillan, 1953.

MAN AS AN ECONOMIC SUBSYSTEM

JOHN C. MALONEY

Northwestern University, Medill School of Journalism, Evanston, Illinois 60201, U.S.A.

Man is an open system, linked in countless ways to his environment. The biochemical raw materials which form his tissues are ingested, inhaled, or absorbed from the environment. The information which forms his hopes, fears, outlooks and plans for action are likewise drawn from the environment in the form of light wave patterns, sound wave patterns, and olfactory, taste and tactile stimuli. These environmental inputs, added to the biogenetic information carried forward from conception and birth, account for all that man is or can become.

In describing the pathway which man has trod enroute to his present biological state Bertalanffy wrote as follows:

> Life spirals laboriously upward to higher and ever higher levels, paying for every step. It develops from the unicellular to the multicellular, and puts death into the world at the same time. It passes into levels of higher differentiation and centralization, and pays for this by the loss of regulability after disturbances. It invents a highly developed nervous system and therewith pain. It adds to the primeval parts of this nervous system a brain which allows consciousness that by means of a world of symbols grants foresight and control of the future; at the same time it is compelled to add anxiety about the future unknown to brutes; finally, it will perhaps have to pay for this development with self-destruction [1].

Human ecologists warn us that man may already be well on his way to self-destruction. They suggest that the human animal, with its new found science and technology, has failed to keep its peace with the biological environment. But much of the ecological jargon of the day seems a bit too simplistic. Modern man is not the primitive hunter, fisherman or farmer that his ancestors were. Individual human beings, acting simply as biological organisms, have relatively little effect on the environment.

To be sure, man must have a concern for the purity of the air he breathes and the water he drinks. He must not waste essential mineral supplies and it is utter folly to despoil the beauty of nature's landscape. But between man and the biosphere we find a mechanized, commercialized, bureaucratized *technostructure* (to use Galbraith's term) [2], or a *noosphere* of human thought processes and artifacts (to use Teilhard de Chardin's term)[3]. A series of agricultural, industrial, educational and cybernetic revolutions has enmeshed individual man in a supraorganismic matrix of overlapping input-output linkages. These form a noospheric web of life as essential to man's survival as the biospheric web of life most commonly discussed by ecologists.

Telegraph, telephone, television, radio and communication satellite provide the nerve fibers which link the computerized ganglia of this supraorganism. Railroads, trucklines, airlines and shipping facilities provide the arteries of distribution. Factories, warehouses and stores provide the organs of production and consumption and the whole is entwined by governmental regulatory bureaucracy. If man is to keep peace with the biological environment he must do so by making proper adjustments within the noospheric environment or technostructure.

Individual and institutional patterns of thinking, acting and deciding must be changed before significant changes can be made in man's biological interactions with nature. We must realize, moreover, that the economic, political, psychological and sociological subsystems of the noosphere or technostructure have become as vulnerable to sudden, violent perturbations as the hydrospheric, atmospheric, lithospheric subsystems of nature.

It is an axiom of ecology that one can never change only one thing. The sudden, ill-conceived effort to redress one imbalance simply leads to other imbalances. In either the biosphere or the noosphere the complex interrelationships among subsystems account for a ponderous resistance to sudden change.

Consider, for example, these few facts about a single portion of the U.S. technostructure, the automotive-transportation complex:

1.   In 1969 alone more than 56,000 Americans died in automobile accidents; countless thousands of others were injured, many maimed for life. (While deaths due to all other accidents are falling in the U.S. auto fatality rates are rising.)

2.   The auto contributes 60% to 70% of all U.S. air pollution and hundreds of thousands of diplapidated autos left abandoned on the streets and highways make up a major portion of the nation's solid waste pollution problem.

Steps are being taken to alleviate these problems but if they are successful and a continued expansion of automobile use is encouraged other problems will grow worse. These include the following:

1.   The auto is the direct source of tension-producing traffic jams and a major source of crowding, urban sprawl and inefficient land use. (Because of space required between fast moving autos and the low person-per-vehicle ratio, 15 to 30 times as much land surface is required to move people in and around cities by automobiles as by bus or rail facilities.)

2.   Auto traffic control places a tremendous burden on the resources and manpower of police organizations and accounts for countless confrontations between police and the citizenry which would not otherwise occur. (Auto theft accounts for 60% of all arrests for serious crimes among Americans under 18 years of age.)

3. While domestic petroleum supplies are dwindling rapidly in the U.S. (despite pollution causing oil drilling in off-shore waters and in the fragile ecology of Alaska) the U.S. auto population has doubled and gasoline consuming auto horsepower has quadrupled in less than twenty years.

4. Though rail travel is safer and causes less crowding, pollution, and fuel consumption on a passenger mile basis, the government approves huge funds for more highway construction while interurban and intraurban rail systems are neglected and allowed to totter on the verge of bankruptcy. (The gasoline tax trust fund, reserved solely for highway construction, is used to pave over more land for more autos to burn more gasoline to provide more tax money for the trust fund, and the trend goes on uninterrupted.)

What accounts for this particular example of runaway positive feedback? Why do we see self-sustaining, geometric growth rates of this sort spiraling out of control? Why do Americans demand more automobiles (and more of everything that depletes raw material supplies and pollutes the environment)?

The answer is to be found in the simple fact that people are so immersed in the noosphere or technostructure that they take it completely for granted. We may note, with regard to the automobile growth syndrome, that hundreds of thousands of Americans earn their livelihoods building, selling or servicing automobiles. Many thousands of others build the highways or provide the concrete, steel, petroleum products, and accessories upon which auto transportation depends.

Well over three out of four U.S. families own an auto and an increasing number of families, already over one-fourth, own more than one. The auto has thus become so close to the heart of the American way of life that it is hard for Americans to imagine being without autos or even being less dependent upon them. Even those young Americans so caught up in the ecological movement, those most eager to rush to the defense of Mother Nature, are resentful of any implication that their ownership or use of the automobile could or should be regulated in any way. This is not too surprising.

In addition to the self-sustaining effects of the mere existence of millions of cars, millions of miles of streets
and highways already built for auto use and the multimillion
dollar gasoline trust fund, such demands are legitimized and
encouraged by mammoth mass persuasion efforts.

In 1969, a bad year for the auto industry when advertising expenditures were lower than in previous years, automobile advertisers in the U.S. spent well over $500,000,000
to advertise their products. Seven oil companies spent
$135,000,000 and four tire manufacturers spent $137,000,000
in traceable advertising expenditures on largely auto related advertising. (*Advertising Age* estimates, August 24,
1970). By comparison, advertising in support of rail passenger service was **negligible**; railroads were seeking approval for further discontinuance of passenger service.

Such figures reflect nothing of the influence which
these same industries exert through their elaborate public
relations groups which produce films and press releases
supportive of "favorable" driver habits. They indicate
nothing of the influence of vast automobile financing and
insurance industries. They indicate nothing of the automobile and highway construction lobbying efforts in Washington and in all state capitals. (Any urban planner in the
U.S. can testify to the effectiveness of the automobile-
highway lobbies in opposing the construction of public mass
transit systems.)

Revising the "Revised Sequence" of Economic Forces

This, then, is but one of many examples we might consider of what Galbraith calls the "revised sequence" of
economic forces at work "as instruction passes not alone
from the sovereign consumer to the producer; it proceeds
also from the producer to the consumer in accord with the
needs of the technostructure" [4].

Boulding calls for a new science of *Eiconics* to change
the symbol meanings and planning assumptions of society —
so that "anti-entropic", organized, patterned forces of
coordinated human understanding may develop fast enough to
offset the entropic (running down or decaying) trends in
the human ecosystem [5].

Platt calls for new mechanisms of persuasion so that long-sighted realists and men of good will can persuade selfish (i.e., short-sighted) men to fall in with society's predicted long range needs [6].

Dubos calls for new communication forms to help the citizen recognize, evaluate and anticipate the social consequences of science and technology and thus avoid the tyranny of the expert. He agrees with many who insist that this is a must for the survival of democratic societies and the survival of their institutions [7].

Von Bertalanffy called for a "new natural philosophy" so that we may have "new glasses through which people look at the world and themselves" [8] and so that science "may be more than an accumulation of facts and technological exploitation of knowledge in the service of the Establishment" [9].

Businessmen [10], government officials [11], and university professors of various disciplines [12] now echo these sentiments. Upon sending the first annual report of the Council on Environemntal Quality to the U.S. Congress (August, 1970) President Nixon similarly declared: "It is also vital that our entire society develop a new understanding and a new awareness of man's relation to his environment. This will require the development and teaching of environmental concepts at every point in the educational process."

Surveys by myself and others reflect a general commitment to such public education by the mass media managers of the nation [13]. But we can not assume that clarion calls for these new forms of mass persuasion will provide an automatic antidote for mankind's problems. Indeed, if such programs are handled with the same haste and reckless abandon as the sciences and technologies which have produced the ecological crisis, the cure could be worse than the disease.

It may be well, then, to consider what past studies of mass communication have to offer a new "Ecological Eiconics". As a part of such a brief review I shall try to suggest what the general system theory orientation might eventually contribute to this new science. (In various working papers I have heretofore used the terms *communifunction theory* and *eccommunication* rather than *general systems theory* and *eiconics*. These terms were meant to describe a functional communication theory for ecological communication. However, out of deference to von Bertalanffy and Boulding's priorities and eminences in these related fields, I am persuaded to use their terminology rather than my own.)

TOWARD AN ECOLOGICAL EICONICS

Thousands of studies of mass persuasion have produced more fragmentary knowledge of mass persuasion processes than I can possibly summarize here. In the U.S. these are typically to be found in such journals as the *Journal of Advertising Research,* the *Journal of Marketing Research,* the *Journal of Marketing, Public Opinion Quarterly,* the *Journal of Social Psychology,* and in countless books on propaganda, advertising, and the psychology and sociology of information diffusion and attitude change.

At the risk of oversimplification, I would offer the following as the most important generalizations from these studies:

1. *Public opinion or attitude change on significant issues comes about gradually.*

People are gradually moved, by mass persuasion efforts, through stages of awareness, interest or curiosity, knowledge-seeking and a mental evaluation of the issues in question. It is only in the latter stages of the persuasion process that people are induced to adopt the publicized product, candidate, or outlook as their own.

For each issue there are likely to be some people who will (because of their interests, occupations of life styles) try or adopt new ideas earlier than others. Some of these will be opinion leaders or "influentials" who are particularly inclined to pick up information from the mass media and pass it along to others by word-of-mouth or example [14].

2. *The mass media seldom work alone to produce significant public opinion change* [15]

No single information source has a monopoly on the attention of the public or even a single segment of the public. Many competing campaigns of mass persuasion thus tend to cancel each other's effects. Moveover, the public's response to new ideas is strongly mediated by social norms and values, and certain economic or technical circumstances make the adoption of some new ideas almost inevitable while the adoption of others may be almost impossible.

3. *People inevitably "see things in the light of past experience".*

Even the most open-minded man reacts to mass communication and all other forms of information in highly selective ways. None of us can understand or believe all that is offered for our enlightenment. We selectively expose ourselves to programs, shows, magazines, newspapers, books, conversations and other information sources in terms of habits, interests and biases which we have already developed at any given time. Once exposed to information in a general way, we selectively attend to or focus upon those messages or facets of the information which are of greatest current interest. Once we attend to such information we selectively perceive ("decode" or understand) it in terms of our wishes, expectations or previously developed capacities for understanding. By the same token, message "belief" is a product of competing tendencies to either distort message meanings to make them conform to existing outlooks or to change present outlooks to accommodate the message.

In this give and take competition between new message meanings and old points of view there are definite limits to the amount of new learning or attitude change which can take place at any one time. Some psychologists refer to this as the "latitude of acceptance".

*4.   Mass persuasion effects are virtually always tentative
      or temporary.*

   Some attitudes and beliefs are more enduring than others, depending upon the extent to which they have been
reinforced by social supports and use and depending upon
the individual's relative isolation or insulation from competing attitudes and beliefs. (Attitudes, like muscles,
are strengthened by repeated use as bases for decision or
action.) However, learning and attitude change are continuous processes for people regularly exposed to uncensored
mass media or a variety of social contacts. Psychologically
speaking, reasonably alert people are always the products
of both their past and very recent or present environments.

*5.   Successful mass persuasion must take account of both the
      informational (cognitive) and emotional (affective) facets
      of public opinion* [16]

   Emotional appeals are often more conducive to public
opinion change than purely rational appeals and much successful persuasion is based on the principle of encouraging
people to see the things they already know in slightly new
contexts. (Most advertising in the U.S. would fall in the
category of "reminder advertising".)

   Even so, emotional appeals or messages devoid of sub-
stantive information will often produce "boomerang" effects
when the communicator is dealing with important issues and
an intelligent or critical audience.

*6.   Finally, communications research has shown that effec-
      tive mass persuasion almost always requires continuous two-
      way communication.*

   As suggested above, the meaning of communicated messages is not inherent in the message itself; it derives,
instead, from an *interaction* between the message and the
existing state of mind of the audience. (Good salesmen and
good diplomats are good listeners as well as persuasive
speakers; they continuously adapt their arguments to the
specific needs, interests, and questions or resistances of
their customers.)

Such two-way communication, or audience-to-persuader feedback, is as important for the educator or persuader using mass media channels as it is in face-to-face communication and a major task of any scientific eiconics is to establish adequate channels for such feedback.

These generalizations characterize hundreds of theories and investigations of anthropologists, sociologists, social psychologists, semantacists, learning theorists and applied researchers in propaganda, advertising, political campaigning, and other fields as well. They confirm an impression that there is nothing sure or simple about the operation of mass persuasion. As is the case with other applications of modern technology, mass persuasion can often produce totally unexpected side-effects.

Given this growing base of fragmentary knowledge there is a challenge for the general system theorists in social science ranks to find the "unifying principles running 'vertically' through the universe of individual sciences" [17]. The mass persuaders in corporate and academic marketing circles have, in fact, been greatly influenced by systems theory during the past decade. In 1965 Professor William Lazer, in an address to the American Marketing Association, described this influence as follows:

> Systems thinking has influenced marketing thought. It has led to the widely hailed marketing management philosophy and marketing concept, both of which emphasize the coordination, the integration and the linkage of marketing ingredients to achieve total system action. It has encouraged the acceptance of functionalism and its emphasis on adjustment, survival and growth. And it has stimulated the study of various aspects of market input-output and open and closed systems [18].

The first task of a systems theory of consumer behavior is a description of the principle features of many different applicable theories. This calls for a surrogate model (or, to use von Bertalanffy's term, a *logical homology*) which can stand in for the language and functions of these disparate views. Fig. 1 provides a preliminary formulation

of such a model resulting from my own systems theorizing in
this area.

The Surrogate Model

In Fig. 1 we see the counterparts of:

- the *stimulus - integration - response* paradigm of
the behavioral sciences;

- the *input - internal processing - output* paradigm of
the communications engineering sciences; and

- the *independent variable - intervening variable -
dependent variable* paradigm of the experimental tradition.

The dashed arrows in Fig. 1 represent the "noises"
of the communication engineer's signal-to-noise ratio; the
background stimuli of the psychologist's and psychophysi-
cist's figure-ground contrast concept; and the exogenous
and extraneous variables of the experimental viewpoint.
This feature of the diagram acknowledges the fact that the
consuming public is exposed to tremendous varieties of information from many sources, and that all compete for the
consumer's attention.

The Crux of the Model: Memory

The information processing or memory functions represented between the stimulus input and the response output
account for a three-fold role: (1) *decoding* (noting and
understanding); (2) *internal storage* (remembering); and
(3) *encoding* (deciding or acting).

The full implications of these memory functions demand
some elaboration since commonplace definitions of the term
memory often confuse the meaning of what is implied here.
The concept of memory, as it is used here is as broad and
at the same time a bit more explicit than Boulding's concept of image [19]. The memory concept includes any information pattern or functional negentropic state of an organism or organization so long as that negentropic state is in
any way self-regulating and selectively responsive to information entering the system. The memory structure results
from any prior information inputs, the organized residues

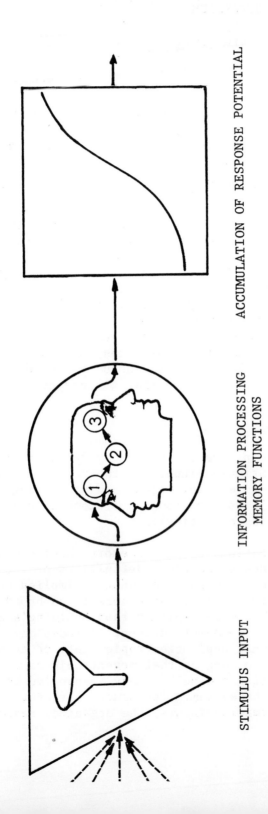

STIMULUS INPUT

INFORMATION PROCESSING
MEMORY FUNCTIONS

ACCUMULATION OF RESPONSE POTENTIAL

Fig. 1   Preliminary view of surrogate model

of which mediate the processing or storage functions of
subsequent inputs. That is to say that the term memory, as
I use it here, refers to all that the noting-understanding-
remembering-deciding mind of man has become as a result of
its psychological (experiential) and biological history.

In this broad sense the memory structure of a whole
consumer population or culture is comprised of the social
norms or public opinions which arise from the total history
of a product, a candidate or an issue in the market-place
or social milieu. (For example, public opinions concerning
technological progress, the free enterprise system, birth
control and abortion are among the *memories* which may be
changed by, and *memories* which will determine responses to,
much of the mass persuasion of the ecological movement.)

From the psychologist's point of view the memory structure of Fig. 1 includes all that is implied by a host of
concepts: the apperceptive mass; the attitude structure
or cognition structure; the hypothetical "engram". From the
neurophysiologist's point of view the memory structure is
embodied in a neural network. This network is shaped by
intracellular and intercellular electrochemical states which
have been conditioned by prior experience and are thus ready,
at any given moment, to facilitate or inhibit a subsequent
pattern of neural response.

Strictly speaking, the memory functions of Fig. 1 must
also be seen to include "genetic memories" such as those in
RNA molecule forms carried forward from the moment of conception as well as residues of ingested, inhaled, injected
or absorbed pharmacological agents which may mediate information decoding or response processes.

The memory functions of Fig. 1, like Boulding's *images*,
are both past and future oriented since they (1) include
internally stored effects of past experiences, and (2) provide expectations about or potential predispositions toward
future inputs or experiences.

As we elaborate the surrogate model (Fig. 2) we must
distinguish between *active memory* and *inactive memory*.
Active memories are the now-in-use memories which guide

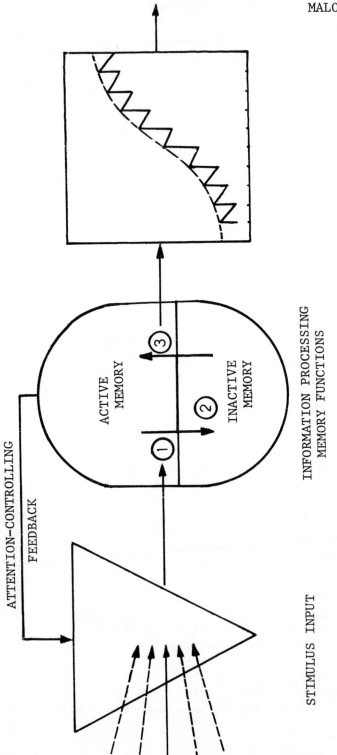

Fig. 2. Elaborated view of surrogate model

understanding-deciding (or decoding-encoding) processes
going on at any one time. These are like the computational
programs of the computer, the reverberating neural traces
within a central nervous system, or the Freudian ego. Inactive memories, on the other hand, account for stored-away-
but-available-for-use information within the system. These
are the memories which provide the templates or standards
of comparison in the "reality testing" or "trial-and-check"
phases of cognition, recognition, apperception or thought
processes as things "are seen in the light of past experience." These would include the stored-in-file memories
of the computer, the latent post-synaptic potentials of the
nervous system or the Freudian id. To paraphrase William
James, these are the memories which are "brought out of
cold storage at the necessary times to do service in the
world" [20, 21].

Since persuasive messages are "believable" only to the
extent that they are compatible with pre-existing patterns
of what people know or think they know about an idea or
issue the study of inactive memory states is of great importance to any new science of Eiconics.

It is the inactive memory of Fig. 2 which defines the
"latitude of acceptance" for persuasive messages. Messages
which are sufficiently compatible with prior learning to be
assimilated within the memory structure are accepted or
"believed". Messages which exceed the latitude of acceptance tend instead to be *contrasted* with the pattern of
things known and are thus rejected through a variety of
message distortion processes.

In the late 1950's academic researchers such as Osgood
and Suci were developing the use of attitude scaling and
factor analytic procedures for studying semantic or meaning
relationships in "semantic space" (i.e., the memory structure) [22]. During the 1960's advertising researchers,
myself included, used these and other psychometric and multivariate analysis techniques to study those portions of
the memory most relevant to a given issue or mass persuasion process. (Though most of this work remains unpublished
it is covered in various commercial research reports and in
mimeographed presentations to advertising or marketing trade

groups. I am presently engaged in a study of the interrelationships among awareness or nonawareness of a variety of
social problems including pollution problems, a variety of
attitudes toward such problems, and the way in which all of
these fit into a variety of general value systems. So far
this effort seems to promise the same kind of help for mass
persuasion in "social marketing" as it provided for earlier
commercial marketing efforts [23].)

Memory Balance and Feedback

Memory structures, like the internal states of all
open systems, strive for internal balance without quite
achieving it. As von Bertalanffy has observed, "Living
structures are not in being, but in becoming. They are
an expression of the ceaseless stream of energy, passing
through the organism and at the same time forming it." [24]

Psychologist Floyd Allport drew upon von Bertalanffy's
insights to describe the systems theory implications for
human perception. He distinguished between true equilibrium,
which does not occur within dynamic organisms, and the maintenance of a dynamic *steady state* condition within structures [25]. The psychological literature otherwise offers
many examples of theories of a similar sort [26, 27, 28,
29, 30].

Most of these theories suggest the operation of some
sort of attention-controlling feedback which regulates the
input screening mechanism of the organism (see Fig. 2).
They use such terms as "surprisal", "tension", "dissonance",
"imbalance", "anastasis", "strain toward symmetry", "need
for closure", or other terms which imply an unfinished business of one sort or another within the memory structure
as the basis for cognitive attempts to achieve a steady
state. The separate theories likewise have their own
terms for the feedback itself: "interest", "curiosity",
"reaction sensitivity", "facilitating neural set", and so
on. (In communications research of recent years a variety
of measures of autonomic arousal — galvanic skin response,
pupillary dilation, and others — have been used as a basis
for inferring the presence of such attention-directing feedback [31].)

Contrary to certain older views of learning or attitude change processes (but in accord with information diffusion theory of gradual change mentioned earlier) this continuously changing, steady state view of memory structures renounces any expectation of sudden conversion from one state to another. It may be enough that a given message simply stimulates curiosity about an issue, for example, thus setting the audience in readiness for further information.

As I have elsewhere indicated, only the most trivial of cognitions, attitudes, intentions, or habits are changed completely by a single message [32, 33]. I submit that most evidences of "sudden conversion" result from the use of artificially discrete information response measures.

In atheoretical terms we might say that certain sorts of experience create a need or openness to further experience of a related kind. Or, questions bring answers which raise new questions.

Many systems and cybernetic theories depict feedbacks as a portion of the system output which feeds back as system input. By comparison the feedback depicted in Fig. 2 may seem a bit strange. The Fig. 2 feedback is seen to arise from the internal state of the system, rather than from outputs, and is seen to function as a regulator of inputs, rather than as an input itself. This may seem heretical, something reminiscent of the Maxwell's Demon of thermodynamic folklore.

Indeed, the Maxwell's Demon analogy does apply particularly to the many instances in which the steady state of the system is restored or maintained by within-the-system, memory-memory "balancing acts". (The feedback process is not confined to the regulation of input-memory balancing regulation.)

We may, for example, observe certain internal trial-and-check processes underlying autistic thinking (e.g., imagination, day dreaming, or contemplation) which provide the basis for humor, insight and much creativity [34]. Such within-the-system feedbacks no doubt have much to do with what learning theorists have called *latent learning* and what communications psychologists have called sleeper effect, terms which describe message perception or information decoding effects which are greater at some time after receipt of a message than they are immediately after receipt of the message.

As I see them, those within-the-system feedbacks operate on a level-to-level basis between hierarchic levels of the memory structure and relate to what I call "pullthrough" phenomena which I shall touch upon later. For those interested in such matters, I should also say that the "demonic" implications of these views do not really defy conservation of energy laws as most Maxwell's Demon hypotheses normally do. I am talking here about semiclosed, not fully closed, systems in which the Demon (i.e., information screening or organizing feedback) derives its energy from metabolic processes which impinge upon the memory structure.

Two Forms of Attention-Controlling Feedback

In the same way that most theories of human response to information imply some sort of distinction between active and inactive memory forms, as suggested in Fig. 2, we must distinguish between two general forms of feedback which call for a more sophisticated model than is shown there. I refer to a distinction which I describe as *continue-cycle feedback* vs. *renew-cycle feedback*.

Continue-cycle feedback is that which sustains an already in progress decoding cycle. Like the "orientation response" of Pavlovian theory it involves a heightened sensitivity for stimuli already in the perceptual field. In the individual it manifests itself in terms of autonomic arousal or the physiological state of the organisms exteroceptors. (The organism "picks up its ears", dilates its pupils, or turns its head to "lock onto" the source of interesting information.) It is continue-cycle feedback, for example, which holds a reader's attention to a page, once a headline, illustration or phrase on the page is found to be of interest.

Renew-cycle feedback, on the other hand, is characterized by a latent curiosity, interest or readiness to respond.

Instead of compelling attention to more of the same stimulus
pattern(s) already present it predisposes the organism to
attend to stimuli of a given general class — at some later
time, if and when they become available. The advertising
research literature abounds with examples of this more pervasive, relatively more time delayed feedback. (For example, magazine readers who have recently bought an automobile
are more likely than the average reader to note and read a
major portion of most automobile advertisements.)

This distinction, like most distinctions to be found
in general system theory, involves relativities rather than
absolutes. The renew-cycle feedbacks are *relatively* more
pervasive and *relatively* longer lived than continue-cycle
feedbacks. (The psychologist may be reminded of the relativities of motivation theorists' distinctions between such
concepts as desires, motives, needs or drive states [35].)

This same distinction might otherwise be described in
terms of "higher order" vs. "lower order" operations of the
surrogate model of Fig. 2, or in terms of system vs. subsystem feedbacks. But before we turn attention explicitly
to such matters let us consider the implications of such
hierarchies for a final feature of the surrogate model
itself: the jolt-and-fade pattern in the accumulation of
response potential.

Jolt-and-Fade of Response Potentials

Many of the output-input linkages between components
within complex systems are chain linked. That is to say
that outputs from one component become inputs for the next
component in the system on an immediate, now or never basis.
(Examples: the ear drum, ossicles and cochlea linkages in
the ear; or tuner, amplifier, and speaker linkages of a
radio.) But many other output-input linkages in complex
systems are cascade linked so that outputs from one subsystem may be stored or accumulated for a time before they
are passed on or put to service as inputs for a larger or
higher order system. Linkages of the latter sort are of
special interest in a broad range of human information processing phenomena.

Thus, a series of sound waves of greater or lesser frequency are summed in the brain to produce a hearing sensation of higher or lower pitch. Sensations are summed to produce symbol recognitions. Word, picture, sound or other sensory symbols are summed to produce tentative message meanings. And over a much longer time period messages, such as advertisements, editorials, or television commercials may be summed to produce the kind of attitude or public opinion change intended by originators of an entire persuasive campaign. The outputs or tentative effects at each level are stored as a special memory form until they are put to use at the next higher level as inputs.

Now, what happens to these lower order memories or tentative effects of lower level information processing while they are in storage, prior to the time that they can be used for higher order processes? For certain mechanical or electro-mechanical devices there is no problem; they are fairly imperishable. For example, magnetic core memory in a computer will not lose its electro-static charge spontaneously at a rate that is troublesome for the computer operator, and one such charge is all that is needed to clearly record stored data on that core.

But the forms of human memory which involve cascade linkages *are* perishable; the memory will fade or be forgotten if it goes too long without being reinforced or put to use as a higher order input. The curve of forgetting seems, moreover, to follow a characteristic shape for most or perhaps all of these memory forms. This is a decelerating, negative curve, like the characteristic half-life curve of radioactive decay or the diminishing pressure curve of gas pressure within a semi-closed container [36].

This jolt-and-fade or learn-and-forget (negentropic-entropic) characteristic of most human memory forms has great practical importance for behavioral scientists, especially those interested in programs of mass persuasion. For example, the communications researcher should pay close attention to the matter of time lapse between stimulus input and the measure of response output. Equally effective television commercials, as a case in point, have been shown to produce markedly different magnitudes of response (i.e., message recall or apparent message comprehension) if

responses are measured at different time intervals (e.g.,
12, 24 or 48 hours) after exposure.

For the same reason large-sample surveys of campaign
effects should be made at intervals of at least monthly
frequency. Reliance upon semi-annual or quarterly surveys,
a common practice in marketing research, often produces
grossly misleading findings. When intensified levels of
competing information are reaching the audience weekly or
even more frequent measures of campaign effects may be required. (Those who watched the public opinion polls in the
closing weeks of the Nixon-Humphrey political campaign of
1968 will recall how rapidly Humphrey was closing the public opinion gap between himself and Nixon during that time.)
Thus each response level has its own time frame for decoding processes and memory decay rates. (Lower order subsystem processes are generally faster, i.e., have shorter
time frames, than the higher order processes to which they
contribute [37].)

In many cases the response potential produced by a
single input will fall far below a threshold level required
for input at the next higher level. Repeated inputs may be
required to accumulate an above-threshold level of response
potential. For such accumulation of response to occur the
successive inputs must be of a certain minimal frequency.
That is to say, each successive input must come soon enough
after the prior input to build upon the memory residue of
that prior input. If the input-to-input time lapse is so
great that the memory produced by earlier inputs is nearly
all decayed (or crowded out by competing inputs) before
subsequent inputs are introduced into the system, each input starts from essentially the same base. For the communications researcher, the jolt-and-fade manner of response
potential accumulation (Fig. 2) has marked implications for
studying the effects of information repetition. Such effects must be studied in terms of the timing or frequency,
as well as the mere number, of inputs for the audience or
organism. It would be almost as fallacious to compare the
effects of six television message exposures during a week
long interval with the effects of six such exposures over
a month long interval as it would be to equate two sound
signal frequencies if one were 3,000 cycles per minute and
another were 3,000 cycles per second [38].

More to the point perhaps are the implications of the principles suggested here for mass persuaders themselves. The manner in which response potential ebbs and flows is a crucial consideration for the political campaigner who wants his persuasive effects to "peak" just before election day, or the advertiser who wants consumer awareness of his product to reach a maximum level during a pre-Christmas buying season. Any eiconic science which ignores these issues of message timing will do so at the cost of losing much of its efficiency.

INFORMATION RESPONSE HIERARCHIES

One might infer from Fig. 2 that man is nothing more than a materialistically or physically determined animal whose every response or output is shaped solely by informational inputs whose memories are all entrained in physiological neural traces. But this is only a partial picture of the complexities of human response to information. For a fuller understanding we must look to a hierarchy of input, memory, and response forms. Thus, while Fig. 3 presents matters in an oversimplified way, it is an important step beyond Figs. 1 and 2 in that it depicts the crucial concept of response hierarchy.

Hierarchies of Form, Function and Information "Chunks"

First of all, it should be understood that as the surrogate model of Figs. 1 and 2 is replicated at each level of this hierarchy the higher levels transcend or encompass lower levels. Public opinions transcend and embrace the attitude structures of those who compose a particular public; attitudes are aggregates of affect-charged cognitions; and so on. But there is an integrity of subsystem functioning at each level.

Von Bertalanffy spoke of the evolutionary emergence of morphological forms in just such terms: "Thus every level — electron, atom, molecule, coloidal unit, cell, tissue, organ, multicellular system organism, and society of organisms — acquires an emergent evolution new characteristics that surpass those of the subordinate system [39]."

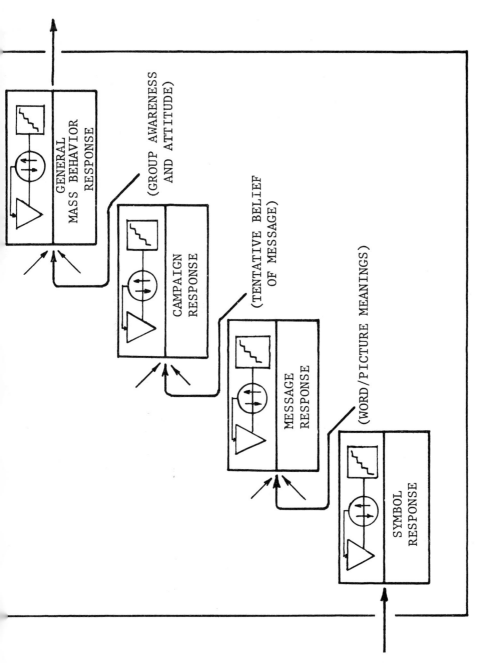

Fig. 3.   The communication response hierarchy

We must understand, moreover, that all such hierarchies
imply *several* parallel hierarchies of form, function, and
a variety of micro-to-macro definitions of input and response. More accurately stated: an organism does not represent one hierarchy that can be described thoroughly in morphological terms. Rather it is a system of hierarchies
that are interwoven and overlapping in many ways, and that
may or may not correspond to levels of the morphological
hierarchy [40].

It would be futile to argue that a purely physical
structure or physical force interpretation is adequate for
our understnading. All memory forms do in fact have an
electro-chemical or neuro-physiological root. But the memory forms which are most pervasive and influential in shaping the behavioral world also have psychological, sociological, anthropological, and historic forms. And each of
these forms has its own reality.

The architect of public opinion or consumer demand
faces the same challenge as the architect of buildings or
cities. He must find the ways in which parts make wholes;
the ways in which subsystems fit together to form larger,
organic, dynamic systems; the ways in which theories applicable to one level of complexity can be made to mesh with
theories applicable to other levels of complexity.

Higher-to-Lower-Order "Pull-Through"

In searching for the key to these part-whole, system-
subsystem, relationships the eiconicist must understand
that causality operates from the top down, as well as from
the bottom up in our hierarchy of response levels. It is
not as though so many pounds or gallons of information of
a given sort pumped into the human nervous system at the
bottom of this hierarchy will lead inevitably to certain
public actions flowing from the topmost level of response.

Given specific impetus for decision or action, man
may decide or act on the basis of very little information.
Many candidates, public issues and products succeed in the
marketplace on little more than what some advertisers call
a "friendly familiarity" — a vague impression that this
seems to be a satisfactory candidate, issue or product to

support to buy. Standing in the voting booth, required to
make a now-or-never decision man acts; confronted with a
special inducement to buy "at this amazing low price — for
a limited time only", he often buys whether or not he is
well informed. This is to say that the transcendent influence of a decision-precipitating circumstance often over-
comes a paucity of information [41]. Lacking any such impetus, man may defer action on even the most thorough or
persuasive information already stored away in his lower
order memory structures. (How many thousands of people
are vaguely resolved to go on a diet or stop smoking cigar-
ettes "one of these days"?)

At the same time, higher order processes regulate the
threshold levels for the filtering of lower order information forms. Renew-cycle feedbacks (the "Maxwell's Demons"
which link each level of the memory structure with lower
levels of the memory structure) make the human organism
something more than a passive transducer of light and sound
waves which become sensations, which become cognitions,
which become attitudes, which become public actions.

In discussing such properties of living systems, Michael
Polanyi speaks in terms of the higher order levels of integration providing the "boundary conditions" which harness
the principles of lower level phenomena in the service of
higher level phenomena. "The higher comprehends the workings of the lower and thus forms the meanings of the lower."
[42]

For the eiconicist this means that while higher order
plans, needs or interests unique to the individual, group
or society are formed and nurtured by things seen and heard
— it is also true that these higher order memory forms determine the relevance, understandability and attention value
of information *still to be* seen and heard. We might say
that certain kinds of public opinions, once they are under
construction, give employment to certain kinds of individual attitudes. These, in turn, create a need for certain
kinds of cognitions or sensations. These, in turn, give
rise to a hypersensitivity for certain kinds of information
as that lowest order "Maxwell's Demon" of the peripheral
nervous system scans the environment for to-be-processed

and to-be-ignored information. (I normally refer to this as the selective, higher-to-lower order "pull-through" of information.)

This all too brief discussion of the principle of information pull-through may indicate the importance of this principle for both researchers and practitioners in the field of mass persuasion. One must expect any mass information campaign to be much more effective for those segments of the audience already "in the market" for the kind of information offered. If an idea's time has not yet come, the mass communicator may have to link the idea to other information which *is* already of interest. Advertisers refer to this as "borrowing attention", a subterfuge which often leads to problems I have discussed elsewhere [43].

The Number-of-Levels Problem

The four levels of the Fig. 3 hierarchy are presented rather arbitrarily. Charles Sanders Peirce, near the turn of the century, hypothesized three response levels for his *semiotic* theory: the *syntactic, semantic* and *pragmatic* levels. Later writers followed his example with three-fold discussions of *technical, semantic* and *effectiveness* levels or *biological, personal* and *social* levels. Still others have developed theoretical structures with four, six, eight or more levels.

The implications of the topmost level in any such hierarchy are also set rather arbitrarily depending upon the scope of phenomena for which the theory is meant to relate. The "general mass behavior response" at the topmost level of Fig. 3 might, for example, relate to the ecological behaviors of a community, a nation, or the entire world [44, 45, 46].

There are, to be sure, certain requirements for level definition or specification within a hierarchy. But level definition is largely a matter of convenience to suit the planning processes and measurement procedures at hand. The four levels of Fig. 3 are chosen to conform with four levels of measurement common to advanced advertising research practices already in use for many product classes marketed in the United States [47]. This general scheme

suggests a prototypical persuasive communications information system based on such a hierarchy. While employed by
a Chicago advertising agency I gradually fitted together
the pieces of such a system several years ago much along
the lines suggested by Figure 4 [48].

In the external loops of this overall system the mass
communicator provides a flow of communicator-to-audience
information through a number of channels and receives a
continuous pattern of feedbacks from the mass communications
audience. Some of these feedbacks are naturally occurring
inferential feedbacks (e.g., product sales data, voting
results) from the topmost, mass behavioral levels of response. These are suggested by solid line feedback in Fig.
4. Other external loop feedbacks are *synthetic feedbacks*
evoked by special research procedures at lower levels of
audience response (the dashed line feedbacks of Fig. 4).

The *synthetic* feedbacks are the crux of the system's
evaluation, planning or control functions. They provide
a series of subsystem measures (like the radio technician's
separate tests of tuner, amplifier, or speaker system) to
diagnose any "malfunctions" in the eiconic system.

In such an information system the topmost levels of
feedback come from a monitoring of the ultimate public behaviors which the mass persuasion effort seeks to induce.
In marketing circles these are commonly provided by monthly
or bimonthly retail sales audits such as are conducted in
the United States and a number of other countries by the
A.C. Nielsen Company. For social marketers or those engaged
in "ecological eiconics" these feedbacks might be provided
by a variety of social indicators (e.g., health or crime
statistics, pollution indices, etc., which are now being
gathered or could be gathered by governmental agencies).
The U.S. literature on "social systems accounting" or "social indicators" has proliferated in recent years to describe many possibilities for such feedback.

For lower levels of the response hierarchy the system
requires a refinement of already existing measures which
satisfy the implications of the surrogate model and otherwise draw upon theories and methods of behavioral science
disciplines most relevant to the level in question.

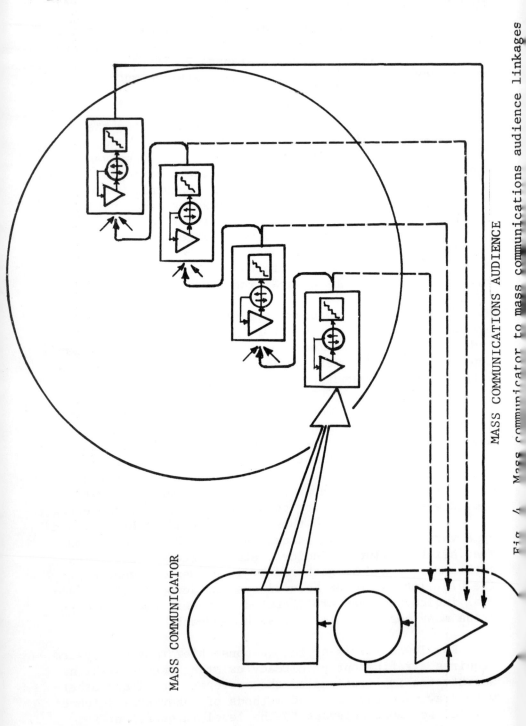

MASS COMMUNICATOR

MASS COMMUNICATIONS AUDIENCE

Fig. 4. Mass communicator to mass communications audience linkages

Campaign (second level) response measures, as a case in point, should use survey research procedures comparable to those used by sociologists or political scientists to forecast election results. Surveys of awareness, attitude and involvement should be conducted among members of the campaign audience at least monthly. Such measures should be correlated with the higher order behavioral response measures to provide a basis for survey data projections of mass behavioral response. These should also be related to higher order "noises in the system" (extraneous variables which facilitate or inhibit the specific mass behaviors in question) in order to achieve a maximal predictive efficiency for survey data. Given the availability of appropriate data a number of multivariate statistical techniques can be used for this purpose.

In my own past research I have obtained message level (third level) feedbacks through the use of telephone interview procedures used with audiences known to have been exposed to the separate messages (e.g., television commercials or programs) in question. Following the implications of the surrogate model as it applies to psychological learning and attitude change theory, these focus upon message content recall, comprehension of intended message meanings and potential changes in attitude toward the publicized product, candidate or issue [49]. Symbol level (fourth or bottom level in Fig. 4) feedbacks (i.e., responses to partially or crudely produced messages) may be measured by laboratory studies.

Within a system of this sort the response measures at each level of the hierarchy automatically provide intermediate criteria against which to validate the immediately lower level measures. This is a matter of considerable importance for certain of these feedbacks, that is the lower level feedback measures, can hardly be expected to be highly predictive of the mass behaviors (top level outputs) sought by the mass persuader. But if symbol level responses predict message level responses; if these predict campaign level responses; and if these, in turn, predict top level mass behavioral responses, one need not worry about the validity of symbol level measures for predicting mass behaviors.

In the sort of system described here the theory and measurement procedures are simultaneously refined by developmental research which strives to maximize level-to-level prediction one step at a time but always with the intent of building a coherent overall information system. The developmental research required to build such a system requires considerable time and resources. A system which functions well for a conventional marketing problem might well require somewhat different feedback measures than one required for a social marketing problem, or an ecological rather than a commercial eiconics. But enough is already known to assure us that such systems can be developed.

Once the validities of the feedback measures are generally established, and once the research team determines how responses measured at one level interact with various mediating factors at the next higher level, the deviations from expected or predicted performance at each level can be highly instructive. It is the ability to identify such surprises (the residual error variance in the system) which permits continuous refinement of the system with use. The importance of this feature of information systems operation, as contrasted with conventional experimental approaches to the study of communication effects, can hardly be overemphasized.

In the experimental or piecemeal approach to communication research, the extraneous variables are pushed aside with the assumption that they are among the "other things" which will operate on an "all other things being equal" basis. But this *ceteris paribus* assumption is seldom valid and the "other things" often have a greater effect on higher level responses than the mass communicator's own efforts. (In discussing information systems for guiding governmental rather than marketing control decisions, Bertram M. Gross points out that the systems approach prevents the *ceteris paribus* from becoming the *ceteris incognitis* [50].)

CONCLUSIONS

As we view the visible spectrum of prehuman and human evolution we see a pattern of growing complexity with the human nervous system and brain becoming the focal point for the negentropic ordering of convergent energies. Sight and sound patterns in the world have been processed and reprocessed, ordered and reordered in the brain and sent back out into the environment in newly complex spoken, painted, printed, modeled, broadcast, or otherwise reconstructed forms to be perceived, ordered and reordered by other men.

As von Bertalanffy pointed out in the quotation at the outset of this paper, the evolutionary emergence of the human brain gave man a consciousness which "by means of a world of symbols, grants foresight and control of the future". In a symbol-rich matrix of man to man input-output linkages, man has imagined himself in control of his own further evolution. But there is obviously something amiss, something which may require man to pay for his evolutionary progress with his own self-destruction.

There is an imbalance in human knowledge which has victimized individual man and subordinated his interests to those of the collectivized, commercialized, bureaucratized technostructure. Man's collective knowledge of physical and biological sciences, commerce and warfare far outrun his knowledge of the laws of human society [51].

As a result, the human society is using up the resources required to keep it in business. We are poisoning the waters and atmosphere required to sustain life. We are paving over the earth and covering it with people, noises, confusion and tension. Food rots in storage in one part of the world, even as the ratio of food supply to population dwindles and millions face starvation in other parts of the world.

My investigations of public understanding of these most basic facets of the ecological crisis suggest that many of the better informed segments of the public are growing pessimistic about the chances for solving these problems. People who see pollution in terms of the soot and stench spewing forth from a neighborhood smoke stack assume that pollution can be stopped. But cosmopolites who see the ecological crisis in terms of the generation-to-generation

degradation of worldwide ecological balances are beginning
to despair. For the latter group there is danger that the
old advertiser's paradigm of successive stages of Awareness-
Interest-Desire-Action will become Awareness-Interest-
Confusion-Apathy.

Those interested in an applied ecological eiconics as
an antidote for these problems face a number of dilemmas.
If they were able to mount a major public education campaign with all of the knowledge and power that a scientific
eiconics might provide, and if they were able to do this
without prior approval of the public, we would be confronted with the prospect of an Orwellian mind-manipulation
machinery of potentially frightening implications. On the
other hand, since the lack of consensus which gives rise to
a need for public information also gives rise to conflict
over support for such efforts, the task is left to fragmented and competing special interest groups.

Each of these fragmented groups, operating with limited
funds and little eiconic sophistication, does its utmost to
attract mass media coverage of their cause. Their principle
assumption is often that "the public must be alerted to
the danger", at least the danger as they see it, whether
or not they have workable answers to the problems which
they publicize. (One often hears the argument that the
major competition for environment - saving funds and efforts
comes from demands for military spending, and since the
public has been sold on vast military spending through fear
they must be sold on vast ecological efforts through fear
[52].)

Thus, the ecological action group, or the expert spokes-
man for such groups, often resorts to extreme statements or
bizarre events to attract attention. Boorstein refers to
these as *pseudoevents,* the success of which is measured in
terms of how widely they are reported. The question of
whether the event is valid is less important than whether
it is newsworthy, and pseudo-events, as Boorstein observes,
spawn other pseudo-events in geometric progression [53].

Surveys which I have conducted at the Northwestern
University Urban Journalism Center suggest that the media

themselves contribute to a peculiar muchrooming of coverage
of events or pseudoevents of this sort. When sensational
news of the ecological crisis hits the headlines, less
prestigious news media follow the lead of the more prestigious media. People begin to become aware of such news,
whether or not they understand it, simply because they see
so much about it in the newspapers or hear so much about it
on radio or television. Media managers then report that
they give the issues in question major coverage because
people seem to be interested in them — and the bandwagon is
off and rolling.

In the U.S. these trends have given rise to the popularity of the "doomsday artist", the expert whose public pronouncements are issued more for publicity effects than for
the valid light they may shed on a problem. One such authority, writing recently in *Science* magazine, called for
more and more propaganda, insisting that ecologists should
use every contact they might have with the mass media to
"maximize symbolic disassurance"; that is, one presumes,
to frighten people as much as possible about the dangers
facing mankind.

What these propagandists fail to understand is this:
when they decide to redirect the flow of human understanding
by altering the patterns of information available to the
public they are tampering with the human ecosystem no less
than the business managers responsible for smokestacks or
sewer drains which pollute the air or water.

The human nervous system is as vulnerable to noospheric
(informational) pollution as the respiratory system or other
vital systems are vulnerable to biospheric pollution. Con-
taminated television signals and newsprint symbols can
potentially affect the chances for ultimate survival as
much or more than the pollution or purity levels of the
oceans, lakes, rivers, or the gaseous environment hovering
over our cities.

In a poetic mood, while discussing his concept of the
noosphere, Teilhard de Chardin once said that "God made the
world round so that love and understanding can flow around
it." Unfortunately, the same communications environment

which can envelop man in a noosphere of love and understanding can surround him with an environment of suspicion or paralyzing fear and confusion.

There is reason to believe that problems of the ecological crisis will yield to a broad enough, deep enough, sufficiently long range sort of *radical-rational* planning — planning that is dedicated to rationality rather than fear-arousing publicity seeking, planning that is radical enough to question any and all institutions which may need reform, radical enough (in the literal sense of the word) to go to the very root of the whole complex of interrelated population-pollution-energy supply crises at all levels — local, national and worldwide.

But, so far, we only know that our present economic, social and political institutions have failed to protect the human environment and seem incapable of making sufficiently radical adjustments to forestall much graver difficulties. We have hardly begun to examine the full implications of the whole ecological crisis. The present problems have obviously resulted from the unexpected consequences of technologies too hastily applied in the name of progress.

How ironic it would be if mass communication programs, seemingly developed as antidotes for earlier technologies, should also be applied too hastily and with too little planning to produce a pollution far worse than the environmental problems they sought to cure.

We should take heart in the knowledge that pattern and order have so far been man's friend in the ontogenetic history of the human race. In the evolution of the earth, in the evolution of living forms upon the earth, and in the evolution of man as a special living form, negentropy has so far kept ahead of entropy. The continued organization of human knowledge should still be more than a match for the tendencies toward disorganization in the environment.

An Ecological Theology

If it is true, as theologian Paul Tillich suggested, that the courage to be comes from the God which appears when God has disappeared in darkness and doubt, we may be overdue for a new vision of God.

Historian Lynn White, Jr. is not alone in insisting that the historical roots of our ecological crisis lie in an implicit faith in perpetual material progress, a faith which was unknown to Greco-Roman antiquity or to the Orient [54]. This faith, according to White and others, has its basis in Judaeo-Christian teleology which has vulgarized the divinity and led to a view of God as a business partner. (The fact that Marxists share this faith merely illustrates, says White, what can be shown on many other grounds: that Marxism, like Islam, is a Judaeo-Christian heresy.)

But current ecological concerns, and our growing awareness of the inadequacy of science and technology alone for coping with the ecological crisis, suggest that the prescientific Christian view of nature as a symbolic system through which God speaks to men may not be too far off the mark.

As a child I said this prayer to the Trinity:

Glory be to the Father,
And to the Son,
And to the Holy Spirit,
As it was in the beginning, is now, and ever shall
be, world without end.

The notion may repel the "enlightened" or "liberated" agnostic or atheist; it may revolt the conservative Christian (It has never been *endorsed* by a theologian or ecclesiastical authority), but I find a courage to be in a slight modification of that old prayer. I think of it as the ecologist's prayer:

Glory be to the Negentropic Order of
Physical Forces throughout the Universe;
Glory be to the Best of Men, the evolved and
evolving offspring of those forces;
Glory be to the Growth of Understanding among men
which may henceforth govern the world.
As it is now and ever can be, to the topmost
spiral of man's growth.

It seems more obvious today than ever before that man must commit himself to negentropy; he must commit himself to

brotherhood and the nurture of the least selfish, most ad-
mirable (divine?) human instincts; he must commit himself
to a cooperative understanding of his fellow man and an
understanding of the negentropic-ecological roots from which
he has emerged.

If ecologists fail to understand this — if they think
that they can lead mankind to its own salvation by teaching
it to hate or fear its own most highly developed cultures
(either communist or capitalist cultures) they will surely
fail. But if they can encourage an optimistic respect for
the human intellect's ability to harmonize with the rest of
nature they will surely succeed. We need not find the final
solution to every ecological problem within a generation.
We need only to keep man on that evolutionary path to which
von Bertalanffy has referred — spiraling laboriously (and
let us hope, joyfully) upward to higher and ever higher
levels.

REFERENCES AND NOTES

1.   von BERTALANFFY, Ludwig, *Problems of Life — An Evalua-
      tion of Modern Biological and Scientific Thought*. New
      York: Harper Torchbook 108, 1961.

2.   GALBRAITH, John Kenneth, *The New Industrial State*. New
      York: Signet Books paperback edition, 1968.

3.   Much of what is offered in this paper is profoundly
      influenced by the writings of Teilhard de Chardin,
      for whom the concept of *noosphere* was crucial. The
      idea is treated importantly in virtually all of his
      books. Within the present context the following re-
      ference seems especially germane: CHARDIN, Pierre
      Teilhard de, *Man's Place in Nature*. New York: Harper
      & Row (English translation,) 79-95, 1966, especially
      Chapter IV on "The Formation of the Noosphere".

4.   GALBRAITH, John Kenneth, *Op. Cit.*,   323.

5. BOULDING, Kenneth E., *The Image: Knowledge in Life and Society*. Ann Arbor; University of Michigan Press, 1956. (See especially chapters entitled, "How Manifest is Destiny?" and "Eiconics; A New Science".)

6. PLATT, John R., *The Step to Man*. New York: Wiley, 101, 1966.

7. DUBOS, Rene, *Reason Awake* New York: Columbia University Press, 206-208, 1970

8. von BERTALANFFY, Ludwig, *Robots, Men and Minds*, New York: George Braziller, 52, 1967.

9. Ibid., 114-115

10. See, for example, "Industry Starts the Big Cleanup" by John DAVENPORT and "What Business Thinks", a report of a survey of corporate executives of the largest American corporations, by DIAMOND, Robert S., *Fortune*, 114 ff., and 118 ff., respectively, 1970.

11. WALTERS, Robert, "FCC Calls for Pollution Issue Shows", *The Washington Evening Star*. A-9, August 18, 1970.

12. For example, KOTLER,Philip and ZALTMAN, Gerald, *Social Marketing: An Approach to Planned Change*, mimeographed, Graduate School of Management, Northwestern University, Evanston, Illinois.

13. For example, MALONEY, John C. and SLOVONSKY, Lynn, "The Pollution Issue: A Survey of Editorial Judgements", in *The Politics of Ecosuicide*, ROOS, Leslie J., Jr. (ed.), New York: Holt, Rhinehart and Winston, 64-78. 1971.

14. See, for example, KATZ, E. and LAZARSFELD, P.F., *Personal Influence: The Part Played by People in the Flow of Mass Communication*. New York: The Free Press, 1955; LIONBERGER, H.F., *The Adoption of New Ideas and Practices*. Ames, Iowa: Iowa State University Press, 1960; or ROGERS, E.M., *Diffusion of Innovations*. New York: Free Press, 1962.

15. KLAPPER, Joseph T., *The Effects of Mass Communication*, Glencoe, Illinois: The Free Press, 6, 1960.

16. For an excellent overview of research findings bearing on this and related issues of persuasive message rhetoric, see KARLINS, M. and ABELSON, H.I., *Persuasion: How Opinions and Attitudes are Changed*. New York: Springer, 2nd edition, 1970.

17. The systems theory definition implied here is from von BERTALANFFY, Ludwig, "General Systems Theory", in *General Systems* von BERTALANFFY, L. and RAPOPORT, A. (eds.), *1*, 2, 1956.

18. LAZER, William, "Development of Marketing as a Discipline," *Marketing and Economic Development*, ed. BENNETT, Peter D., Chicago: American Marketing Association, 794, Fall 1965.

19. See BOULDING, Kenneth E., *The Image: Knowledge in Life and Society*, Ann Arbor: The University of Michigan Press ,1956.

20. Although modern systems theory in the biological sciences reveals that the distinction is more apparent than real, a further difference between active and inactive memories might be this: *active memories are patterned energy states* involved in information decoding or encoding, while *inactive memories are latent energy states or patterned states of matter* recorded, for example, in the synaptic states of the nervous system.

21. From the psychologist's vantage point the interaction between active and inactive memory forms in the "reality testing" or "trial-and-check" phases of decode-encode processes has been studied in some detail. One of the leaders in such research has been Milton Rokeach of Michigan State University whose studies reflect a difference between inhibiting response sets characterized by *rigidity* and *dogmatism*. He has developed cognitive-style scales to measure each tendency. In advertisers' terms we might say that the dogmatic

thinker is disinclined to pay any attention to the
advertising message. The rigid thinker, on the other
hand, might pay attention but be especially inclined,
because of a predeliction in favor of Product A, to
sharpen, level or otherwise distort the message of
Product B. (ROKEACH, Milton, *The Open and Closed Mind*.
New York: Basic Books, Inc., 182-195, 1960.)

22. see, for example OSGOOD, C.E., SUCI, G.J. and TANNEN-
BAUM, P.H., *The Measurement of Meaning*. Urbana, Illinois:
University of Illinois Press, 1957.

23. For commercial marketing problems I have found a "mode
of evaluation framework" helpful for studying the rational, sensory reward, social reward and ego-supportive
motives or attitudes which may underlie purchase
decisions for a given product or service. (MALONEY,
John, C., "Marketing Decisions and Attitude Research"
in *Effective Marketing Coordination*. BAKER, George L.
(ed.), Chicago: American Marketing Association, 595-
618, 1961). In a number of unpublished studies these
dimensions have been supported by factor analyses. My
present work in "social marketing" focuses more explicitly on a framework with a "social circumference"
dimension (concern about self, concern about family,
concern about neighborhood, region or nation, and concern about all mankind) and a "content" dimension (concern with health, concern with environmental aesthetics,
concern with survival, economic concern, etc.). It
is hoped that these investigations will reveal much of
value for helping the mass persuaders in "social marketing" to know what to say and how to say it believ-
ably. At this point I can only say that these latter
efforts show promise.

24. von BERTALANFFY, Ludwig, *Problems of Life - An
Evaluation of Modern Biological and Scientific Thought*.
New York: Harper and Brothers, First Harper Torch-
book Edition, 181, 1961.

25. ALLPORT, F.H., *Theories of Perception and the Concept of Structure*. New York: John Wiley and Sons, 467-530, especially 471, 1955.

26. HEIDER, F., "Attitudes and Cognitive Organization", *Journal of Psychology, 21*, 107-112, 1946.

27. CARTWRIGHT D, and HARARY, F.,"Structural Balance: A Generalization of Heider's Theory", *Psychological Review. 63*, 277-293, 1956.

28. OSGOOD, C.E. and TANNENBAUM, P.H., "The Principle of Congruity in the Prediction of Attitude Change", *Psychological Review. 62*, 1955

29. FESTINGER, L., *A Theory of Cognitive Dissonance*. Evanston, Illinois: Row Peterson 1957.

30. NEWCOMB, T.M., "An Approach to the Study of Communicative Acts", *Psychological Review. 60*, 393-404, 1953.

31. See, for example, HESS, E.H. and POLT, J.M., "Pupil Size as Related to Interest Value in Visual Stimuli", *Science, 132*, 349-350, 1960. Or, KRUGMAN, H.E., "Some Applications of Pupil Measurement", *Journal of Marketing Research*. 15-19, November 1964. Early uses of such measures in advertising research were based upon some unduly simplistic assumptions about the affective response evoked by stimulus patterns. Dilation was assumed, for example, to indicate liking while pupil contraction was taken as evidence of aversion to ads, pictures or other stimuli. More recent discussions reveal a more realistic appraisal of what is reflected by such measures. See, for example: BLACKWELL, R.D., HENSEL, J.S., and STERNTHAL, B., "Pupil Dilation: What Does It Measure?", *Journal of Advertising Research*. 15-18, August 1970.

32. MALONEY, John C., "Is Advertising Believability Really Important?", *Journal of Marketing. 27*, No.4, 1-8, October 1963. Or, MALONEY, John C., "Ist die Glaubhaftigkeit der Werbung so wichtig wie wir meinen?", *Schweizer Reklame*. 215-221, April 1967.

33. MALONEY, John C., "Curiosity vs. Disbelief in Advertising", *Journal of Advertising Research.* 2, 2-8, June 1962.

34. Arthur Koestler, in his brilliant analysis of creativity, describes such delayed insights as bisociations — the sudden coming together of cognitions or knowledge from two different "logical matrices" or planes of the memory structure. KOESTLER, Arthur, *The Act of Creation.* New York: The MacMillan Company, 1964.

35. Indeed, in the present context feedbacks and motivational states are synonymous. Both refer to internal-to-the-organism input filtering or behavior directing conditions which must be inferred from tensions within the organism or from selective behaviors which involve the organism with a portion of the environment. Though motives, but not feedbacks, are sometimes inferred from certain input deprivations (the food deprived rat is assumed to be hungry) this would not seem to be an adequate basis for distinguishing between motivation and input filtering or behavior regulating feedbacks.

36. The specific slope of such curves depends upon a number of factors, not the least of which is the investigator's choice of memory measures. Certain measures commonly used in consumer research (such as the "recognition" measures or "aided recall" measures) tend more than others to reinstate memories in the process of measuring them. These naturally produce flatter appearing curves.

37. See, for example, von BERTALANFFY, Ludwig, *Problems of Life — an Evaluation of Modern Biological and Scientific Thought.* New York: Harper and Brothers, First Harper Torchbook Edition, 135, 1961.

38. I am tempted to elaborate the surrogate model to make a further distinction between stimulus frequency and stimulus intensity and thereby accomodate the principle implied by psychology's Fechner Law. The evidence is less compelling than that which may be adduced for the universal application of other model features already

described. But the Fechner law (which states that
response increases with the logarithm of stimulus intensity) seems to apply over a broad range of stimulus-
response or input-output relationships. An increase
in advertisement size, for example from quarter page
to half page to full page, increases advertisement
noting and recall but the increase in the latter is
less than linearly proportional to the increase in
the former. The same applied to noting and/or recall
of television commercial messages of various lengths.
Limited evidence suggests that the principle *tends*
to apply to campaigns with varying intensities of
"reach" and "frequency" against a given audience.

39. von BERTALANFFY, Ludwig, *Problems of Life*. 197.

40. Ibid., 42

41. A "Decision-precipitating circumstance" (or a "pull-
through situation") is one which calls for action or
decision whether or not the person in that circumstance
is fully prepared for action — whether or not he or
she has made up his mind about which product to buy,
which candidate is worthy of support, or whatever.

42. POLANYI, Michael, "Life's Irreducible Structure",
Science. 1308-1312, June 21, 1968.

43. See my discussion of the problems of "misindexing by
borrowed attention" in: MALONEY, John C., "Is
Advertising Believability Really Important?",
Journal of Marketing. *27*, No. 4, 1-8, October, 1963.

44. Systems theory has been increasingly applied to problems of macroeconomic analysis in which whole industries or nations are studied as subsystems within broader national or international systems. Inputs and
outputs (purchases and sales or imports and exports),
manufacture and storage, and exchange functions are
examined to explain the interactions occuring at the
interfaces of such large scale subsystems. And these
interactions often provide the keys to the nation's or
industry's potential for growth and self-regulation.

Several years ago a Conference of the American Marketing Association was largely devoted to national
economic reforms based on such principles. (BENNETT,
Peter D.,(ed.),*Marketing and Economic Development*.
Chicago: American Marketing Association, Fall 1965).

45. For an example of relevant Soviet literature see
     Kiberneticu na Sluzhbu Kommunizmu, ed. BERG, A.I.,
     available as a Technical Translation from the Office
     of Technical Services, Washington, D.C., under the
     title, *Cybernetics at the Service of Communism*. See
     especially contributions by BELKIN, V.D. on "Cybernetics
     and Economics" and KITOV, A.I. on "Cybernetics and
     Control of National Economy".

46. Relevant literature from American writers includes:
     ROSTOW, Walt W., *The Stages of Economic Growth: A.
     Noncommunist Manifesto*. Cambridge University Press,
     1960.

47. I first discussed this four level hierarchy in a re-
     port to the Advertising Research Foundation in New
     York in the Fall of 1963 — MALONEY, John C., "Copy
     Testing — What Course is it Taking?", in *Advertising Re-
     search at the Crossroads*. New York: Advertising Re-
     search Foundation, October 1963.

48. At the heart of this information system was a monthly
     mail survey of "consumer demand profile" measures
     (Awareness-Acceptance-Preference-Recent Trial-
     Satisfaction) for a variety of products frequently
     purchased by housewives. These surveys, drawing upon
     a different sample of over 1,000 U.S. households each
     month over a period of more than two years, were anal-
     yzed according to housewives' advertising exposures
     and according to the mediating effects of point-of-
     purchase influences. Response-to-advertising curves
     were empirically developed and the survey data were
     correlated with independent audits of product sales
     through retail stores. Such product-moment correlations,
     consistently in the order of .90 and higher, demonstrate
     a very clear relationship between survey measures and
     broad-scale consumer purchase behavior. In more recent

years my graduate students have obtained comparable
correlations with audited sales figures by using similar survey procedures with much cruder and smaller
samples. Recent attempts to adapt the survey procedure to telephone surveys have produced good results,
though problems of obtaining adequate advertising exposure data in this way have not yet been adequately
overcome. (The two year mail survey experience has
been summarized in MALONEY, John C., "Attitude
Measurement and Formation", an unpublished paper presented at the Test Market Design and Measurement Work-
shop. American Marketing Association, Chicago,
Illinois, April 21, 1966.)

49. A study indicating the validity of procedures which I
     developed in the early 1960's for enhancing the rele-
     vance of such tests has recently been reported in
     LEAVITT, Clark, WADDELL, Charles and WELLS, William,
     "Improving Day-After Recall Techniques", *Journal of
     Advertising Research*. 13-17, June, 1970.

50. GROSS, BERTRAM M., "Social Systems Accounting", in
     Social Indicators. ed. BAUER, Raymond A., Cambridge,
     Mass.: The M.I.T. Press, 185, 1966.

51. von BERTALANFFY, Ludwig, *General System Theory*. New
     York: Braziller, especially 51-53, 1968.

52. From a purely pragmatic point of view this approach
     may have some merit. For those with little or no in-
     terest in or concern about a given issue, fear appeals
     can be expected to enhance the attention value of per-
     suasive messages and to stimulate supportive word-of-
     mouth communication about the issue. However, if fear
     appeals arouse greater fear than can be assuaged by
     available and acceptable actions people can be expected
     to eventually desensitize themselves to such communi-
     cation. (Among the many recent reviews of research
     on the topic is: RAY, Michael L. and WILKIE, William
     L., "Fear: The Potential of an Appeal Neglected by
     Marketing", *Journal of Marketing*. 54-62, January 1970.)

53. BOORSTEIN, Daniel J., *The Image: A Guide to Pseudo-events in America*. New York: Harper Colophon Books, 1961. See especially Chapter I, "From News Gathering to News Making: A Flood of Pseudo-Events", 7-44.

54. WHITE, Lynn, Jr., "The Historical Roots of our Ecological Crisis", in *The Environmental Handbook*. De BELL, Garrett, (ed.), New York: Ballantine Books, 12-26, 1970.

A CYBERNETIC INTERPRETATION OF INTERNATIONAL CONFLICT

J. DAVID SINGER

University of Michigan
Mental Health Research Institute, University of Michigan,
Ann Arbor, Michigan 48104, U.S.A.

INTRODUCTION

In all too many intellectual disciplines, there is still the notion that scientific inquiry and social concern are incompatible, and that the scholar who fails to keep the distinction clearly in mind is somehow suspect. It is to von Bertalanffy's everlasting credit that, while offering an impressive number of conceptual innovations and scientific discoveries, he remained involved and productive in a number of public policy areas as well. Thus, even as he played a key role in bringing the biological, physical, and social sciences increasingly under a single theoretical rubric, he addressed himself to such applied problems as higher education, social ethics, medical practice, and mental illness. The important point, however, is that he does not treat these as two separate and distinct spheres of activity in which the scholar must remove his "scientific hat" and replace it with his "concerned citizen hat".

Following his example, I should like in this brief paper to bring together a scholarly concern and a policy concern within my own area of specialization: international politics. I shall, moreover, do so in terms of those general systems concepts which von Bertalanffy has done so much to develop and utilize in his efforts to move us closer to a unified and coherent science of man and his environment.

INTERLOCKING POLITICAL SYSTEMS: NATIONAL AND INTERNATIONAL

In any examination of global politics, there are at
least five levels of analysis available to the observer.
First, there are the three which are most frequently utilized in the discipline: the individual, the national state,
and the international (or global) system. For the period
from approximately the Treaty of Utrecht (1713) up to perhaps World War II, these three system levels turn out to be
more or less sufficient; but for a longer historical view,
into the future as well as into the past, two additional
levels of analysis seem essential. Let me refer to them in
general terms as sub-national entities and extra-national
entities. With the individual, plus these four classes
of social system, one can put together a fairly complete
description — cross-sectional or longitudinal — of global
politics for any epoch. In this section and the next, I
will focus primarily on the national and the global levels,
and will re-introduce the sub-national and extra-national
levels later in my argument.

One of the more important but less obvious characteristics of modern international politics is the fact that a
single set of individuals finds itself playing the dominant
role in both national and international politics. These
are, of course, the national political elites — those individuals who comprise what is variously called the government, the regime, the administration, or, less frequently,
the court. *Within* the national state there may well be
other elites with a fair degree of autonomy who dominate
provincial or local politics but who are subordinate to
those who comprise the national regime. On the other hand,
however, there does not yet exist any legitimate authority
above the hundred-odd national regimes. Given the extra-
ordinary durability of the doctrine of national sovereignty,
most influence in international politics is exerted in a
horizontal direction (nation vis-a-vis nation) and almost
none in a downward vertical direction. There are, of course,
many international organizations and even some supra-national
ones, but they remain largely the creatures of their nation
members; hence we speak of the global system as "sub-system
dominant" (Kaplan, 1957).

One consequence of this state of affairs is that national elites constitute the major actors in both national and international politics. Moreover — and of central concern to us here — the demands of these two systems are often quite incompatible. Behavior which leads to success in one environment may often lead to failure or disaster in the other, and vice-versa. The balance of this paper will be addressed to: (a) the nature of the conflicting incentives, temptations, and constraints which are generated by both sets of systems; (b) the resulting inadequacy of their homeostatic mechanisms; and (c) some possible short-run modifications of a self-correcting nature which might reduce the magnitude of those conflicts which are so inevitable a part of international politics.

What makes a certain level of such conflict almost inevitable? In the global system, given the absence of legitimate supra-national authority, national elites have relied on the ultimate threat of military power as a means of defending "national interests" against possible interference by other nations. This traditional reliance on force as the final arbiter has, in turn, inhibited the growth of an alternative basis for inter-nation harmony: a widely accepted normative code which might permit more adaptive solutions to the inescapable conflicts and clashes of interest. In the absence of both coercive authority and normative consensus, and in the presence of many material and psychic scarcities, the only remaining basis for cooperative behavior is a utilitarian one — a payoff matrix which rewards short-run restraint and accomodative strategies.

And there is the rub. If two nations become involved in a conflict, the general options are two. The most natural, and probably the most frequent, response is to stand firm on the original conflict-inducing position, or perhaps to even increase the original demands. Within most well-integrated national societies, this response tends to be applauded, and the data suggest that it generally enhances the popularity of the regime. Moreover, this behavioral response tends to reinforce the existing norms of world politics ("this is the way things are done") and hence the probability that other nations will handle subsequent

conflicts in the same general manner [1]. But this is
a fairly standard and stylized opening-round routine, and
not particularly pregnant with danger. The critical question is whether the protagonists now succeed in "backing
off" sufficiently so that normal diplomatic procedures
can be brought into play, or whether one or both parties
continue to press their claims in the original and more
vigorous fashion.

     The other general option is to recognize the opening
moves for what they are and then to initiate and recipro-
cate moves of a more conciliatory nature. But the probabilities are all too high that the competence, courage, or
patriotism of one or both sets of elites will then be challenged by the domestic opposition, be it a legitimate political party in a democratic system or a less institutional-
ized faction in a more autocratic system. Moreover, the
efficacy of that challenge from the "outs" will generally
be high, due largely to the prior actions of the "ins".
That is, political elites cannot man an army and finance a
military machine without some sort of psychological mobilization. In persuading an appreciable sector of their society that preparedness is necessary, they inevitably create
a climate which must be relatively responsive to jingoistic
appeals from the opposition. As a matter of fact, had some
minimum psychic and material preparedness *not* existed prior
to the conflict, there might well have been no conflict;
had the nation been militarily weak or psychologically un-
prepared, the competitor would probably have had its way
without any diplomatic conflict.

     Having suggested the general linkages between the na-
tional and the international systems, creating largely incompatible sets of demands on the national elites, let me
now describe the feedback processes in greater detail. My
purpose here is to indicate more precisely where the self-
aggravating tendencies are greatest, and then to suggest
some possible feedback mechanisms whose effects might tend
more in the self-correcting, and less in the self-aggravating, direction.

SOME SELF-AGGRAVATING LINKS IN THE FEEDBACK PROCESS

Given the limitations of space here, the most feasible
procedure is to bypass any thorough description of the
structural, cultural, and physical setting within which
foreign policy decisions are made and executed, and concentrate rather on those few variables which are critical to
the scheme outlined here. In my judgment, one of the reasons for our failure to understand and more fully control
inter-nation conflict is the tendency to treat such conflicts as discrete and separable events. By viewing them
rather as part of an oft-recurring feedback process, we
might better appreciate that the way in which any single
conflict is handled is both a consequence of prior experiences and a predictor of the way subsequent ones will be
handled. The position taken here is that intra-national
and inter-national events all impinge on one another in a
cyclical and ongoing process within which the self-
aggravating propensities frequently exceed the self-
correcting ones by an unacceptably large amount. As I see
it, there are four points at which the self-aggravating
effects of positive feedback are particularly critical during
the inter-nation conflict. Let us discuss them, one at a
time, noting how the traditional notions of confrontation
between a government and its citizenry have been replaced
by highly symbiotic relationships.

Regime and Opposition [2]

The first point is found precisely at the apex of the
foreign policy hierarchy within the nations themselves.
The political elites, often unwittingly, "paint themselves
into a corner" in order to accomplish two short-run objectives when engaged in diplomatic conflict. One objective
is to demonstrate to the *foreign* adversary that they have
both the intent and the capability to stand firm, and the
other is to head off any potential *domestic* attack based on
the inadequacy of that intent and capability. In order to
satisfy both these objectives, however, the elites will
ordinarily resort to the kind of rhetoric which does little
more than "raise the ante" all around. The intended message to the adversary may be merely one of firm determination, but since it will be heard at home as well, it cannot

be too conciliatory; as a matter of fact, by making a commitment audible to the domestic audience, the decision makers may hope to make their foreign policy threats more
credible, given the domestic costs, real or apparent, of
capitulation.

Assuming for the moment that the early verbal behavior
has demonstrated the appropriate degree of firmness abroad
and at home, what are the likely consequences? The adversary's regime, of course, "will not be intimidated", and he
so responds in public messages to the several relevant audiences. At this point in the scenario, if we are fortunate, the interactions shift toward quiet diplomacy, both
domestic oppositions turn their attention to other matters,
and the publics forget the episode in short order. Suppose,
however, that the prior episodes had been so handled by
the regime, the opposition, and the media, that there was
sufficient public hostility toward this particular adversary, and, further, that the opposition prefers not to let
the issue drop out of sight. Quite clearly, the regime
takes a fairly serious domestic risk if it ignores the cries
for justice, revenge, national honor, and so forth; but it
takes a different (and also far from negligible) risk of
escalating the conflict if it tries to satisfy the domestic
critics.

Military and Psychological Mobilization

In order to examine the second point at which positive
feedback can get us into serious trouble, we can focus on
another set of factors. Let us assume, reasonably enough,
that both nations in the conflict are moderately well-armed
by contemporary (but non-nuclear) standards, but that one
enjoys a discernible superiority over the other in the relevant military categories, and that neither can turn to close
allies for diplomatic or military support. The regime of
the disadvantaged protagonist, having permitted the conflict
to pick up some momentum, now has the choice of (1) bluf-
fing; (2) retreating; or (3) delaying while improving its
military position. The first can lead to a sharpening of
the conflict and a more humiliating retreat later (or even
a stumbling into war), and the second makes it vulnerable
to political attack at home. Thus, there is always some

temptation to try to close the manpower and weapons gap
in order to bargain from a position of parity or even of
greater strength. If this route is taken, the regime will
first need to launch a program of psychological mobilization, without which neither the volunteers and conscripts
nor the funds for weapon acquisitions might be forthcoming.
In the process of mobilizing public and sub-elite support
for these preparedness activities, however, two new conditions are generally created. First, the adversary is not
likely to sit idly by, watching its superiority disappear,
and its regime therefore embarks on a similar set of programs. Second, both publics must become more persuaded of
the need to resist the menace to their nation's security,
and as a consequence, offer a more fertile ground for any
militant domestic opposition. Given the almost irresistible
temptation to exploit this state of affairs, the net effect
is to raise hostility levels in both nations and therefore
to raise the expectations as to what would constitute a
satisfactory settlement, negotiated or otherwise. Since
these rising expectations tend to be fairly symmetrical,
neither regime is in as good a position to compromise as it
was during the first round of the conflict. The probability of further escalation, diplomatic rupture, or war itself
is now appreciably greater.

Amplification via the Media

Let me now turn to a third source of danger in the
cyclical conflict processes which seem to characterize so
much of international politics. To this point, the role of
the media has had little attention, yet mass communications
would seem to play a particularly central role in helping
the self-aggravating process along. Again, the differences
between a highly autocratic and a relatively democratic
nation are seldom as profound as contemporary Westerners
prefer to believe [3]. At almost any point along the
autocratic-democratic continuum, the political elites need
the media and the media need the political elites, be they
regime or opposition. The regime relies on the media to
help mobilize the population, to bargain with and ridicule
the domestic opposition, and even to communicate with other
nations.

    While it may be simpler to arrange when the party in
power exercises *formal* control over its media, any effective and stable regime has little difficulty "managing the
news". First of all, the words and actions of the elite
are, by definition, newsworthy, and therefore widely transmitted. Secondly, members of the regime have information
available which can be of great help to the reporter or
commentator to whom it is made available. Thus, by judicious release or righteous restraint, government officials
can all too readily help or hinder the careers of many media
employees. Thirdly, as regimes become more conscious of
the need — and possibilities — of domestic propaganda, they
begin to recruit media people into their ranks as "public
information" officers. Many newsmen are therefore involved
in competition for these often attractive bureaucratic positions, and one way to stay in the running is to describe
the appropriate agency's activities in a generally favorable fashion. While access to, and control over, the media
may not be quite as simple for the "outs" as for the "ins",
factions or parties in legal opposition are not without
the sorts of media amplifiers they need to berate the regime for being "soft on --------", devoid of courage, or
incapable of defending the nation's honor. In some nations,
each political party has its own newspaper, magazine, or
radio station, and in others, the possibility of the opposition coming to power can make the media somewhat more responsive than might be expected.

    I am not, in this section, arraigning the media of
most nations on charges of "selling out", although the
charge would be far from groundless. Rather, despite the
existence of a vigorous and independent sector in the media
services of many nations, the general impression is that
the incentives work to make these institutions a major factor in amplifying inter-nation conflicts and contributing
to the positive feedback process [4].

The Redistribution of Domestic Power

    The fourth and final factor to be considered in this
analysis is the effect which a nation's participation in an
escalating conflict can have upon the distribution of social, economic, and political power within the society.

Without accepting those conspiratorial models which see
generals and "munitions makers" actively fomenting rivalry,
conflict and war, one must be extraordinarily naïve to expect no systematic biases in the foreign policy preferences
of those who comprise the military-industrial complex.
Even more than with newsmen, questions of ambiguity will regularly tend to be resolved in the hard-line direction by
many military officers, corporate executives, labor leaders,
government bureaucrats, civil defense specialists, and technical consultants, as well as by the standard phalanx of
patriotic organizations. Given the state of our knowledge
about international politics, most foreign policy problems
are indeed matters of opinion, rather than fact, and in
matters of opinion the point of view which usually gets the
benefit of the doubt (i.e., the conventional wisdom) can be
expected to win out most of the time.

The problem here, of course, is that in most nations
the major positions of power — as well as the public plau-
dits — go to those who are in the ideological mainstream;
this seems to hold even if the mainstream of the moment is
allegedly pragmatic and non-ideological, as in the United
States of today and (probably) the Soviet Union of tomorrow.
Having acquired power, prestige and credibility by advoca-
ting, or acquiescing in, the modal foreign policy positions,
these middle elites are seldom likely to shift too far in
their views; and they are particularly unlikely to shift
toward a position which could be interpreted (or mis-
interpreted) as giving aid and comfort to the enemy, whoever
the enemy of the moment may be.

Furthermore, as the intensity of the inter-nation conflict increases, the higher becomes the value of the professional and extra-curricular services of these middle
elites. On top of this, as their individual influence and
status increases, the *size* of their sector also increases.
When the armed forces expand, officer promotions acceler-
ate, and when more weaponry is being designed and produced,
more engineers and technicians are promoted and recruited;
even academics in the social and physical sciences find
that foreign policy conflicts lead to increased opportunities for money, status, and influence in the modern world.
The high energy physicist or the professor of biology has

his role to play in the preparedness program, just as the political scientist or anthropologist finds himself consulting on log-rolling tactics in international organizations, military strategy, or counter-insurgency. If for no other purpose than to give intellectual legitimacy to the conventional wisdom, academics are almost as likely to be co-opted into the foreign policy mainstream as are the more obvious members of the military-industrial complex.

My point here is that is does not take a so-called totalitarian regime to mobilize key sectors of the society. The basic properties of the sovereign national state in the industrial age are such that this mobilization occurs with little effort. No secret police, no dictatorial government, not even any veiled threats are required to generate the joint "conspiracies" of silent acquiescence and noisy affirmation once a nation becomes embroiled in a conflict of any intensity or a preparedness program of any magnitude. For the past century or so, the self-correcting mechanisms have gradually withered, despite the assumptions of economic liberalism and classical democratic theory. In the absence of vigorous countervailing forces within the nations or in the larger global community, the self-correcting mechanisms of international politics are feeble indeed, with the consequence that all too many of the inevitable conflicts among nations are free to grow into costly rivalries and, occasionally, into tragic wars.

Is the interaction between and among nations in global politics as dismal as I have painted it here? Is the relative potency of our self-correcting mechanisms this much less than that of the self-aggravating ones? Considering the paucity of scientific, data-based research on global politics, and the absence of much evidence at either the micro- or macro-level, it is a bold man indeed who will take so dim a view and embrace so pessimistic an analysis. The picture may, admittedly, be overdrawn for the sake of emphasis, and it may even be that as a science of global politics develops, this characterization of the nation-state system will turn out to have been seriously incomplete or inaccurate. Be that as it may, responsible scholars must act on the basis of the little that *is* known, even while working to enlarge that knowledge base, and the interpretation offered here will therefore have to suffice for

the moment. The word "act" is used quite literally, since
I intend in this section to shift from the interpretive mode
to that of prescription. Having described how these aspects
of the global system look to me, let me summarize a few
modifications that might possibly reduce the probability of
any given conflict erupting into war, and of any given war
converting great parts of humanity into a nuclear rubble.
With so much at stake, it is embarrassing to propose so
little, but the approach offered here may possibly generate
some self-amplifying processes of its own.

SOME POSSIBLE SELF-CORRECTING MECHANISMS

Assuming that this formulation is essentially correct,
and having emphasized that a great deal more rigorous research is called for, I would single out the communication
and norm-setting nodes in the national societies as among
the more high-priority points of intervention. Until decision makers become aware of the many ways in which their
own behavior exacerbates conflicts, and converts the possibility of win-win outcomes into zero-sum ones, the chances
are they will continue to act in the traditional manner,
and often find themselves, unexpectedly, in situations from
which extrication is costly or impossible [5]. Journalists
and commentators, for example, could pay more attention to
the effects of such moves on the inter-nation conflict itself, and less to the effects on the regime's popularity
vis-a-vis its domestic opponents (Waltz, 1967). The various private or semi-independent groups that exist to influence foreign policy or the public's attitudes toward it
could devote as much of their attention to the regime's
conflict management techniques — and the opposition's acquiescence in, or exploitation of, such techniques — as they do
to pursuing their own particular and narrow goals or ap-
plauding "our side" in world politics.

Perhaps more critical, but demanding much more in the
way of short-run self-sacrifice, is the need for the political "outs" to play a less opportunistic game. Support for
a "vigorous defense of the national interest" may win the
opposition a word of thanks from the regime, and criticism
of "a policy of appeasement" may win it some support from

a large sector of the public, but neither of these tactics is likely to make the regime's diplomacy any more successful.

Nor will they have led to any improvement in the future. This is an utterly critical phenomenon in all social processes, but it is very rarely acted upon, or even appreciated, and may deserve more than this passing allusion. Consider, for a moment, the relationship between two classes of phenomena in any social system: beliefs (including norms, values, and expectations) and behavior (including verbal, decisional, and physical). Every public action, especially if taken by a highly visible reference figure, exercises some impact, however minor and however indirect, on the beliefs and attitudes of those who observe or hear about the act. It may lead to the strengthening and reinforcement of some attitudes among some people, and to the weakening or modification of some attitudes among others. Given this dynamic interdependence, it behooves us to pay attention to the possible consequences of every foreign policy action that occurs. Each act of the opposition — no matter how weak its power, or how cynical the public — helps shape those attitudes which will, in turn, shape the behavior of many of the participants in the foreign policy process. If, for example, the "ins" and the "outs" are seen to agree on the rights and wrongs of a foreign policy conflict, many citizens will conclude that there is no other reasonable position. And if they disagree to the extent that the regime is accused of appeasement, the regime will either modify its policy in a more militant direction, or try to *appear* as if the policy were indeed at least as militant as that advocated by the opposition "outs". Either way, citizen attitudes will be strengthened in a more nationalistic and short-range direction [6]. Unfortunately, many of those so influenced will be reference figures who, themselves, are "opinion influentials".

The importance of these positive feedback mechanisms is relevant not only *during* conflicts and crises, but before and after. If a conflict is finally resolved in a more or less satisfactory fashion, the contending regimes are likely to emphasize the diplomatic "victory" they have achieved by their firmness in the face of the adversary. Once again, this may enhance their prestige for a few weeks or months, but the main effect is to increase the popular expectation that all subsequent conflicts will end in victory-through-firmness. If it ends unsatisfactorily for one side, the norm is a refusal to acquiesce in the "unjust" outcome, and a pledge to redress the nation's grievances at the earliest opportunity. In either case, the prognosis for peaceful resolution of future conflicts is not favorable. Likewise, there is a great and naive myth in many more or less democratic societies that elections have one function and one alone: to decide which party or faction shall be in power. Thus, the campaign strategists first try to ascertain the dominant views of the various voting blocs and then proceed to pander to these views. With few exceptions, then, election campaigns — because they receive fairly wide and sustained publicity — tend to serve as a powerful reinforcement for existing views on many domestic and some occasional foreign policy issues. And, as I have already mentioned with some frequency, these are not views which make it easy for decision makers to pursue peace abroad and honor at home.

For the information channels to play a useful part in reducing the dominance of positive over negative feedback mechanisms in inter-national conflict, several groups will have to contribute. Scholars need to identify which points are most critical in different classes of conflict and which behavioral patterns account for most of the self-aggravating as well as self-correcting tendencies. Journalists and other media people need to take a more detached and critical view, accepting the important difference between their professional roles and those of politicians [7]. Politicians need to appreciate the trade-off between short-run tactical gains vis-a-vis the domestic opponent and the middle-run liabilities that accrue when, in negotiating with foreign elites, they find little room to maneuver.

At first blush, these look as if they might indeed be steps which individuals and groups in each nation could take on a unilateral basis. If they could be taken unilaterally, one might feel somewhat more optimistic, but the fact is that too much progress along these lines in any single nation could put that nation at a modest (some would say disastrous) disadvantage vis-a-vis other nations in the global system (Osgood, 1962). After all, each of these

steps implies — almost by definition — some reduction not
only in the level of political and psychological mobilization within the affected nation, but a longer-range trend
toward public resistance to the standard mobilization appeals. When the attentive public in a nation becomes more
sophisticated, far-sighted, and tolerant of compromise with
foreign powers, its regime may be at a disadvantage in diplomatic bargaining. As a matter of fact, a favorite ploy
in such bargaining is to inform the adversary that one's
own public (or legislature, or press, etc.) just would not
accept a particular settlement, and certain concessions
must therefore (and regrettably) be requested in order to
get an agreement which could be "sold" at home. If this is
indeed an accurate portrayal, the only way to start the
trend toward more realistic diplomacy is for the initiative
to be taken by those nations which are clearly in the strongest bargaining position in any such negotiations, despite
the modest risks.

In addition to the possibility of certain unilateral
measures, a number of *negotiated* arrangements should also
be mentioned. Given my emphasis on the role of the media
in exacerbating many conflicts, let me begin there. One
approach might be to establish, in line with Quincy Wright's
proposal (1957), an international "intelligence" center,
whose mission would be to monitor a representative sample
of the world's radio, film, TV, and newspaper output, in
order to ascertain the levels and growth rates of self-
aggravating (and self-correcting) emissions. Using computerized content analysis techniques (Holsti, 1969; Singer,
1963; Stone, 1966) such an agency could publish weekly reports, thus providing a type of "early warning" to the governments and publics of the world.

Another approach might be a treaty or agreement, perhaps initiated by a group of non-aligned middle-powers,
obliging governments to match each allocation of resources
to military preparedness with an equivalent or larger allocation to a specified non-military activity. Given the
upper limit on all nation's resources, the need to increase
expenditures in agriculture, housing, education, or research,
for each preparedness expenditure, might well help to cur-
tail preparedness programs and all that follows in their

wake. A variation on this theme might be to base a nation's contribution to the United Nations system on military expenditure levels rather than on gross national product or access to hard currencies.

A third possibility — lying somewhere between the unilateral move and the negotiated arrangement — is what I have called elsewhere "negotiation by proxy" (Singer, 1965). Very simply, the idea is that several nations begin to experiment with the hiring of international law firms to handle certain types of diplomatic negotiations. The assumption is that foreign ministry officials, despite the folklore to the contrary, are indeed susceptible to the domestic political pressures which we discussed earlier, and that international bargaining could be partially depoliticized by assigning the task to skilled "mercenaries". With the intelligent design of procedures and fee schedules, some of the basic incentives for failure in negotiation could be replaced by incentives for success.

CONCLUSION

In this paper, I have tried to describe those relationships and behavioral propensities which account for a great deal of the positive feedback in the international system, and which therefore convert many minor disputes into major conflicts (Deutsch, 1963; Milsum, 1968). Now some will urge that the mechanisms which I propose in order to strengthen some of the negative feedback tendencies are little more than short-run palliatives, and that the system is basically inadequate in its present design. The charge is probably a fair one, but it is also somewhat beside the point; this is the nature of the system as it now stands, and our immediate concern is to devise those homeostatic mechanisms which will keep the fluctuations in conflict within the safe range. Moreover, there may well be some "natural" tendencies toward more self-correcting behavior even in the absence of such innovations. For example, war by and large has not been a particularly effective conflict resolving technique in this century, and the nature of the cost-benefit ratio is increasingly appreciated. Certainly, nuclear weapons and missile delivery vehicles can do nothing but increase the ratio — even if they do contribute somewhat

to the tendency toward pre-emptive attack. Likewise, the
drive for overseas possessions — once a major source of
international conflict — has become less and less attractive.
Colonialism, at least in its older form, just did not pay.
A third element of built-in stability may be the increasing
disenchantment with national states and nationalism; many
of the world's people are beginning to look for alternative
and more efficient forms of human organization (Singer,
1969). If this trend continues, many regimes will find it
increasingly difficult to mobilize support for traditional
foreign policies.

Despite these favorable possibilities, the need for
supplementary control mechanisms nevertheless remains. We
must of course explicitly differentiate between mechanisms
which are designed to perform a largely homeostatic function, such as those outlined here, and those designed to
initiate a self-reinforcing feedback process which might
lead to fairly radical system transformation. We have merely alluded to some potential tendencies in this direction,
and the need for further investigation is crucial.

My major concern, then, has been to point out those
properties of the international system which seem most maladaptive, to frame them in general systems terms, and to
indicate some possible short-run mechanisms of a more adaptive and self-correcting nature. If certain unilateral
and multilateral innovations can be made, we may still be
able to keep the basic self-aggravating tendencies within
safe limits, and thus have at least one more opportunity
to design a global system which is fit for human habitation.

NOTES

1. Lest there by any misunderstanding, the analysis sug-
    gested here does not necessarily apply to *every* conceiv-
    able inter-nation conflict. While most such conflicts
    are, in my judgment, matters of routine incompatibilities
    between and among traditionally defined national inter-
    ests, some do indeed raise legitimate issues of justice
    and morality. Unfortunately, we have not yet developed
    any generally accepted criteria for distinguishing be-
    tween the two types of cases, and even if we could,
    nationalistic appeals would often overwhelm them.

2.   For the sake of simplicity here, I not only assume
      that there is a viable opposition in most nations but
      that the political spectrum is largely based on a two-
      faction, quasi-pluralistic division, with one or the
      other in power at a given time. These are, of course,
      drastic simplifications, but do not affect the argu-
      ment which concerns us here.

3.   As I write these lines, the radio newscast, reports
      that "American aircraft carried out fifty-two sorties
      in the Hanoi-Haiphong area" but that "Vietcong terror-
      ists continued their campaign of terrorist tactics
      against unarmed civilians in an effort to disrupt the
      forthcoming democratic elections!" Redundancy in the
      name of patriotism is, of course, a virtue.

4.   Some informative and suggestive interpretations of
      the media's role in foreign policy are Cohen (1963),
      Kruglak (1963), Reston (1966), Nimmo (1964), and Hale
      (1964).

5.   In almost every government agency or corporation, there
      is a controller (or comptroller) whose major assign-
      ment is to watch budgetary income and outgo, and to
      issue warnings when they tend to get out of balance,
      or look as if they might do so. Perhaps every foreign
      ministry ought to have an analogous officer whose sole
      responsibility is to watch for those trends which sig-
      nal a potential loss of diplomatic maneuver.

6.   There is an extensive literature on bipartisanship in
      U.S. foreign policy, but it tends to look at only one
      part of the problem. Revering the traditional doctrine
      that "politics must stop at the water's edge" in the
      name of patriotism, it seldom notes the frequency with
      which bipartisanship produces a conspiracy of silence.
      Since foreign policy is rarely an issue in national or
      local elections, the electorate is most unlikely to
      hear any criticism (thoughtful or otherwise) of the
      regime in this regard. And when it *is* an issue (usu-
      ally too late in the game) the parties usually seek to
      out-do one another in simplistic appeals.

7.   They could probably get some reinforcement in this
      task from the more alert and concerned consumers of
      national media. One possible mechanism might be the
      establishment of some sort of readers' pressure group
      which could single out certain newspapers and period-
      icals from time to time, publicize the more serious
      distortions which they perpetuate and try to organize
      "subscribers' strikes". If such errors of fact and
      interpretation were called to the attention of publis-
      hers and editors by a readership which is in a posi-
      tion to impose a temporary boycott, some progress
      might be made. And since much of the propagandistic
      material in the newspaper and radio reports must be
      traced to the wire services, these transmitters might
      then begin to demand higher standards from UPI, AP,
      Reuters, Tass, and the rest.

REFERENCES

COHEN, Bernard C., *The Press and Foreign Policy*.
Princeton, N.J.: Princeton University Press, 1963.

DEUTSCH. Karl W., *Nerves of Government*. New York: Free
Press, 1963.

HALE, O.J., *The Captive Press in the Third Reich*. Princeton
N.J.: Princeton University Press, 1964.

HOLSTI, Ole R., *Content Analysis for the Social Sciences
and Humanities*. Reading, Mass: Addison-Wesley, 1969.

KAPLAN, Morton A., *System and Process in International
Politics*. New York: John Wiley and Sons, 1957.

KRUGLAK, Theodore E., *The Two Faces of Tass*. New York:
McGraw-Hill, 1963.

MILSUM, John (ed.), *Positive Feedback*. Oxford: Pergamon,
1968.

NIMMO, Dan, *Newsgathering in Washington*. New York:
Atherton Press, 1964.

OSGOOD, Charles E., *An Alternative to War or Surrender*.
Urbana, Ill.: University of Illinois Press, 1962.

RESTON, James, *The Artillery of the Press*.   New York:
Harper and Row, 1966.

SINGER, J. David, "Media Analysis in Inspection for
Disarmament", *Journal of Arms Control*. 1/3, 248-60, July
1963.

SINGER, J. David, "Negotiation by Proxy", *Journal of Conflict Resolution*. 9/4, 538-41, December 1965.

SINGER, J. David, "The Global System and its Sub-Systems:
A Developmental View", *Linkage Politics: Essays in National
and International Systems*. ROSENAU, James, (ed.),
New York: Free Press, 1969.

STONE, Philip et al., *The General Inquirer*.   Cambridge, Mass.:
M.I.T. Press, 1966.

WALTZ, Kenneth, "Electoral Punishment and Foreign Policy
Crises", *Domestic Sources of Foreign Policy*.   ROSENAU,
James N., (ed.), New York: Free Press, 1967.

WRIGHT, Quincy, "Project for a World Intelligence Center",
Journal of Conflict Resolution.   1/1, 93-97, March, 1957.

THE CHALLENGE OF A LEAP-EPOCH IN HUMAN HISTORY

F.C. HAPPOLD*

Salisbury, Wilts., England

When I received an invitation to be one of the contributors to this volume of essays in honour of Professor
Ludwig von Bertalanffy, I was both surprised and pleased;
surprised because I have had no scientific training, pleased
because I have never claimed to be a scholar in the usual
sense. So, though I have gratefully accepted what for one
of my intellectual calibre is a very high honour, it has
been with some trepidations. Could one who, though endowed
with a multi-dimensional outlook and able to range fairly
freely over a number of fields of knowledge, is primarily
a rather skillful populariser, write at the level which
such a book as this demanded? I feel at the outset I should
make my apologies to my fellow contributors, so much more
eminent and learned than myself. I do not wish to sail under
false colours.

Until comparatively recently I was not acquainted with
the work of Professor von Bertalanffy. A connection between us was established as a result of a book I had written
on Mysticism which came into his hands. Since then we have
corresponded with each other, and it has become increasingly
clear that, starting from very different points, with very
different environments, engaged on different fields of study
and activity, we have throughout a great part of our lives
been engaged on the same quest, on an adventure in search of
a synthesis, of a unity in all experience and in all life.
Both of us have been profoundly influenced by that great
fifteenth-century thinker, the Cardinal Nicholas of Cusa
(Cusanus), and by historians such as Oswald Spengler; both
of us have known experiences which Maslow calls "peak" and

---

* Deceased

which I am prepared to label "mystical" experiences. Both
of us, I think, regard such experiences as windows opening
on to something essentially real. Both of us can say with
Ishak in the last scene of James Elroy Flecker's play
Hassan:

> We are the Pilgrims, Master, we shall go
> Always a little further; it may be
> Beyond that last blue mountain barred with snow,
> Beyond that angry or that glimmering sea.
>
> White on a throne or guarded in a cave
> There lives a prophet who can understand
> Why men were born: but surely we are brave
> Who take the Golden Road to Samarkand.

As one surveys the long history of the evolution of life
on this planet, it is possible to see points where history
entered on a new phase, when, in its early stages after millenia of adaptations and gropings, *leaps* were made, and life
and history rose to a new level. The greatest of these *leaps*
occurred at the point at which what Teilhard de Chardin calls
hominisation took place, i.e., the emergence of *Homo sapiens;*
of a creature no longer governed solely by instinct, but
able to reflect on his experience. At that point man started
on his pilgrimage.

A long period of "pre-history" [1] followed, marked by
such *leaps* as those brought about by the domestication of
animals, by the development of agriculture, and by such vital
discoveries as those of fire, tools, metals, etc. With the
discovery of writing a new era of human history began; an
era of only six thousand years, infinitely small in relation
to man's history as a whole, in which experience could be
passed on through written records. The tempo of development
immensely quickened.

This era saw the rise of great civilizations, centring
around the chief river valleys of the world. Great cities
were built; new forms of governmental organization evolved;
the arts and crafts developed; knowledge, spiritual and
intellectual, expanded and became more and more refined.

In the millenium before the birth of Christ the spirit
of man moved onto a new plane. In different parts of the
globe, to a great extent apparently unconnected with, and
uninfluenced by, the others, there occurred what is perhaps
the most significant *leap* in this era of written history,
a veritable revolution in human thought and spiritual insight. Man's conception of the That which he calls God [2],
of his own nature, and of the universe was, in different ways,
expanded and refined. This *leap* manifested itself in China
in Confucius and Lao-tse; in India in the development of
the religio-philosophy of the Vedanta, set out in the *Upani-
shads*, and in the rise of Buddhism; in Persia in Zoroas-
tianism; in the rise of the great Hebrew prophets in Pales-
tine; and in the emergence of the conception of a rational
universe, which could be explored and comprehended by the
human mind, in the Classical philosophy of Greece.

A primarily spiritual *leap*, if such it can be called,
of great insight and significance took place some five hundred years later, in the refinement of the Krishna image in
Bhagavad Gita [3], in the emergence of the Bodhisattva ideal
in Mahayana Buddhism, and in the interpretation of the nature
of Jesus Christ evolved by the early Christian Church. This
movement in religious thought is characterized by a person-
alizing and humanizing of the God-image. Its origin can be
traced not only in the insights of the earlier *leap*, but
also in the archetypal imagery of earlier religious mythology.

It is of the nature of civilizations to rise, blossom
and decay. Oswald Spengler, in *The Decline of the West* and,
more convincingly, Arnold Toynbee, in *A Study of History*,
have attempted the heroic task of trying to analyse these
culture-epochs and to account for their rise and fall.

With the decline of the power of the Roman Empire in the
West, a new civilization came into being in Western Europe,
our own Western European culture-epoch. Within this epoch
of Western European culture it is possible to detect a number
of "crises", that is, minor *leaps* within a particular culture,
when that culture moved into a new phase. Historians have
sometimes called these crises Renaissances. One occurred in
the ninth century, the so-called Carolingian Renaissance.
It was not, however, permanent and was followed by another

period of chaos. A permanent turning point was not reached
until the end of the eleventh century. The following century saw the rise of towns, the beginnings of Gothic architecture, the emergence of vernacular literature, the re-
vival of Latin studies and the founding of the first European universities; and, through contacts with the Moslem
world, the re-discovery of Greek science.   Side by side
with these advances in the secular sphere there was a re-
vival of spiritual and mystical life.

A further crisis is seen in the Renaissance of the Fif-
teenth Century, which was at the same time the final flowering of the so-called Middle Ages and the dawn of our own
Modern World. It was characterized by the birth of humanism,
to be followed by what arose out of it, that Scientific
Revolution of the Seventeenth Century, which, with its practical outcome in modern technology, has been the most potent
factor in the emergence of the pattern of the life and
thought of our own age.

Now in our time, we are certainly living at a crisis
point, not only of our own culture, but also of world culture.
It is not an untenable hypothesis to assume that what we
see happening around us is much more than that; that our
age is, indeed a *leap-epoch,* an epoch in which the collective consciousness of mankind is painfully moving into a
new dimension of awareness. Such is the thesis of this
essay.

The three interlocking elements which have led to, and
which dominate, the character of this crisis of the Twentieth
Century are:

1. *The development of scientific thought* since the Seventeenth, and its passing into a new phase in the Twentieth,
Century. There is no space here - nor is there need, since
it is known to the readers of these essays - to trace the
development of scientific discovery and thought since the
time of Galileo, Copernicus, and Newton. What is important
for our purpose is that transformation of the scientific
world-view which has occurred during our own century, that
opening-up of a new dimension of the physical universe which
has resulted from the discoveries of twentieth-century astronomers and quantum physicists, and of a new dimension of the
spiritual universe laid bare by depth psychology.

The widely held scientific view of the Nineteenth Century, that matter was solid and indestructible, and that the universe was governed by laws which were inflexible and causally determined, has given way to the conception of matter as a concentrated form of energy, which cannot in any real sense be *known*. The knowledge of the scientist is seen rather as one of a *pattern of actions*, of the *structure of a set of operations*. Scientists are now content to study relationships, by which means it is possible to predict the likelihood of happenings. The *absolute object* of the older science has disappeared, as has also the idea of absolute time, i.e., the idea of three-dimensional space passing simultaneously, moment by moment, through time. Rather we are compelled to conceive the universe in terms of a multi-dimensional space-time continuum, in which time is one of the dimensions.

Thus we are led into a new dimension of knowledge, thought, and intuition, into the conception of a *physico-spiritual* universe in which the idea of *spirit* is no longer alien. It is no longer uncritical to assume that there may be regions of personality which lie outside the orbit of normal conciousness and in which the categories of time and space may be inappropriate, that man in his completeness dwells in a realm which embraces infinity and which cannot be rationally known. Further it has become evident that our apprehension of the sum-total of reality is carried out only in part by the rational mind, that much comes out of that unconscious (or perhaps better super-conscious) in which, according to Jung, is stored up the most profound collective insights of mankind. It is now accepted that in part our knowledge of the universe is a knowledge of something in ourselves; it is not completely objective.

An intuitive spiritual awareness, with its source in the super-conscious, however the nature of that super-conscious may be interpreted, is a part of the sum-total of man's apprehension of the universe in which he lives. This type of awareness, through the knowledge which comes out of it can only be partially translated into intellectual concepts; though, in the use of it, "the proud spirit of Reason"[4] may no longer occupy an exclusive throne and we are compelled to accept as valid the notions of "darkness" and "unknowing" of the mystics; and the "docta ignorantia (learned ignorance)"

of Nicholas of Cusa, while it may be called *non*rational, is
not *ir*rational.

In a fully integrated personality there is a fertile
interplay of intuitive and rational thought, out of which
can come a *spiritualized rationalism*, which is, in a real
sense, an expansion of perceptive awareness and leads to a
deeper knowledge of the true nature of things. The importance of Ludwig von Bertalanffy lies to a great extent in
the fact that the workings of his mind are controlled by a
capacity for this spiritualized rationalism; and it is this
capacity which has enabled him not only to evolve his organismic conception and general system theory, but also to arrive
at what he calls a "perspectivist" philosophy, in which different forms of experience mirror, as it were, different
aspects of reality.

2. *The immense and widespread impact of technological
advance on the life of mankind.* The effects of this technological advance cannot be exaggerated. Political structures
and social groupings have been thrown into the melting pot.
The whole pattern of living has changed. Vast possibilities
of the good life have been opened up. Further, it must be
accepted that the political, social, and technological patterns of any era exercise a profound influence on the collective thought-patterns and attitudes of that era.

3. *The elimination of distance* through the vastly improved
means of communication which has been made possible by this
technological revolution. Our globe has veritably become
one. There is now only one world of which each of us is a
part, with a consequent change in our attitudes and thought
patterns. Not long ago it was possible for a Nineteenth
Century poet to write: "East is East and West is West, and
never the twain shall meet". That is no longer true; for,
in addition to the elimination of physical distance, a process of what Teilhard de Chardin has called "psychic inter-
penetration" is taking place and increasing in momentum.
Western and Eastern modes of thought are intermingling and
cross-fertilizing each other.

A *leap-epoch* in human history, in which mankind is moving
into a new area of expanded consciousness - such is the thesis
of this essay. This Twentieth-Century *leap* has affinities

with that which took place in the millenium before the birth
of Christ, to which we have already referred, It is, however, on a much wider scale and, owing to the evolution of
knowledge and thought which has taken place during the last
two and half millenia, contains elements which were not present in the earlier *leap*.

A *leap* offers a hard challenge. It calls for new modes
of thought, for an openness of mind and for original approaches and interpretations. It will be the task of the
remainder of this essay to consider how the challenge of our
age may be met, to examine possible modes of thought and apprehension and to suggest certain key principles and concepts.
I would ask, however, that all that I shall now write shall
be regarded as exploratory and tentative, as the speculation
of one, trained as a historian, who has had throughout a long
life a burning spirit of curiosity and adventure, which has
impelled him to stretch out into the intellectual domains
of the physicist, the biologist, the psychologist, the philosopher, and the theologian. Let anything that I write be
regarded solely as the fruits of the spiritual and mental
explorations of one man only, myself.

As one surveys the story of mankind and the evolution
of man's thought and perception during the era of written
history, it seems to have been characterized by two determining principles. The first of these may be called the
Principle of Possibility. By that is meant that it has only
been when knowledge and perception has reached a certain
stage of evolutionary development that it has been possible
for the new thoughts to be thought, the new concepts to be
grasped, and the new synthetic vision to shine forth.

The second of these determining principles may be called
the *Principle of Forgetting*. The mind of man at its present
stage of development cannot contain more than a certain
amount at one time. In order to be able to glimpse, explore,
and grasp new aspects of reality, older insights have to
fade out and be forgotten out. There comes a time, however,
when human consciousness moves into a new dimension, in which
old and new insights are gathered togetherm old and new
visions of reality merge, and the outlines of a new and wider
synthesis are seen.

This sort of gathering together and merging of old and
new visions is clearly evident in our time. Not only has
the transformation of the scientific world-view resulted in
the modern scientists' picture of the cosmos becoming one
which can, not inaptly, be called a picture of a "spiritual"
universe; but also side by side with the present predominant
"secular" temper of thought there is a widespread longing
for and a stretching out into a world which is not that of
time and history.

In the Epilogue of my book, *Religious Faith and Twentieth Century Man,* I wrote these words:

> Our analysis of the present situation has led to
> the hypothesis that we are in the midst of one of those
> evolutionary mental and spiritual "leaps" which have
> happened before in history, that what we see happening
> around us is an enlargement of human consciousness, a
> widening of perception and a natural growth in the col-
> lective soul of mankind. Is-ness (*the meaning of this
> term is explained below*) discloses itself to us in ways
> different from those in which it disclosed itself to our
> forefathers, so that we are compelled to interrogate and
> interpret the universe in a way which our knowledge of
> the operation of mystical consciousness and insight im-
> pels us to call mystical. I have therefore called this
> "disclosure" or "discernment" situation (to use terms
> which some writers are now using) a movement into the
> realm of the mystical.

A movement into the realm of the mystical. It will be
apparent to one familiar with the literature of mysticism
that I am using the term *the mystical* in a way different
from that in which it is normally used by writers on the
phenomenon of mystical experience; giving it a more extended connotation, so that it embraces a variety of spiritual and mental experiences which, on my examination of the
evidence, I have come to regard as falling within the same
continuum. I am using it to describe at the same time a
particular level of perception, and particular ways of ap-
prehending, interrogating, and interpreting the nature of
reality, the Is-ness of the universe all of which have affinities with those of the acknowledged mystic.

One is compelled to recognize more than one mode of cognition, more than one way of valid knowing. Let us call them the rational, the intuitive, and the mystical. While there is a close similarity between the last two, it is desirable to make a distinction. The manifestation of the intuitive mode of perception as seen, for instance, in scientific exploration, is different from its manifestation in the contemplative saint. In the highest manifestation of *the mystical* there is a fading out of the rational altogether and a passing into a state of naked awareness which, though it has a Noetic quality, is emptied of all images, symbols, and concepts. In order to avoid the difficulty of always having to try to distinguish between the intuitive and the mystical let us coin the term "intuitive-mystical".

These different modes of cognition are found in different combinations in different people. Sometimes one, sometimes another predominates. In some the rational is so dominant that the intuitive-mystical seems to be entirely absent; in others, for instance, in the contemplative saints and in some poets, the intuitive-mystical predominates. In some highly developed individuals, however, for instance in intellectual mystics such as St. Augustine and Nicholas of Cusa, and in some of the great scientists, there has been an exquisite balance between the rational and the intuitive-mystical. In his Autobiography, that great pioneer of quantum physics, Max Planck, could write out of his own experience: "When the pioneer in science sends forth the groping fingers of his thoughts, he must have a vivid intuitive imagination, for new ideas are not generated by deduction, but by an artistically creative imagination".

So when we use the phrase, "a movement into the realm of *the mystical*", as a description of the temper of thought of our age, we are not confining *the mystical* to that fading out of the rational and analytical, which is found in the most highly developed types of mystical experience, but are including in it all manifestations of a fertile interplay between the rational and the intuitive-mystical modes of knowing.

The thesis I am putting forward may be a breaking of comparatively new ground and may consequently not be easy for one unfamiliar with it to grasp. May I, therefore, try to make it clearer by first considering Wittgenstein's notion of the *mystical-inexpressible*, then Meister Eckhart's concept of *Is-ness*, and finally analyzing the several manifestations of *the mystical*.

1. In his *Tractatus Logico-Philosophicus* the Logical Empiricist philosopher, Ludwig Wittgenstein, argued that, in the totality of human experience, there is much which does not fall within the domain of science, the only domain, he maintained, in which meaningful language can be used. Science does not, indeed cannot, answer every question. There always remain the questions which life, in its fullness, poses. This realm of reality Wittgenstein called the *mystical*, and to explain what he meant he coined the phrase: "Not *how* the world is, is the mystical, but *that* it is". This mystical world, he argued, though it cannot be spoken of or described meaningfully, is a *real* world, a world which can be *felt*, and, in a real sense, *known*. He called it the *inexpressible*. "There is indeed the inexpressible", he wrote, and continued, "this *shows* itself; it is the mystical".

2. "Not *how* the world is, is the mystical but *that* it is". With a somewhat similar meaning the medieval mystic, Meister Eckhart, used the term, *Is-ness*. The That we call God, however imaged, *is*; the world *is*; each has the quality of *Is-ness*; each *shows* (or *discloses, reveals*) itself. What any particular individual can apprehend of the disclosure of Is-ness is dependent on his degree of sensitivity and his range of awareness. The Is-ness of God is, by definition, inexpressible, changeless and unconditioned. But the disclosure of Is-ness, not only of the world, but also of God, changes from age to age as human consciousness evolves and moves to new levels of awareness, and as human knowledge increases. The history of both religion and of science is strewn with abandoned "images" and discarded "models".

3. *The mystical* is contained in the totality of perception and experience of the human race. It manifests itself, however, at different levels and in different ways.

    (a) Throughout man's history, in all parts of the world, in all religions, and in every age, there have been those who have been endowed with a range of perception and awareness different from that of ordinary men. This expansion of perception and awareness enabled them not only to undergo experiences which, though interpreted differently according to different religio-philosophies, have the same character and may be presumed to have the same origin; but also to enter into permanent states of consciousness variously called Illumination, Union with God, Enlightenment, Nirvana, etc. Further, these experiences resulted in an apprehension of reality, including the reality of the phenomenal world, more intimate and profound than is possible to the unaided rational, analytical mind. These men and women are recognized as the mystics in the fullest sense, as the true contemplatives and seers. In them *the mystical* is manifested in its highest and most specialized form. Let us call this manifestation *the mystical in the first degree.*

(b) There is also a type of mystical experience which is known to many, who are in no sense contemplatives, affirm, which is clearly in the same continuum. It is, however, usually of a transitory nature, infrequent, occurring perhaps only once or twice in a life-time. Yet such experiences are clearly recognizable by those who have experienced them. They have a unique quality; they stand out from every other experience; they have a particular sort of objectivity. Further, they carry with them a tremendous sense of certainty, a sure conviction that, as it were, a curtain had momentarily opened on a part of reality, which had not been previously apprehended, or at least not with the same certainty and intimacy. In *Watcher on the Hills,* Dr. Raynor Johnson describes and examines thirty-six cases of this type of mystical experience. This manifestation of the mystical may be called *the mystical in the second degree.*

(c) The experience of the mystical in the second degree is, however, comparatively, but only comparatively, rare. What we may call *the mystical in the third degree,* the experience of "the unattended moment, the moment in and out of time", is more common. One type of it is described by T.S. Eliot in *The Dry Savages,* the third of his *Four Quartets:*

> the unattended
> Moment, the moment in and out of time,
> The distraction fit, lost in a shaft of sunlight,
> The wild thyme unseen, or the winter lightening

> Or the waterfall, or music heard so deeply
> That it is not heard at all, but you are the music
> While the music lasts.

Eliot continues:

> These are only hints and guesses,
> Hints followed by guesses.

These experiences must be described as "feeling" states, in the sense that they convey a "feel" about the nature of reality, rather than a rational apprehension of it. Nevertheless they have a definite noetic quality; they reveal something of the nature of things; they may thus be regarded also as "knowledge" states.

(d) There is, however, a fourth manifestation of the *mystical*, in which rational and analytical thought plays a greater part. This manifestation breaks through when what is primarily a process of rational thought culminates in a flash of contemplative insight. It is as if the pieces which have been moving about in a mental kaleidoscope suddenly fall into a significant and revealing pattern. For instance, one has been reading and brooding over a passage in a book or pondering on some scientific or other hypothesis. Suddenly, something in it is illuminated, is seen from a fresh angle, and takes on a new and vivid meaning. Is-ness (to use the word we have already used) shows itself in a new guise. The rational and the non-rational, the analytical and the intuitive-mystical, coalesce.

What one finds in the *mystical*, at whatever level it manifests itself, is consciousness and cognition operating in a particular way; a way in which, as it were, an inner non-rational light is communicated, through which the mind is enabled to apprehend something which would otherwise remain in darkness. While the higher manifestations of *the mystical* are known to few, it is possible for one who is in no way a contemplative and who has never known any unique mystical experience, to *think and apprehend mystically*, and so to arrive at a *mystical* interpretation of the nature of things.

The ability to think mystically is thus to expand one's range of perception and to enable one to penetrate more deeply and fully into the ultimate truth.

We have now reached a point where it is possible to set out three, albeit tentative, interlocking definitions of *the mystical*.

1. *The mystical* is the complexion which reality, whether it be the reality of God or of the world, assumes when perception and thought have moved into a particular dimension of consciousness.

2. *The mystical* is the response to the disclosure of Is-ness, whether of God or the world, of one who has attained to some degree of mystical cognition.

3. *The mystical*, particularly in its manifestations in the fourth degree, is the point of intersection of rational and non-rational thought and perception.

As over the years my thought has developed and expanded, certain key conceptions have become increasingly dominant as direction posts, pointing to that more complete vision in which the whole universe is seen as a unity, a vision similar to that which Ludwig von Bertalanffy has glimpsed.

1. The first of these, that of Unity and Polarity, is summed up in a passage of Nicholas of Cusa's *The Vision of God*:

I have learnt that the place where Thou (i.e., God) art found unveiled is girt round with the coincidence of contradictories, and this is the wall of Paradise wherein Thou dost abide, the door of which is guarded by the proud spirit of Reason, and, unless he is vanquished, the way will not be open. Thus 'tis beyond the coincidence of contradictories Thou mayest be seen and nowehere this side thereof [5].

Here we have the conception of an Undivided Unity, a Primal Meaning, which Nicholas of Cusa calls God; which in its fullness must ever remain concealed from sense perception and rational thought, conditioned as they are by the presence in them of polar-opposites. Nothing can be

conceived except in relation to its opposite, e.g., light
and darkness, above and below, before and after, etc. Only,
says Nicholas of Cusa, by the vanquishing of "the proud
spirit of Reason" can the door of the "coincidence of contradictories" be unlocked and everything seen as it really
is, a unity. That is, another way of knowing, which he
called "docta ignorantia" (learned ignorance), must be
brought into play. And, let it be remembered, Nicholas of
Cusa was not only a mystic, but also one of the keenest in-
tellects of his age.

This idea of an underlying Unity in everything, concealed in the polar-opposites of human perception, runs
through the whole of the speculation of mankind on the nature of Ultimate Truth. It is found in the Genesis myth of
the Old Testament, in which it is told how, by eating of
the fruit of the Tree of the Knowledge of Good and Evil,
the first parents of the human race were expelled into a
world of polar-opposites. It is found also in the religious
philosophy of ancient China, in which the phenomenal universe is envisaged as brought into existence by *a coming out
of Tao*, the Ultimate Principle of Everything, through the
pulling asunder of polar-opposites; in the rise of non-
dualistic thought in Hinduism; in the speculations of the
Greek philosopher-scientist, Heraclitus; and, in a most
striking and subtle way, in the conception of complementarity of the quantum physicists.

Once one has grasped this notion of Unity and Polarity
the whole of one's thinking is affected. One realizes that
no statement can be more than a partial truth, never complete, true only within its own particular setting. There
is always another statement, apparently contradictory,
which must be combined with it to arrive at the most complete statement.

2. The conception of Unity and Polarity leads to the second key conception: *the distinction between Truth, i.e.,
that which is completely and ultimately true, and "truths",
i.e., those things which are true within their own particular settings.* Each partial truth may be true within its
own sphere, but is only a fragment of Truth in its fullness;
and, owing to the limits of human perception, there is not

seldom a conflict between different truths. Truthfulness
within each different truth is determined by whether or not
it conforms with the accepted criterion of truthfulness
within its particular field. Thus one may speak of statement being scientifically, or historically, or mathematically,
or psychologically, true, if it conforms with the criterion
of truthfulness within their own fields of knowledge.

"All we know of truth", wrote Nicholas of Cusa, "is that
absolute truth, such as it is, is beyond our reach... The
quiddity of things... is unattainable in its entirety; and
though it has been the object of all philosophers, by none
has it been found as it really is. The more profundly we
learn this lesson of ignorance, the closer we draw to truth
itself" [6].

3. How close is it possible to get? What is the most fertile line of approach? We have reached our third key conception, the conception of the *Totality of Experience*. The
task of science is primarily the quantitative study of the
material universe. Within this field scientists have evolved
their own proved and effective methods and their own conception of what constitutes scientific truth. There are,
however, other aspects of life and experience which are no
concern of the scientist as scientist; and beyond them, part
of the Totality of Experience, immortal longings, intima-
tions of something which is neither of time nor of history.

If we are to draw as close as it possible to draw to the
quiddity, the Totality of things, surely it can only be by
taking as our province the Totality of Experience, not the
experience and insights of the scientist only, but also the
experience and insights of the poet, the artist, the musi-
cian and the religious mystic; not only our own individual
insights and experience or those of our own Western European
culture only, but the total experience of the human race,
both past and present.

To take the whole of human knowledge and experience as
one's province calls for an ability to think and feel *multi-
dimensionally*. How, however, is that possible in our age?
The vast accumulation of knowledge in our time has resulted
in greater and greater specialization. Simply to work

effectively in his own chosen field, it has become more and
more common for a man to know more and more about less and
less. Specialization is a necessity if knowledge is to expand. Yet the challenge of our age calls for multi-dimensional minds which, while refined and sharpened by their
own specialities, are at the same time able to range over
a variety of fields, to grasp their interconnections and
relevancies, and thereby to arrive at a synthesis, a conception of reality as a whole and not merely of one small
aspect of it.

That does not mean that a man should strive to know
everything about everything. Such would be an impossible
task. Nor is it necessary; for out of the co-ordination
of the separate items of knowledge in each particular field
of knowledge there emerge key ideas, general principles and
unified notions, which an intelligent man, who has trained
his mind to do so, can without difficulty understand and
assimilate.

In his B.B.C. Reith Lectures on *Science and the Common
Understanding*, Professor Robert Oppenheimer said:

> But if these examples indicate, as we should expect
> from the nature and conditions of scientific enquiry,
> that what science find does not and cannot uniquely
> determine what men think as real and important, they must
> show as well that there is *a kind of relevance* - a rele-
> vance which will appear different to different men and
> which will be responsive to many influences outside the
> work of science. This relevance is a kind of analogy,
> often of great depth and scope, in which views which have
> been created or substantiated in some scientific enter-
> prise are similar to those which ought to be held with
> regard to metaphysical, epistemological, political and
> ethical problems [7].

To lay bare these relevancies must be the constant task
of those who are called upon to lead the human advance in
our age. It is needful for them to be animated by an urge
to discover the interlocking of each separate part in the
complete pattern, to unify the knowledge and insights contained in each separate "truth", in order to penetrate so
far as is possible into the Truth which contains them all.

In my book, *Religious Faith and Twentieth Century Man*, from which I quoted earlier in this essay, I called this multi-dimensional temper of mind *Intersection*. Intersection I defined as a mental attitude, characterized by intellectual charity and humility and an acceptance of one's limitations and conditioning by race, environment, heredity, education and experience, which enables one to throw one's mind open to the impact of the totality of human knowledge and experience. For one who would tread the way of Intersection it is not enough to follow the path of science alone, nor the path of art and imagination alone, nor the path of social and political action, however dedicated, alone; not even the sublime "wayless way" of the contemplative saint. Nothing less than the throwing open of the mind to the Intersection of all knowledge and all experience is sufficient for those who would attain to the highest wisdom and so be most fully fitted to serve their time and generation in this *leap-epoch* of man's history.

REFERENCES

1. That is, the period before *recorded* history.

2. Whatever my own personal religious faith may be, in this essay the word "God" does not necessarily carry any specific theological connotation.

3. I have accepted the most recent dating of the *Gita*, i.e., about 100 B.C. to 200 A.D. The *Gita* is, however, probably a composite work, the earliest parts of which are several centuries older.

4. NICHOLAS OF CUSA, *The Vision of God*.

5. Translated by E.G. Salter (Dent).

6. NICHOLAS OF CUSA, *Of Learned Ignorance* (De Docta Ignorantia), translated by Fr. Germain Heron, London: Routledge and Kegan Paul, 1954.

7. Published by Oxford University Press.